MEDICINAL PLANTS OF INDIA
Volume 2

OTHER RELATED BOOKS

A Manual of Ethnobotany (2nd Ed)	*Jain, S.K.*
Betelvine Cultivation and Management of Diseases	*Chaurasia, J.P.*
Bibliography of Indian Ethnobotany, 2002	*Jain, S.K.*
Ethnic Aphrodisiac Plants	*Sood, S.K. et al.*
Ethnic Indian Plants in Cure Diabetes	*Sood, S.K. et al.*
Ethnobotany and Medicinal Plants of India & Nepal Vol. 1-2	*Singh, V. et al.*
Ethnobotany and Medicinal Plants of Indian Subcontinent	*Maheshwari, J.K.*
Ethnobotany of Rajasthan (India)	*Singh, V. et al.*
Flavouring and Fragrant Plants of Ethnic India	*Sood, S.K. et al.*
Flora of Andhra Pradesh (Vol. 1-5)	*Pullaiah, T. et al.*
Flora of Western Tribal Madhya Pradesh	*Samvatsar, S.*
Floristic Biodiversity of Barda Hills and its Surrounding	*Nagar, P.S.*
Flowering Plants of Thrissur Forest	*Sasidharan,N. et al*
Flowers and Vegetables of India	*Sud, R.K. et al.*
Glossary of Medicinal Plants used in Ayurveda	*Saroya, A.P. Singh*
Handbook of Indian Medicinal Plants	*Joshi, M.C.*
Handbook of Legumes of World Economic Importance	*Duke, J.A.*
Herbs, Culinary, Medicinal, Aromatic	*Sud, R.K. et al.*
Herbs of Tribal Land, Jharkhand, India	*Jaipuriar, M.K.*
Identification of Common Indian Medicinal Plants	*Naik, V.N.*
Leafy and Edible Plants of North-East India	*Kumar, S.*
Medicinal Plants of Bombay Presidency	*Agharkar, S.P.*
Medicinal Plants of North-East India	*Kumar, S.*
Monograph on Indian *Leucas* R. Br. (Dronapushpi) Lamiaceae	*Singh, V.*
Monograph on Indian Subtribe Cassiinae (Caesalpiniaceae)	*Singh, V.*
The Economic Plants of North East India	*Kumar, S.*
वनस्पति औषद्य विज्ञान	*भूत्या, रमेश कुमार*
वनस्पति शब्दकोश	*जैन, एस.के.*
कुमाऊँ हिमालय का लोकवनस्पति विज्ञान	*पाण्डे, पी.सी.*

MEDICINAL PLANTS OF INDIA

[A Guide to Ayurvedic & Ethnomedicinal uses of plants]

With

Identity, Botany, Phytochemistry, Ayurvedic properties, Clinical & Ethnomedicinal uses

Volume - 2

DINESH JADHAV

Guest Faculty
Department of Botany,
Govt. Arts & Science College,
RATLAM (M.P.)

SCIENTIFIC PUBLISHERS (INDIA)

P.O. BOX 91 JODHPUR

Published by:
Pawan Kumar
Scientific Publishers (India)
5-A, New Pali Road, P.O. Box 91
Jodhpur - 342 001 (Raj.)
Tel.: +92-291-2433323, 2624154
E-mail: info@scientificpub.com
www.scientificpub.com

ISBN: 978-81-7233-545-8 (Set)
978-81-7233-547-2 (Vol. 2)
978-81-7233-546-5 (Vol. 1)

Typed by:
Narendra Parihar (Johny)
Parihar Solutions, Ratlam

Cover design: Tanay Sharma

Lasertype Set: Rajesh Ojha
Printed in India

Dedicated to

The Memory of My Grandmother

Late Mrs. **Kanchan Devi Jadhav**

PREFACE

Medicinal plants belong to the earliest known health care products that have been used by the mankind. In India, the earliest reference to the medicinal value of plants appears in *Rigveda*, in which a brief reference to the healing property of plants has been made. However, it is in the *Ayurveda* that definite properties and uses of drugs and drug yielding plants have been discussed. In fact, Ayurvedic medicine had its origin from the works of *Ayurveda*. The later works of *Charak* and *Susruta*, namely *Charak-Samhita* and *Susruta Samhita* added invaluable knowledge to the science of medicinal plants.

Most of the drug plants are found in the tropics growing in wild condition and are mainly used by herb doctors and Ayurvedic vaidyas, who refer to them as *jari-butis*. In the modern age with the fast emergence of western modern medicine and synthetic drugs, the importance of plants and herbs started declining as more and more attention was paid to the development of synthetic drugs. However, with these synthetic drug came the problems of side effects and other clinical complications; the reason in the increasing awareness about the limitations of the synthetic drugs. Because of natural herbal drugs are safe and effective; now herbal medicine and natural products are in big demand all over the World.

This book is an effort to put together the vast variety of medicinal plants found in India. The plants selected in the present book are fairly widely used in India for millennia. This book well helps in generating a global interest in *Ayurveda* and medicinal plants in India.

I hope that this compilation of most commonly used medicinal plants will be of use to Ayurvedic practitioners, students, Ethnobotanists and researchers as well as to medical and scientific communities.

Dinesh Jadhav
'Kanchan',
72 B, Rajiv (Kasturba) Nagar,
Ratlam 457 001 (M.P.)
E-mail: dinj2ad@yahoo.com

ACKNOWLEDGEMENTS

First and foremost I express my deep sense of gratitude and indebtedness to Respected Dr. Shri. Anil K. Goel, Deputy Director, Botanic Garden, National Botanical Research Institute (NBRI), Lucknow (Uttar Pradesh) for encouragement and valuable suggestions.

I offer my sincere thanks to all Respected Senior Professors of Govt. Arts and Science College, Ratlam (M.P.) for suggestions and kind cooperation in all respects. I owe my respect to all the non-teaching staff of Govt. Arts and Science College, Ratlam (M.P.) for valuable cooperation and encouragement.

It is also a pleasure to thank Mr. Manish Solanki, Library incharge, Central Library, Pt. Shivshakti Lal Sharma Ayurvedic Medical College and Hospital, Ratlam (M.P.) for allowing me to use the library.

Lastly, I take this opportunity to express my gratitude to Respected Shri. Pawan Kumar Ji, Managing Editor, Scientific Publishers (India), Jodhpur, for accepting the Manuscript and also for guidance and helpful suggestions. Without his encouragement and support this book would not have been completed.

Dinesh Jadhav

ABBREVIATIONS USED IN THE BOOK

A.ma.	:	Abhidhanamanjari
A. vi.	:	Ayurveda vigyan
Bha.pra.	:	Bhavprakash
Bri.ma.	:	Brind Madhav
Ca. ka.	:	Carakasamhita kalpasthanam
Ca.su.	:	Carakasamhita Sutrasthanam
Dha.ni.	:	Dhanvantarinighantu
Dra.gu.sam.	:	Dravyagunasamgraham
Dra.vi.	:	Dravyagunavijnan
Kai.ni.	:	Kaiyadevanighantu
Ni.ra.	:	Nighanturatnakaram
Ra.ni.	:	Rajanighantu
Sha. ni.	:	Saligramanighantu
Sa.ni.bhu.	:	Saligramanighantubhusanam
So.ni.	:	Sodhalanighantu
Syn.	:	Synonyms
Vern.	:	Vernacular name

KEY TO TRANSLITERATION

Sanskrit	Transliteration key	Sanskrit	Transliteration key
अ	A, a	ट	ṭa
आ	Ā , ā	ठ	ṭha
इ	I, i	ड	ḍa
ई	Ī, ī	ढ	ḍha
उ	U, u	ण	ṇa
ऊ	Ū, ū	त	ta
ऋ	Ṛ, ṛ	थ	tha
–	$\bar{\text{Ṛ}}$, $\bar{\text{ṛ}}$	द	da
ए	E, e	ध	dha
–	Ē, ē	न	na
ऐ	Ai, ai	प	pa
ओ	O, o	फ	pha
–	Ō, ō	ब	ba
औ	Ou/ ou	भ	bha
अं	aṃ/ ama	म	ma
अः	aḥ	य	ya
क	ka	र	ra
ख	kha	ल	la
ग	ga	व	va
घ	gha	ष	ṣa
ङ.	naa	श	śa
च	ca	स	sa
छ	cha	ह	ha
ज	ja	ळ	ḷa
झ	jha	क्ष	kṣa
ञ	ña	ज्ञ	gna

CONTENTS

INTRODUCTION

Man has depended on plants from time immemorial; plants have been a rich source for therapeutics. Medicinal plants belong to the earliest known health care products that have been used by the mankind. Over three-quarters of the World population rely on the use of traditional medicines for their primary health care needs. The medicinal plants are not only major components of the many formulations used in indigenous systems of medicine but also of a large number of drugs in Allopathy. In India, with one of the oldest ethnobotanical tradition in the World, medicinal plants are the backbone of all major systems of medicine. One of the earliest references to the Medicinal properties of plants is in the *Rigveda* (3500-1800 BC). *Ayurveda*, the ancient Indian system of medicine based on that medicinal property of plants. There are many more useful medicinal plants has been described under Ayurvedic medicinal system by several authors at that time i.e. *'Charakh'* and *'Susruta'* etc. Their Ayurvedic text manifests that an incredible 1600 of the 2000 old Ayurvedic formulations are plant based. After that there are many more books have been written under heading medicinal plants of India, but those books could not fulfil all the requirements of research scholar and readers. The present book is focused on medicinal plants of India. This book is differing from other books on medicinal plants because in this book each taxon contains ethno-medicinal uses with their Ayurvedic medicinal value. The ethno-medicinal value of the taxa is updated upto 2006. The sources of information included survey of published literature including primary, secondary and tertiary sources related to medicinal plants. The description on each plant species includes regional names, Distribution, Taxonomic description, Chemical constituents, Ayurvedic Medicinal properties, medicinal uses and Ethnomedicinal uses. This book is helpful for ethnobotanists, Ayurvedic medical practitioner, students and researchers as well as other reader's interested in the field of ethno-medicine.

Arrangement- This book deals with 200 plants species of Angiosperms. Species of plants are presented in Alphabetical order of their Botanical names. In dealing with each species, after its Botanical name, all available Synonyms are mentioned. This is followed by names popularly used in English and in other Indian languages with its distribution. To help to identify the plant species, the taxonomic description is given. Available information about the chemical constituents of each species is given. Sanskrit Shlokas from relevent Nighantus describing the Ayurvedic Medicinal properties are first given in Devnagari script followed by its rendering in Roman script using Internationally recognized transliteration markings. This is followed by giving its action and uses according to Ayurvedic therapeutics. Information about its use in Ethnomedicinal practice is given then.

ABELMOSCHUS ESCULENTUS (L.) Moench. (MALVACEAE)

Syn.: *Hibiscus esculentus* L.

Regional Names : *Bengali* – Dherash; *English* - Lady's finger; *Gujarati* - Bhindu; *Hindi* - Bhindi; *Kannada* - Bhende; *Malayalam* - Vendakkai; *Marathi* – Bhendi; *Sanskrit* – Asrapatraka, Dindisa; *Tamil* - Vendakkai; *Telugu* - Bhendakaya.

Distribution: Cultivated throughout India.

Taxonomic description: Hispidly hairy herb, with 3 to 7-lobed leaves and yellow flowers with purple centre. Fruits cylendric, 5-angled, beaked.

Medicinal parts: Root, Fruits, Seeds.

Taste: Bitter.

Chemical Constituents: Fruits contain 5-hydroxytryptamin, oxalates, iodine, flourine, Calcium, phosphorus, Magnesium, vitamin-C, fats, carbohydrates, fibres, Amino-acids, Polyphenols.

Medicinal properties -

डिण्डिशो रूचिकृद् भेदी पित्तश्लेष्मापहः स्मृतः ।
शिशिरो वातलो रूक्षो मूत्रश्चाश्मरीहरः ।। (भा. प्र.)

"Diṇdiṣo rucukṛd bhedī piṭtaṣleṣmāpahaḥ ṣmṛtaḥ
ṣiṣiro vātalō rukso muṭralaṣcāṣmarīharaḥ" (Bhā. Pṛa.)

Fruits- Aphrodisiac, constipating, cooling, demulcent, diuretic, emollient, stomachic.

Seeds- Antispasmodic, aphrodisiac, demulcent, emollient, stimulant.

Medicinal uses: Fruits - Abdominal disorders, anaemia, diarrhoea, dysuria, gonorrhoea, Pruritus, spermatorrhoea.

Seeds- Gonorrhoea.

Ethno-Medicinal uses: Fruits- Abortifacient (Tarafder, 1983); Itchy eruptions, fever during teething, dysentery, diarrhoea (Jha *et al.,* 1997); Venereal diseases (Singh *et al.,* 1997); Diabetes (Ghosh, 2006).

Leaves- To make black and silky hair (External application) (Jadeja *et al.,* 2006).

ACACIA LEUCOPHLOEA (Roxb.) Willd. (MIMOSACEAE)

Syn.: *A. alba* Willd; *Mimosa leucophloea* Roxb.

Regional and Other Names: *Bengali* – Safed babul; *English* – White babool; *Gujarati* – Bhabhal; *Hindi* – Safed babul; *Kannada* – Bilijali; *Malayalam* – Velvelam; *Marathi* – Hewar; *Sanskrit* – Arimedah; *Tamil* – Velvelam; *Telugu* – Tellatumma.

Distribution: Throughout India.

Taxonomic description: Trees, with stipular-spines in pairs. Pinnae 3-15 pairs with concave glands in between and 5-30 pairs of leaflets. Heads pale-yellow, in terminal panicles. Pods flat, linear.

Medicinal parts: Bark.

Taste : Astringent.

Chemical constituents: Stem Bark contain n-hexacosanol, β-amyrin, β-sitosterol, tannin, isookannin, cyanin, leuoxol.

Heartwood contain n-hexacosanol, β-amyrin.

Medicinal properties:

अरिमेदः कषायोष्णो मुखदन्तगदास्रजित् ।
हन्ति कण्डूविषश्लेष्मकृमिकुष्ठविषव्रणान् ।। (भा. प्र.)

"Arimedaḥ kasāyosṇo mukhadāṇtagadaṣṛajit.
Haṇti kaṇduvisaṣleṣmakṛmikuṣthavisavṛaṇāṇ." (Bhā. Pra.)

Bark - Alexeteric, anthelmintic, antipyretic, astringent, bitter, constipating, demulcent, expectorant, styptic, thermogenic, vulnerary.

Medicinal uses: Bark - Bronchitis, cough, diarrhoea, dysentery, erysipelas, fever, inflammation, leprosy, leucoderma, pruritus, skin diseases, ulcers, vomiting, wounds.

Ethno-Medicinal uses: Root - Abortfiacient (Maheshwari & Singh, 1987); fever (Bhatt *et al.*, 2003).

Bark- Astringent (Sebastian & Bhandari, 1984); ulcer (Apparanantham & Chelladurai, 1986); dysentery (Kataria & Gauchan, 2006); astringent (Basak, 2006); diarrhoea (Srivastava *et al.*, 1992; Kataria & Gauchan, 2006); stomachache (Kothari & Londhe, 2003); bronchitis, leprosy, blood diseases (Nayak *et al.*, 2003).

Leaf- Fever (Kothari & Londhe, 2003); hair complaints (Kshirsagar & Singh, 2003).

Flower- Diabetes (Bhatt *et al.*, 2003).

ACACIA SINUATA (Lour.) Merr. (MIMOSACEAE)

Syn.: *Mimosa sinuata* Lour.; *M. concinna* Willd.; *Acacia rugata* (Lamk.) Merr.; *A. Concinna* (Willd.) DC.

Regional and Other Names: *Bengali* – Banritha; *English* – Soapnut-acacia; *Gujarati* – Chikakai; *Hindi* – Satala, Koci; *Kannada* – Sege; *Malayalam* – Carmalanta; *Marathi* – Shikakai; *Sanskrit* – Saptala; *Tamil* – Cikaikkai; *Telugu* – Sikaya.

Distribution: Throughout India.

Taxonomic description : A scandent spreading spiny shrub; leaves pinnately compound; flowers in globose head, yellow-whitish or pink; fruits fleshy, beaked & constricted.

Medicinal parts : Pods.

Taste : Bitter.

Chemical constituents: Leaves contain Tartaric, citric, oxalic, succinic & ascorbic acids, tartaric racimase, rutin, tannin along with alkaloids-colycotomine & nicotine.

Pods contain Saponins.

Seeds contain Saponins which possesses β-amrine, acacinin A & B, Carbohydrate glucose, arabinose, xylose, fucose & rhamnose.

Medicinal properties:

सातला कफपित्तघ्नी लघु तिक्ता कषायिका।
विसर्पकुष्ठ विस्फोटव्रणशोफनिकृन्तनी ।। (रा. नि.)

"Sātalā kaphapịttaghnī laghu tịktā kasāyikā.
Visạrpauṣtha vịsphotavranaṣḥophanikṛṇtnī." (Rāj. Ni.)

Pods - Anthelmintic, astringent, bitter, cooling, depurative, detergent, diuretic, emetic.

Medicinal uses: Pods - Burning sensation, constipation, eczema, erysipelas, leprosy, leucoderma, strangury.

Ethno - Medicinal uses: Pods - Constipation, Dandruff, Skin diseases (Singh & Pandey, 1980).

Pods & Seeds - Hair growth (Sadhale *et. al.,* 1991).

Leaves - Laxative (Hemadri & Rao, 1989).

ACONITUM HETEROPHYLLUM Wall. ex Royle. (RANUNCULACEAE)

Regional and Other Names: *Bengali* – Ataicha; *English* – Atis root; *Gujarati* – Ativakh; *Hindi* – Atis; *Kannada* – Ativisa; *Malayalam* – Ativitayum; *Marathi* – Atavish; *Sanskrit* – Ativisa; *Tamil* – Ativadayam; *Telugu* – Ativasa.

Distribution: Sub-Alpine and Alpine zones of the Himalayas.

Taxonomic description: Small herb; leaves heterophyllus, radical leaves near the root pentapalmate, upper cauline leaves small & dentate; flowers blue or greenish blue.

Medicinal parts: Roots.

Taste: Bitter.

Chemical constituents: Atisine, Atidine, Histsine, Isoatisine, Atisinine, Isoasitisine, Dihydroatisine, Heteratisine, Hetidine, Hetisine, Hetidine, Hetisinone, Heterophyllisine, Heterophylline, Heterophyllidine.

Medicinal properties:

विषा सोष्णा कटुस्तिक्ता दीपनी पाचनी हरेत्।
कफपित्तातिसारामविषकासवमिकृमीन् ।। (भा. प्र.)

"Visā soṣṇa katuṣtiḳta pācani dīpanī hareṭ.
Kaphapiṭtatisārāmavisakāsavamikṛmīṇ." (Bhā. Pra.)

Roots- Acrid, alexeteric, anitperiodic, bitter, digestive, expectorant, stomachic, thermogenic.

Medicinal uses:

Roots - Diarrhoea, dysentery, fever, haemorrhoges, helminthiasis, stomach disorders, vomiting.

Ethno- Medicinal uses: Root-Anthelmintic (Dhar & Siddique, 1993; Singh *et al.,* 1997; Dobriyal *et al.,* 1997; Singh *et al.,* 1980; Arya & Ved Prakash, 2003); snake bite (Malhotra & Balodi, 1984; Tiwari *et al.,* 1990); stomachache, snake bite (Jain & Puri, 1994); cough (Gaur *et al.,* 1983); diarrhoea (Uniyal, 1968; Srivastava *et al.,* 1981; Jadeja *et al.,* 2006); dysentery (Srivastava *et al.,* 1981; Gupta *et al.,* 1981; Jadeja *et al.,* 2006); fever (Ballabh & Chaurasia, 2006; Shah, 1982; Uniyal, 1968; Koelz, 1979; Shah & Joshi, 1971); worms, piles (Srivastava *et al.,* 1981); Rheumatism (Chhetri, 2005); toothache, headache (Ballabh & Chaurasia, 2006); dyspepsia, tonic (Ara & Naqshi, 1992); malaria fever (Jain & Puri, 1994; Kapur & Nanda, 1992); gastric problem (Singh, 2003); abdominal trouble in children (Beigh *et al.,* 2003); headache (Nautiyal *et al.,* 2003).

Leaves - Analgesic (Balodi & Singh, 1997); Malaria fever (Chauhan & Chauhan, 1988).

Rhizome - Cough (Singh & Aswal, 1992); toothache (Ganai & Nawchoo, 2003); dyspepsia, stomachache (Nautiyal *et al.,* 2003); fever, diarrhoea, dysentery (Singh & Aswal, 1992); (Nautiyal *et al.,* 2003).

ACONITUM NAPELLUS L. (RANUNCULACEAE)

Regional and Other Names: *Bengali* – Mitha zahar; *English* – Indian aconite; *Hindi* – Bachnag; *Kannada* – Vatsanabhi; *Malayalam* – Vatsanabhi; *Marathi* –Bachneg; *Sanskrit* - Vatsanabhah; *Tamil* - Vasanavi; *Telugu* - Vatsanabhi.

Distribution: Northern Himalayas of Nepal & Kashmir.

Taxonomic description: A biennial herb with tuberous roots with an erect stem; flowers blue in loose racemes; fruits follicles.

Medicinal parts: Roots.

Taste - Bitter, Acrid.

Chemical constituents: Aconitine, aconine, picroaconline, neopelline, neolin, napellin, mesaconitine, hypaconitine.

Medicinal properties:

सिन्दुवारसदृक्पत्रो वत्सनाभ्याकृतिस्तथा।
यत्पार्श्वेन तरोर्वृद्धिर्वत्सनाभः स भाषितः।। (भा. प्र.)

"Siṇduvārasadṛakpaṭro vaṭsnāḅhyākṛtiṣtathā.
Yaṭpāṛṣvena taroṛvṛdḍḥiṛvaṭsanābhaḥ sa bhāsitaḥ." (Bhā. Pra.)

Root - Anodyne, anti-inflammatory, appetizer, carminative, depurative, diaphoretic, digestive, diuretic, expectorant, febrifuge, narcotic, sedative, stimulant, stomachic, sweet, thermogenic.

Medicinal uses:

Root - Amenorrhoea, asthma, bronchitis, colic, cough, dysmenorrhoea, dyspepsia, flatulence, gout, hypotension, inflammations, leprosy, neuralgia, paralysis, sciatica, skin dieases, spermatorrhoea, strangury.

ACORUS CALAMUS L. (ARACEAE)

Regional and Other Names: *Bengali* – Bach; *English* – Sweet flag; *Gujarati* - Gandhilovaj; *Hindi* – Bace; *Kannada* – Baji; *Malayalam* – Vayampu; *Marathi* – Wekhand; *Sanskrit* – Vaca; *Tamil* – Vasampu; *Telugu* – Vasa.

Distribution: Throughout India.

Taxonomic description: Small aquatic or marshy herb, with tuberous fleshy, creeping aromatic cylindrical rhizome; leaves linear, strap shaped.

Medicinal parts: Rhizomes.

Taste: Bitter, Pungent.

Chemical constituents: Rhizome contains Essential oil, Glucoside-Acorin.

Leaves contain Oxalic acid, Calcium, Asarone, Chlorpromazine.

Medicinal properties:

वचोग्रगन्धा षडग्रन्धा गोलोमी शतपर्विका।
क्षुद्रपत्री च मङ्.गल्या जटिलोग्रा च लोमशा ।। (भा. प्र.)

"Vacog̣ragaṇdhā sadg̣raṇdhā golomī ṣatapaṛvikā.
Ksuḍrapatrī ca maṇgaḷyā jatilogṛā ca lomaṣā." (Bhā. Pra.)

Rhizome- Acrid, anodyne, anti-inflammatory, antipyretic, antispasmodic, aphrodisiac, aromatic, bitter, carminative, emetic, laxative, nervine tonic, sedative, stomachic, sudorific, thermogenic.

Medicinal uses: Rhizome - Amenorrhoea, bronchitis, calculi, colic, cough, depression, dysentery, dysmenorrhoea, dyspepsia, epilepsy, fever, flatulence, gout, helminthiasis, hoarseness, inflammations, otalgia, skin diseases, strangury, tumours.

Ethno-Medicinal uses: Rhizome-Ringworm (Bajpai *et al.,* 1995); snake bite (Chauhan & Chauhan, 1988; Singh & Aswal, 1992; Kapur, 1993; Singh, 1996; Siddque *et al.,* 1995; Mohanty *et al.,* 1996; Tiwari & Majumdar, 1996; Chetty *et al.,*1998; Nagendra Prasad & Abraham, 1984); rheumatism (Jain & Puri, 1994; Chhetri, 2005); dysmenorrhoea (Borthakur, 1993; Borthakur & Goswami, 1995); Abdominal pain (Malhotra & Balodi, 1984); cough, cold, bronchitis (Maheshwari *et al.,* 1980, 1981); dysentery, febrifuge, snake bite, stomachache (Nagendra Prasad & Abraham, 1984); epilepsy (Goel *et al.,* 1984; Shah, 1982); headache (Uniyal, 1968; Kharkonger & Joseph, 1981); hysteria (Goel *et al.,* 1984); Cough, cold, asthma, malaria, eczema (Janmeda *et al.,* 2006); Fever (Tomar & Singh, 2005; Chhetri, 2005); pneumonia (Kadaval & Jisha, 2006).

Stem- Toothache (Rao *et al.,* 1996).

Root - Menstrual disorders (Singh *et al.,* 1997); fever (Dobriyal *et al.,* 1997; Kumar & Jain, 1998; Baruah *et al.,* 2006).

ADENANTHERA PAVONIA L. (MIMOSACEAE)

Regional and Other Names: *Bengali* – Ranjan; *English* – Coralwood tree; *Gujarati* – Manjadi; *Hindi* – Baragunci; *Kannada* – Manjatti; *Malayalam* – Mancati; *Marathi* – Thorligunj; *Sanskrit* – Tamarakah; *Tamil* – Yanai kuntumani; *Telugu* – Mansenikotta.

Distribution: Throughout India.

Taxonomic description: A medium sized, handsome deciduous tree. Flowers in short-peduncled spike-like racemes, axillary or panicled at the ends of the branches. Corolla pale-yellow. Pods flat, falcate, 8-15 seeded.

Medicinal parts: Bark, Leaves, Seeds, heartwood.

Taste: Bitter, Astringent.

Chemical constituents: Bark conatains Octacosanol, dulcitol, glucosides of β-sitosterol and stigmasterol.

Seed contains Stigmasterol and its glucoside, dulcitol, polysaccharides; non protein amino acids as γ-methylene glutamic acid, γ-methlene fatty acids as palmitic, stearic, arachidic, lingoceric, oleic, linoleic acid.

Heartwood contains Srobinetin, chalcone, butein, ampelopsin and dihydrorobinetin.

Medicinal properties:

स्वादुतिक्तकषायोऽसौ पित्तभ्रान्तिवमिज्वरान् ।
रक्तवातं च शमेयत् वृष्यस्तृष्णाहरश्च सः ।।

"Ṣvādutiktakasāyoasaū pịttabhṛāṇtivamijvarāṇ
Raktavātaṃ ca ṣamayeṭ vṛṣyaṣṭṛṣṇāhavaṣca saḥ"

Bark & Leaves - Aphrodisiac, astringent, vulnerary.

Seeds - Antiemetic, aphrodisiac, astringent, bitter, cooling, febrifuge, sweet.

Heart wood - Aphrodisiac, astringent, haemostatic.

Medicinal uses: Bark & Leaves - Gout, ulcers.

Seeds - Burning sensation, fever, gout, vomiting.

Heart wood - Dysentery, Haemorrhages.

Ethno- Medicinal uses: Leaves & Bark- Rheumatism (Shah & Gopal, 1982).

Seeds - Dysmenorrhoea (Sarma *et al.,* 2006); abortifacient (Gopal & Chandra, 2003).

AERVA LANATA (L.) Juss. ex Schultes (AMARANTHACEAE)

Syn.: *Achyrantuhus lantana* L.; *Celosia lanata* L.

Regional and Other Names: *Bengali* – Chaya; *Gujarati* –Bur; *Hindi* – Gorakhganja; *Kannada* – Bilihindisoppu; *Malayalam* – Cerula; *Marathi* – Kapurmadhura; *Sanskrit* – Bhadra; *Tamil* – Cerupulai; *Telugu* – Pindicettu.

Distribution: Throughout India.

Taxonomic description: Perennial herbs, with suborbicular to lanceolate leaves. Flowers bisexual, in axillary spikes passing into long leafy inflorescence. Fruits rotund, compressed.

Medicinal parts: Whole plant.

Taste: Bitter.

Chemical constituents: α-Amyrin, campesterol, β-sitosterol, palmitic acid, betuline, syringic acid, vanllic acid, feruloyltyramine, aervine, methylervine, aervoside, aervolanine.

Medicinal properties:

गोरक्षगांजा तुवरा सतिक्ता।
लघ्वी च तीक्ष्णा परमुष्णवीर्या।
कफपित्तहृन्मूत्र विरेचनीया।
प्रभावतोऽप्यश्मरिनाशनी स्यात्।। (द्र.गु. वि.)

"Gorakṣagānjā tuvarā satiḳtā
Laghvī ca tīḳṣṇā paramuṣṇavīryā
Kaphapiṭtahṛṇmutra virecanīyā
Pṛabhāvatoapyaṣmarināṣanī ṣyāṭ." (Dṛa. Gu. Vi.)

Plant- Astringent, bitter, cooling, diuretic, emollient, suppurative, vermifuge.

Medicinal uses: Plant - Boils, Cough, Strangury.

Ethno- Medicinal uses: Whole plant- Anthelmintic (Tripathi *et. al.*, 1996; Basak, 1997; Sudhakar & Rolla, 1985); cuts, wounds (Goel *et. al.*, 1984); headache, skin diseases, swelling (Singh & Pandey, 1980); Malaria (Srivastava & Varma, 1981); Burn healing (Goel *et. al.*, 1984; Upadhay *et. al.*, 1998); diuretic (Tripathi *et. al.*, 1996; Basak, 1997); to dissolve kidney and gall bladder stones (Sudhakar & Chetty, 1998); renal stone (Thomas & Britto, 2003; Rosakutty *et al.*, 2003); strangury, cephalalgia (Nayak *et al.*, 2003).

Leaf- Malaria fever (Ahmad, 1995; Singh & Singh, 1992); Ear complaint (Saxena *et. al.*, 1931; Srivastava *et al.*, 1992); stones in urinary bladder, burning of the male genitalia (Satapathy, 1992); cuts (Saren *et al.*, 2003); eye diseases (Srivastava *et al.*, 2003).

Root- Boils (Ramachandran & Nair, 1981); Diarrhoea (Mohanty *et. al.*, 1996); kidney stone (Deokule, 2006); abnormal bleeding in menstruation (Sur *et al.*,1992); jaundice (Bhatt *et al.*, 2003).

Plant juice- Kidney stone (Kiruba *et. al.*, 2006).

Fruit- Dysentery, constipation (Srivastava *et al.*, 2003).

Bark-Diarrhoea, dysentery, stomach disorders (Srivastava *et al.*, 2003).

Seed- Diabetes (Bhatt *et al.*, 2003).

ALBIZIA ODORATISSIMA (L.f.) Benth. (MIMOSACEAE)

Regional and Other Names: *Bengali* – Kakur shirish; *English* – Black Siris; *Gujarati* – Kalosarasio; *Hindi* – Kala siris; *Kannada* – Bilvara; *Malayalam* – Pulivaka; *Marathi* – Chikunda; *Sanskrit* – Bhusivisah; *Tamil* – Karuvakai; *Telugu* – Cinduga.

Distribution: Throughout India.

Taxonomic description: A medium sized unarmed tree; leaves pinnately compound; flowers white, mfragrant, sessile, numerous, in small globose heads; fruits shortly stacked pods.

Medicinal parts: Bark.

Taste: Bitter, Astringent.

Chemical constituents: The bark contains tannins composed of d-catechin, isomers of leucocyanidin and melacidin, a leucoanthocyanidin as lebbecacidin, friedelin, β-sitosterol & machaerinic acid.

Medicinal properties:

श्रूषा तु भूशिरीषः शिरीषको ध्वांक्षिकः सफला।
तरूधूमो दुरदरिकः कनीयशीर्षोऽतिदुर्बला ज्ञेया।। (अ. म.)

"Sṛusā tu bhuṣirīsaḥ sirīsako ḍḥvāṃksikaḥ saphalā
Tarudhumo duradarikaḥ kanīyaṣisoatiduṛbalā jneyā." (A. Ma.)

Bark- Acrid, astringent, cooling, depurative, expectorant.

Medicinal uses: Bark-Bronchitis, burning sensation, cough, diabetes, erysipelas, leprosy, skin diseases, ulcers.

Ethno- Medicinal uses: Flowers- Skin diseases (Chandra *et al.,* 1989).

Bark - Leprosy, ulcers (Kapoor & Kapoor, 1980); dysentery (Sinha *et al.,* 2006); cough, cold, cuts, wounds (Manandhav, 2003).

Leaves - Cough (Kapoor & Kapoor, 1980).

ALLOPHYLUS SERRATUS (Roxb.) Kurz. (SAPINDACEAE)

Syn.: *A. cobbe* (L.) Rausch.

Regional and Other Names: *English* – Tippani; *Hindi* – Togaratti; *Malayalam* – Makkannapperuku; *Marathi* –Tipani; *Sanskrit* – Triputah; *Tamil* – Amalai; *Telugu* – Eravalu.

Distribution: Throughout India.

Taxonomic description: A small tree or large shrub; leaves trifoliate, crowded at the end of branchlets, leaflets ovate or elliptic; flowers white in axillary racemes.

Medicinal parts: Whole plant.

Taste: Bitter, Sweet, Astringent.

Chemical constituents: Leaves contain Benzylamide, Ph-acetamide and alkaloids.

Medicinal properties:

कषायतिक्तमधुरं समूलं शोफनाशनम् ।
अतिथभङ्गहरं प्रोक्तमङ्गमद्र्दव्रणापहम् ।।

"Kasāyatiktamadhuraṃ samūlaṃ ṣophanāṣanaṃ
Asthibhaṇgaharaṃ p̣roktamaṇgamaṛḍdavṛaṇāpahaṃ".

Plant- Anti-inflammatory, astringent, bitter, carminative, constipation, digestive, sweet, vulnerary.

Medicinal uses: Plant-Bone fractures, diarrhoea, dyspepsia, Inflammations, ulcers, wounds.

Ethno- Medicinal uses: Leaf- Cuts (Upadhye *et al.*, 1986).

ALPINIA GALANGA (L.) Willd. (ZINGIBERACEAE)

Regional and Other Names: *Bengali* – Kulanjan; *English* – Greater galangal; *Gujarati* – Kolinjan; *Hindi* – Kulanajn; *Kannada* – Doddarasagadde; *Malayalam* – Aratta; *Marathi* – Koshtkulayan; *Sanskrit* – Rasna; *Tamil* – Arattai; *Telugu* – Dumparastramu.

Distribution: Throughout the Western ghats.

Taxonomic description: A perennial, aromatic rhizomatous herb, with fragrant greenish white flowers & capsule fruits.

Medicinal parts: Rhizome.

Taste: Bitter, Acrid.

Chemical constituents: Essential oil, quercetin, kaempferol, isorhamnetin, kaemferide, quercetin-3-methyl ether, galangin, 1-acetoxychavicol acetate, 1-acetoxyeugenol acetate, galangal A & B, galanolactone.

Medicinal properties:

रास्ना युक्तरसा रस्या सुवहा रसना रसा ।
एलापर्णी च सुरसा सुगंधा श्रोयसी तथा ।। (भा. प्र.)

"Rāṣnā yuḳtarasā raṣyā suvahā rasanā rasā
Elāpaṛṇī ca surasā sugaṇdhā ṣreyasī tathā." (Bhā. Pra.)

Rhizome- Acrid, aphrodisiac, aromatic, bitter, carminative, expectorant, febrifuge, stimulant, stomachic, thermogenic.

Medicinal uses: Rhizome - Asthma, bronchitis, cough, diabetes, dyspepsia, hiccough, inflammations, obesity.

Ethno- Medicinal uses: Rhizome- Skin diseases (Rao & Haridsana, 1991; Sasidharan & Augustine, 2006; Sharma *et al.,* 2003); Indigestion, stomachache in children (Ganesan *et. al.,* 2006); Fever, joint pain (Janmeda *et. al.,* 2006); dyspepsia (Jadeja *et al.,* 2006); leucoderma, piles (Singh *et al.,* 1992); diabetes (Gogoi *et al.,* 2003); abortion (Singh & Singh, 2003); fever (Sharma *et al.,* 2003); rheumatic pain (Gogoi *et al.,* 2003; Sharma *et al.,* 2003); rheumatism, stomachic, tonic, bronchial catarrh, carminative (Behura & Rout, 2003).

Seeds- Diarrhoea (Janmeda *et. al.,* 2006).

Tuber- Intestinal worms (Janmeda *et. al.,* 2006).

ALSTONIA VENENATA R. Br. (APOCYNACEAE)

Regional and Other Names: *English* – Alstonia; *Hindi* – Visagni; *Kannada* – Addasoppu; *Malayalam* – Analivegam; *Sanskrit* – Visaghni; *Tamil* – Sinnappalai.

Distribution: Western Peninsula.

Taxonomic description: A small tree, with white flowers and follicle fruits.

Medicinal parts: Root, Fruits.

Taste: Bitter, Astringent.

Chemical constituents: Root contains Alkaloids: Alstovenine, venenatine, 3-dehydroalstovenine, reserpine, venoxidine, kopsinine, venterpine; 16-epivenenatine, 16-epialstovenine, venoxidine, 5, 22-dioxokopsane, venoxidine, 5-methoxt-1-oxotetrahydre-β-carboline.

The fruits in addition of alkloids contains β-amyrin acetate, lupeol ester of β-hydroxy acid and ursolic acid and echitosperpine.

Medicinal properties:

सप्तच्छदसमानं स्याद्गुणे त्वक्कुष्ठनाशिनी ।।

"Saptacchadasamānaṃ ṣyāḍguṇe tvakkuṣthanāṣinī ".

Root - Anodyne, astringent, bitter, depurative, febrifuge, thermogenic.

Medicinal uses: Root- Epilepsy, erysipelas, fatigue, fever, leprosy, skin diseases.

Ethno- Medicinal uses: Stem bark- Skin diseases (Saxena & Dutta, 1975); Snake bite (Rakhakrishnan *et al.,* 1996).

Fruit- Syphilis, epilepsy (Ahluwalia, 1968; Rao & Sreeramulu, 1985).

Root- Injury, viper bite (Nadanakunjidam, 2003).

AMMANIA BACCIFERA L. (LYTHRACEAE)

Syn.: *A. salicifolia* Hiern.; *A. vesicatoria* Roxb.

Regional and Other Names: *Bengali* – Dadmari; *English* – Blistering ammania; *Gujarati* – Jalaagiyo; *Hindi* – Dadamari; *Malayalam* – Nirummel-neruppu; *Marathi* – Bhar jambhula; *Sanskrit* – Kurandika; *Tamil* – Kalluruvi; *Telugu* – Agnivendrapaku.

Distribution: Throughout India.

Taxonomic description: Erect or ascending herbs, with oblong or elliptic leaves and sessile flowers lacking petals and style. Capsules globose, reddish.

Medicinal parts: Whole plant.

Taste: Bitter, Pungent.

Chemical constituents: Hentriaconite, Dotriacontanol, Betulinic acid, Lupeol, Ellagic acid, Quercetin, Lawsone.

Medicinal properties:

कुरण्डिका क्षेत्रभूषा कुरण्टी क्षेत्रनाशिनी ।। (शा. नि.)

"Kuraṇḍikā kseṭrabhūsā kuraṇṭī kseṭranāṣnī." (Sa. Ni.)

Plant - Acrid, aphrodisiac, appetizer, bitter, cooling, diuretic, laxative, rubifacient, stomachic.

Medicinal uses: Plant - Burning sensation, colic, dyspepsia, fever. Flatulence, rheumatism, seminal weakness, strangury.

Ethno- Medicinal uses: Whole plant - Fever (Singh & Pandey, 1980; Joshi, 1982; Srivastava *et al.,* 2003); Rheumatism (Singh & Pandey, 1980; Samvatsar & Diwanji, 2003; Nayak *et al.,* 2003); guinea- worm expulsion (Sharma & Sharma, 1992); pain, ringworm (Srivastava *et al.,* 2003); colic, intermittent fever (Nayak *et al.,* 2003).

Leaf- Rheumatism (Shah *et al.,* 1981); Ringworm (Saxena & Vyas, 1983; Srivastava *et al.,* 2003); Skin diseases (Goel *et al.,* 1984; Gopal & Chandra, 2003); pain, fever (Srivastava *et al.,* 2003).

AMOMUM SUBULATUM Roxb. (ZINGIBERACEAE)

Regional and Other Names: *Bengali* – Bara elach; *English* – Greater cardamon; *Gujarati* – Elacho; *Hindi* – Badi Ilayaci; *Kannada* – Doddayelakki; *Malayalam* – Perelam; *Marathi* – Mote veldode; *Sanskrit* – Bhadraila; *Tamil* – Perelam; *Telugu* – Pedda elakkaya.

Distribution: In the Eastern Himalayas.

Taxonomic description: A herb with leafy stem upto 90-100 cm in height, leaves oblong-lanceolate, glabrous. Flowers white in globose shortly peduncled spikes; fruits reddish brown, densely echinate globose capsules, seeds many.

Medicinal parts: Seeds.

Taste: Bitter, Acrid.

Chemical constituents: Seed contains α-terpinylacetate, flavonoids, essential oils.

Medicinal properties:

एला स्थूला च बहुला पृथ्वीका त्रिपुटाऽपिच ।
भद्रैला बृहदेला च चन्द्रबाला च निष्कुटिः ।। (भा. प्र.)

"Elā ṣthulā ca bahulā pṛthvīkā ṭriputāapi ca
Bhadṛailā brhadelā ca candṛabālā ca niṣkṛutiḥ." (Bhā. Pra.)

Seeds- Acrid, appetizer, aromatic, bitter, carminative, constipating, digestive, diuretic, febrifuge, stomachic, sudorific, thermogenic.

Medicinal uses: Seeds - Bronchitis, colic, cough, diarrhoea, dysentery, dyspepsia, fever, flatulence, gonorrhoea, pruritus, skin diseases, ulcers, vomiting, wounds.

Ethno- Medicinal uses: Seed - Gonorrhoea, fever, piles (Singh & Aswal, 1992; Singh, 1993); hairs washed with seed powder become silky (Jadeja *et al.,* 2006); blood purifier, asthma, stomach ulcers, coughs (Sharma *et al.,* 2003).

Leaf- Respiratory diseases (Nath & Maiti, 2003).

ANAMIRTA COCCULUS (L.) Wight & Arn. (MENISPERMACEAE)

Syn.: *A. paniculata* Colebr.; *Cocculus suberosus* DC.; *Menispermum cocculus* L.

Regional and Other Names: *Bengali* – Kakamari; *English* – Fish berries; *Gujarati* – Kakmari; *Hindi* – Kakamari; *Kannada* – Kakamari; *Malayalam* – Polla; *Sanskrit* – Kakamari; *Tamil* – Kakamari; *Telugu* – Garalaphala.

Distribution: Throughout India.

Taxonomic description: A large, woody, climbing shrub; leaves large simple, long-petioled, broadly ovate, cordate at base; flowers greenish in long panicles; fruits drupes.

Medicinal parts : Leaves, Fruits.

Taste: Bitter, Acrid.

Chemical constituents: Pericarp contains Alkaloids: Menispermine, Paramenispermine.

Stem & Roots contain Alkaloids: Berberine, Palmatine, Magnoflorine, Columbamine.

Medicinal properties:

काकमारी काकवैरी तिक्ता कीटविनाशिनी ।
विचर्चिकरक्षतदोष जरात्वग्दोषनाशनी ।। (आ. चंद्रिका.)

"Kākamārī kākavaīrī tiḳtā kītavināṣanī.
Vicaṛcikaraksatadosa jarāṭvagdosanāṣanī."
(Āyuṛvedartha Caṇḍṛikā)

Fruits - Anthelmintic, antifungal, astringent, bitter, depurative, expectorant, thermogenic.

Medicinal uses: Fruits-Bronchitis, flatulence, inflammations, ringworm, skin diseases.

Ethno-Medicinal uses: Seeds - Seeds are used to kill lice (Chetty & Rao, 1989).

ANANAS COMOSUS (L.) Merrill (BROMELIACEAE)

Syn.: *A. sativa* Schult. f.

Regional and Other Names: *Bengali* – Anarash; *English* – Pineapple; *Gujarati* – Aninas; *Hindi* – Ananas; *Kannada* – Anasahannu; *Malayalam* – Kaitaccakka; *Marathi* – Ananas; *Sanskrit* – Anamnasam; *Tamil* – Annasippalam; *Telugu* – Annasapandu.

Distribution: Throughout India, Cultivated.

Taxonomic description : A spiny herb with underground stem. Leaves radicle in cluster, long with dentate spiny margin, fruit composite, spiny, large, rough, red-orange from inside.

Medicinal parts: Fruits, leaves.

Taste: Sweet.

Chemical constituents: Leaves contain Ergosterol peroxide, β-sitosterol, campesterol, stigmasterol & campestanol, 5-stigmasten-3b, 7 α-diol, stigmasterol.

Fruit contains Methyl-β-hydroxy-octanoate, methyl-β-acetoxyoctanoate, methyl-trans-3-octanoate, ethyl-trans-3-octanoate, ethyl-trans-3-hexanoate, butane-2, 3-dioldiacetate, pentanol, butanols, caffic acid, ferulic acid, sinapic acids, amino acids, vitamins A,B,C, minerals, glucose, sucrose, fructose, enzyme-bromelain.

Medicinal properties:

अनंनासं पारवती चामं कौतुकसंज्ञकम् ।। (नि. र.)

"Anaṃnāsaṃ pāravati cāmaṃ kaūtukasaṃjnakaṃ." (Ni. Ra.)

Ripe fruits - Carminative, cooling, digestive, diuretic, emollient, febrifuge, styptic, sudorific, sweet.

Leaves- Abortifacient, anthelmintic.

Medicinal uses: Ripe fruits - Cardiac debility, colic, dyspepsia, flatulence, haematemesis, jaundice.

Leaves - Abortion, amenorrhoea, dysmenorrhoea, helminthiasis, whooping Cough.

Ethno- Medicinal uses: Fruits - Abortifaceint (Maji & Sikdar, 1982).

Leaves - Anthelmintic (Borthakur, 1996; Datta & Nath, 1998; Bhattacharjee *et. al.,* 1980; Kadaval & Jisha, 2006; Basak, 2006; Bora, 2003); purgative (Borthakur, 1996; Datta & Nath, 1998); intestinal worms (Gupta *et. al.,* 1997; Nath & Maiti, 2003); jaundice (Gupta *et. al.,* 1997); malaria (Deka *et al.,* 2006); asthma, diabetes (Sharma *et al.,* 2003).

Fruit - Indigestion (Jamir, 1990); jaundice (Banerjee & Banerjee, 1986); Abortifacient (Maji & Sikdar, 1982; Sharma *et al.,* 2003); worms, stomach trouble (Das & Sharma, 2003); purgative (Sharma *et al.,* 2003).

ANETHUM GRAVEOLENS L. (APIACEAE)

Syn.: *Peucedanum graveolens* (L.) Hiren.; *P. sowa* Roxb.; *Anethum sowa* Roxb. ex Flem.

Regional and Other Names: *Bengali* – Sowa; *English* – Dill; *Hindi* – Soya; *Kannada* – Sabbasige; *Malayalam* – Satakuppa; *Marathi* – Balantashopa; *Sanskrit* – Satapuspa; *Tamil* – Satakuppi; *Telugu* – Satakuppivittulu.

Distribution: Throughout India, Cultivated.

Taxonomic description: A glabrous aromatic annual herb; leaves pinnately compound; flowers yellow, in compound umbels.

Medicinal parts: Fruits.

Taste: Bitter, Acrid.

Chemical constituents: Fruits contain Vicenin, Phellandrene, Dillapiol, Carvone, Dihydro carvone, D-limonene, A new xanthone glycoside-dillanoside.

Seed oil contain Essential oil, Tripetroselinin, Petroselinicdiolein, Dipetroselinicolein.

Medicinal properties:

शतपुष्पा सूक्ष्मपत्रा पीतपुष्पाऽतिछत्रका।
प्रसिद्धा क्षेत्रविख्याता दीपनोक्ता महर्षिभिः ।। (शा. नि.)

"Ṣatapuṣpā sukṣmapaṭrā pītapuṣpāatichaṭrakā.
P̣rasiddḥā kseṭravikḥyātā dīpanoḳtā mahaṛsibhiḥ." (Ṣhā. Ni.)

Fruits - Acrid, alexeteric, anodyne, anthelmintic, antidysenteric, anti-inflammatory, antispasmodic, bitter, carminative, digestive, diuretic, expectorant, febrifuge, stomachic, sudorific, thermogenic.

Medicinal uses: Fruits - Amenorrhoea, asthma, colic, cough, dysmenorrhoea, dyspepsia, flatulence, hiccough, inflammaitons, intestinal worms, skin diseases, strangury.

Ethno- Medicinal uses: Fruits - Stomach complaints in children (Shah *et. al.,* 1981); flatulence (Vishwanathan, 1995); dyspepsia (Jadeja *et al.,* 2006); gout (Jadeja *et al.,* 2006).

ANISOMELES MALABARICA (L.) R. Br. (LAMIACEAE)

Regional and Other Names: *English* – Malabar catmint; *Gujarati* – Gholochodharo; *Hindi* – Codhara; *Kannada* – Karitumbi; *Malayalam* – Karintumpa; *Marathi* – Chodhara; *Sanskrit*–Vaikunthah; *Tamil* – Peyimarutti; *Telugu* – Mogabiraku.

Distribution: Throughout South India.

Taxonomic description: An erect shrub, with quadrangular & softly white-tomentose stems & branches; leaves thick, aromatic, oblong-lanceolate, softly woolly; flowers purple.

Medicinal parts: Whole plant.

Taste: Bitter, Acrid.

Chemical constituents: Plant contains-β-sitosterol; 2 diterpene lactones-ovatodiolide & anisomelic acid; monocyclic diterpenes, anisomelolide, malbaric acid, anisomelin.

Medicinal properties:

अन्या चैव महाद्रोणा कुरूम्बा देवपूर्वका।
दिव्यपुष्पी महाद्रोणी देवीकाण्डा षडाह्वया ।। (रा. नि.)

"Aṇyā caīva mahādṛoṇā kuruṃbā devapūṛvakā
Diẏyapuṣpī mahādṛoṇi devīkāṇdā sadāḥvayā." (Rā. Ni.)

Plant - Acrid, anthelmintic, aromatic, bitter, febrifuge, stomachic, sudorific.

Medicinal uses: Plant - Colic, diarrhoea, dyspepsia, epilepsy, fever, flatulence, gout, hysteria, intestinal worms, swelling.

Ethno- Medicinal uses: Leaves - Cough, cold (Sudhakar & Chetty, 1998; Vijaykumar & Pullaiah, 1998); stomachache (Sikarwar & Kaushik, 1993); snake bite, scorpion sting (Thomas & Britto, 2003); gastric problem (Rosakutty *et al.,* 2003).

Root - Snake bite (Sebastian & Bhandari, 1984; Jain & Sahu, 1993).

ANNONA RETICULATA L. (ANNONACEAE)

Regional and Other Names: *Bengali* –Nona; *English* – Bullock's heart; *Gujrati* – Ramphal; *Hindi* – Raamphal; *Kannada* –Raamphala; *Malayalam* – Manilanilam; *Marathi* –Ramphal; *Sanskrit* –Ramaphala ; *Tamil* – Raamsila; *Telugu* – Raamaaphalamu.

Distribution: Native to tropical America, particularly the West Indies. Naturalized & common cultivated in India.

Taxonomic description: Small trees; flowers yellow-green; ripe fruits round yellowish brown.

Medicinal parts: Bark, fruits, seeds, leaves.

Taste: Sweet.

Chemical constituents: Root bark contains - Alkaloids: Oxoushinsunine, Iiriodenine, anonine, norushinsunine, michelabine, reticulin.

Fruits - Protein, fat, minerals: Calcium, phosphorus, iron, riboflavin; vitamin-C & niacin. Carotene.

Medicinal properties:

पक्वं रामफलं स्वादु मधुरं कफवातलम् ।
अम्लं रूचिकरं दाहक्षुत्पित्तज्जमनुत्परम् ।। (नि.र.)

"Pakvaṃ rāmaphalaṃ ṣvādu madhuraṃ kaphavātalaṃ
Aṃlaṃ rucikaraṃ dāhaksutpiṭtaṇjamanuṭparaṃ" (Ni. ra.)

Root- Insecticidal, purgative.

Seed- Stringent, insecticidal.

Leaves- Anthelmintic, insecticidal.

Stem- Insecticidal.

Bark- Astringent, vermifuge.

Fruit- Anthelmintic, antidysentric, sweet.

Medicinal uses: Leaves- Inflammatory tumors.

Bark- Dysentery, tonic.

Fruit- Diarrhoea, dysentery.

Ethno- Medicinal uses: Leaves- Boils (Tarafder, 1984).

Bark-Astringent, antidysenteric, vermifuge (Shah *et al.,* 1981).

Seeds-Boils (Tarafder, 1984)

Fruits-Dysentery (Deokule, 2006); biliousness, diseases of blood (Mukhopadhyay, 1992).

APHANAMIXIS POLYSTACHYA (Wall.) Parker (MELIACEAE)

Syn.: *Amoora rohituka* Roxb.

Regional and Other Names: *Bengali* – Tikatarai; *English* – Rohituka tree; *Gujarati* – Ragtarahido; *Hindi* – Harin-hara; *Kannada* – Mullumuntala; *Malayalam* – Cemmaram; *Marathi* – Rohada; *Sanskrit* – Rohitakah; *Tamil* – Malampuluvan; *Telugu* – Sevamanu.

Distribution: Throughout India.

Taxonomic description: A medium to large sized tree, with large imparipinnately compound leaves; male flowers numerous in axillary panicles, female or bisexual flowers in supra-axillary solitary spikes. Seeds with scavlet aril.

Medicinal parts: Bark, seeds.

Taste: Bitter, Acrid, Astringent.

Chemical constituents:

Seed contains Essential oil, limonoid (rohitukin), a fixed oil, fatty oil.

Fruit shell contains Aphanamixin (A triterpene).

Bark contains β-sitosterol, stigmasterol, tetranorterpenoid (Aphanamixinin), glycosides, terpenoid glucoside (betulin-3β-O-D-xylopyranoside), saponin.

Medicinal properties:

रोहितकः प्लीहघाती रूच्यो रक्तप्रसादनः ।। (भा. प्र.)

"Rohitakaḥ plīhaghatī ruçyo raḳtapṛasadanaḥ." (Bhā. Pṛa.)

Bark - Acrid, anthelmintic, astringent, depurative, digestive, bitter, refrigerant, vulnerary.

Seeds- Acrid, anodyne, anthlemintic, laxative, refrigerant.

Medicinal uses: Bark - Burning sensation, jaundice, leucorrhoea, liver disorders, rheumatism, tumour.

Seeds - Burning sensation, intestinal worms, otopathy, skin diseases, ulcers.

Ethno- Medicinal uses:

Bark - Spleen complaint. liver complaint (Das *et. al.,* 1983; Kumar, 1992); teeth problem (Jamir, 1990; Rao & Jamir, 1982).

Seed-Rheumatism (Das *et. al.,* 1983; Kumar, 1992).

Leaf- Skin diseases (Rao & Jamir, 1982).

AQUILARIA AGALLOCHA Roxb. (THYMELEACEAE)

Syn.: *A. malaccenisis* Lamk.

Regional and Other Names: Bengali – Agaru; English – Aloe wood; Gujarati – Agar; Hindi – Agar; Kannada – Krisnagaru; Malayalam – Akil; Sanskrit – Aguruh; Tamil – Agar; Telugu – Krsnagaru.

Distribution: In the forest of Bhutan, Assam & Myanmar.

Taxonomic description: A large evergreen tree; leaves linear-lanceolate to ovate-oblong; flowers small, greenish in shortly peduncled umbels; fruits capsules.

Medicinal parts: Fragrant resinous wood & oil.

Taste: Bitter, Acrid.

Chemical constituents: Oil (Agar oil) contains Agarospirol (A Sequiterpenoid), holocellulose, ligin, pentosans.

Medicinal properties:

अगरू प्रवरं लोहं राजार्हं योगजं तथा।
वांशिकं कृमिजं चापि कृमिजग्धमनार्यकम् ।। (भा. प्र.)

"Aguru pṛavaram lohaṃ rājārhaṃ yogajaṃ tathā.
Vāṃsikaṃ kṛmijaṃ cāpi kṛmijagdhamanāṛyakaṃ." (Bhā. Pṛa.)

Wood - Acrid, bitter, carminative, digestive, rejuvenating, sudorific, thermogenic.

Oil - Acrid, alexeteric, antileprotic, astringent, bitter, depurative, thermogenic.

Medicinal uses: Wood - Asthma, cardiac debility, cough, dyspepsia, inflammations, leprosy, rheumatism, skin diseases.

Oil -Asthma, bronchitis, cough, leprosy, skin diseases.

Ethno- Medicinal uses: Leaves - Itching throat (Kumar *et. al.,* 1980).

Wood- Dyspepsia, cordiac debility, leprosy, cough, asthma, hiccough, skin diseases (Gantait *et al.,* 2006).

ARACHIS HYPOGAEA L. (PAPILIONACEAE)

Syn.: *A. asiatica* Lour.

Regional and Other Names: *Bengali* – Chineybadam; *English* – Groundnut; *Gujarati* – Mandavi; *Hindi* – Mung-phali; *Kannada* – Nilakadali; *Malayalam* – Nilakkatala; *Marathi* –Bhui mug; *Sanskrit* – Mandapi; *Tamil* – Verkkaltalai; *Telugu* – Verusenagalu.

Distribution: Throughout India, cultivated.

Medicinal parts: Seed, oil.

Taste: Sweet.

Chemical constituents: Seed contains α-Resorcylic acid, P-hydroxy-benzoic acid, Cis & Trans – P – Coumaric acid, Phloretic acid, Vanillic acid.

Medicinal properties:

मण्डपी मधुरा स्निग्धा वातला कफकारिका।
ग्राहिका बद्धवर्च्चश्च तत्तैलं तद्गुणं स्मृतम् ।। (शा. नि.)

"Maṇdapī madhurā ṣnigdhā vātlā kaphkārikā
Gṛahikā baddḥvaṛçcaṣca tattaīlaṃ taḍgunaṃ ṣmṛitaṃ" (Ṣa. Ni.)

Seeds- Aphrodisiac, constipating, sweet.

Oil- Emollient, purgative, sweet.

Medicinal uses: Seeds - Diarrhoea, general debility.

Ethno- Medicinal uses: Seeds - Galactagogue (Deokule, 2006); stomach problems (Singh, 2003).

ARECA CATECHU L. (ARECACEAE)

Regional and Other Names: *Bengali* – Gua; *English* –Betal palm; *Gujarati* – Supari; *Hindi* – Supari; *Kannada* – Adike; *Malayalam* – Kavunnu; *Marathi* – Supari; *Sanskrit* – Pugah; *Tamil* – Pakkumaram; *Telugu* – Vakka.

Distribution: Cultivated throughout India.

Taxonomic description: A slender tall palm tree, 40-60 feet high; flowers in large spadix.

Medicinal parts: Roots, Leaves, Fruits.

Taste: Acrid.

Chemical constituents: Nuts contain Alkaloids: Arecoline, Arecaidine, Guvacine, Isoguvacine, Leucocyanidin.

Medicinal properties:

भेदी सम्मोहकृत् पूगं कषायं स्वादु रोचनम्।
कफपित्तहरं रूक्षं वक्त्रक्लेदमलापहम् ।। (ध. नि.)

"Bhedī saṃmohakṛt pugaṃ kasāyaṃ ṣvādu rocanaṃ
Kaphapiṭtaharaṃ ruksaṃ vaḳṭraḳledamalāpahaṃ." (Dha. Ni.)

Nuts - Anthelmintic, aphrodisiac, astringent, cooling, digestive, diuretic.

Medicinal uses: Nuts - General debility, urinary disorders.

Ethno- Medicinal uses : Leaf - Abortifacient, leucorrhoea (Tarafder, 1987).

Root- Liver complaint (Tarafder, 1987); rheumatism (Islam & Jha, 2003).

Nuts- Mouth ulcer (Ghosh & Sensarma, 1997).

ARISTOLOCHIA BRACTEOLATA Lam. (ARISTOLOCHIACEAE)

Regional and Other Names: *English* – Worm Killer; *Gujarati* – Kidamari; *Hindi* – Kiramar; *Kannada* – Sanajalihallu; *Malayalam* – Attukottappala; *Marathi* – Kidamar; *Sanskrit* – Kitamari; *Tamil* – Atutinnappalai; *Telugu* – Gadidagadapaku.

Distribution: Bengal, Western Peninsula, Gujrat, Deccan, Kerela, Karnataka.

Taxonomic description: Erect herbs, with diffuse branches. Leaves ovate to reniform. Flowers purple, solitary axillary; capsules oblong-ellipsoid.

Medicinal parts: Roots, Leaves.

Taste: Bitter.

Chemical constituents: Leaves contain Ceryl alcohol, β-Sitosterol, Aristolochic acid, KCl.

Roots contain Aristolochic acid, KCl, KNO_3.

Medicinal properties:

कीटारिः कीटमारी च भृङ्.गी कीटकहा तथा।। (शा. नि.)

"Kītārih kītamārī ca bhṛṇgī kītakahā tathā." (Sa. Ni.)

Roots & Leaves - Acrid, anthelmintic, anti-inflammatory, antiperiodic, appetizer, bitter, cathartic, sudorific, thermogenic, vulnerary.

Medicinal uses: Roots & Leaves - Amenorrhoea, boils, colic, constipation, dysmenorrhoea, dyspepsia, eczema, inflammations, intsestinal worms, gonorrhoea, skin diseases, syphilis.

Ethno-Medicinal uses: Whole plant - Anthlemintic (Singh, 1945; Sudhakar & Rolla, 1985); purgative (Sudhakar & Rolla, 1985); snake bite (Singh, 1945); menstrual disorder (Rosakutty *et al.,* 2003); snake bite (Subramani & Goraya, 2003).

Leaf - Eczema (Sudhakar & Rolla, 1985; Kapoor & Kapoor 1980; Poddy *et. al.*, 1991; Deokule, 2006; Deokule & Magdum, 1992); piles, ulcers (Kapoor & Kapoor 1980; Poddy *et. al.*, 1991); swelling, rheumatism (Rajendra & Rengaswami, 2006); foul & ulcers (Thomas & Britto, 2003); dandruff (Ganesan & Kesavan, 2003); Diabetes (Bhatt *et al.*, 2003).

Seeds - Purgative (Singh & Pandey, 1980).

Root - Intestinal worms (Kapoor & Kapoor, 1980; Deokule & Magdum, 1992; Thomas & Britto, 2003); ulcers (Balaji Rao *et. al.*, 1996); snake bite & scorpion sting (Hemadri *et. al.*, 1980).

ARTEMISIA NILAGIRICA (Clarke) Pamp. (ASTERACEAE)

Syn.: *A. vulgaris* auct. (non L.)

Regional and Other Names: *English* – Indian wormwood; *Hindi* – Nagdona, Dauna; *Kannada* – Urruvalu; *Malayalam* – Masipatri; *Marathi* – Gathona; *Sanskrit* – Damanah; *Tamil* – Makkippu; *Telugu* – Masipatri.

Distribution: Throughout India.

Taxonomic description : A tall aromatic perennial shrub; lower leaves deeply pinnatified, uppermost smaller, trifid or entire, lanceolate; flowers in subglobose heads; fruits achenes.

Medicinal parts: Leaves, Flowering tops.

Taste: Bitter, Astringent.

Chemical constituents: Essential oil contain P-cymene, L-linalool, β-thujone, Azulene, Thujyl alcohol and an unidentified Hydrocarbon. Artemisia Ketone, a Pentacyclic Triterpene, Thujone, a-amyrin & its acetate, Ferneol, Stigmasterol and β-sitosterol.

Medicinal properties:

दमनः कफपित्तास्रहृत् सुगन्धि रसायनः ।। (सो. नि.)

"Damanaḥ kaphapiṭtāsṛahṛt sugandhi rasāyanah." (So. Ni.)

Leaves & Flowering tops - Acrid, alexeteric, anodyne, anthelmintic, anti-inflammatory, aphrodisiac, appetiser, aromatic, astringent, bitter, depurative, digestive, diuretic, febrifuge, stomachic, thermogenic.

Medicinal uses: Leaves & Flowering tops - Amenorrhoea, asthma, bronchitis, colic, cough, dysmenorrhoea, dyspepsia, fever, flatulence, hysteria, inflammations, intestinal worms, leprosy, pruritus, skin diseases, strangury.

Ethno- Medicinal uses: Leaves - Anthelmintic (Sharma *et. al.,* 1979); antiseptic (Sharma *et. al.,* 1979; Uniyal, 1968); asthma (Nautiyal, 1981); ear complaint (Jain, 1984); peptic ulcer (Apparanantham & Chelladurai, 1986); skin diseases (Dhasmana, 1986); Malaria fever (Singh, 1997); cuts & wounds (Chuhan & Chauhan, 1988; Singh, 1997; Nautiyal *et al.,* 2003); abdominal pain, chest pain (Radhakrishnan *et. al.,* 1996); allergies (Jamir, 1990); piles, headache (Singh *et al.,* 1992); check nose bleeding (Kapur & Nanda, 1992); itching in eyes during summer months (Sharma & Rana, 2003); boils (Nautiyal *et al.,* 2003); cuts (Dash *et al.,* 2003); nasal bleeding, mouth sores, septic wounds (Srivastava *et al.,* 2003).

Whole plant - Antiseptic (Das *et. al.,* 1983); asthma (Dhasmana, 1986; Rao *et. al.,* 1981); stomachache, epilepsy, nervous disorders (Dhasmana, 1986); measles (Kapur & Nanda, 1992).

Root - Stomachache (Singh, 1997).

Flower bud- Liver disorders (Dash *et al.,* 2003).

ARTOCARPUS HETEROPHYLLUS Lam. *(MORACEAE)*

Syn.: *A. integrifolia* auct. non Linn.

Regional and Other Names: *Bengali* – Kanthal; *English* – Jackfruit tree; *Gujarati* – Vanas; *Hindi* – Kathal; *Kannada* –Halasu; *Malayalam* – Plavu; *Marathi* – Phanas; *Sanskrit* – Panasah; *Tamil* – Palamaram; *Telugu* – Panasa.

Distribution: Throughout India.

Taxonomic description: Tree with dense, cariaceous elliptic leaves. Stipules glabrous. Male receptacle cylindric and female receptacle tuberculed. The receptacles are lateral on trunk and branches, on special branchlets. The inflorescence is enclosed in 2 large, lathery yellowish stipules belonging to the leaf.

Medicinal parts: Root, leaves, fruits, seeds, wood, latex.

Taste: Sweet, Astringent.

Chemical constituents: Leaves contain Cycloartenone, cycloartenol, β-sitosterol, tannin.

Fruit contains β-carotene, amino acids, aurantiamide acetate, vitamin- A & C; iron phosphorus.

Bark contains Betulinic acid, cycloheterophyllin, iso cycloheterophyllin, cycloartenyl acetate, cycloartenol, cycloartenone.

Heartwood contains Morin, dihydromorin, cyanonaclurin, artocarpin, isoartocarpin, cyclo artocarpin, artocarpesin, cycloartocarpesin, artocarpetin, artocarpanone, Sucrose, ellagic acid.

Latex contain Cycloartenon, cycloartenol, B-sitosterol, butyrospermol, leucine, isoleucine, tyrosine, valine, cycloartenol.

Medicinal properties:

पनसं शीतलं पक्वं स्निग्धं पित्तानिलापहम् ।
तर्पण बृहणं स्वादु मांसलं श्लेष्मलं भृशम् ।। (भा. प्र.)

"Panasaṃ ṣitlaṃ pakvaṃ ṣnigdhaṃ piṭtānilāpahaṃ
Taṛpaṇaṃ bṛṃhaṇaṃ ṣvādu maṃsalaṃ ṣleṣmalaṃ bṛṣaṃ"
(Bhā. Pra.)

Unripe fruit- Acrid, astringent, carminative, tonic.

Ripe fruit - Aphrodisiac, cooling, latex, sweet, tonic.

Seeds - Aphrodisiac, constipating, diuretic, sweet.

Medicinal uses : Unripe fruit - Dyspepsia, general debility.

Ripe fruit - Biliousness, burning sensation, constipation, seminal debility, ulcers, tonic.

Seeds - General tonic, tuberculosis.

Latex - Abscesses, swellings.

Ethno- Medicinal uses: Leaves - Anthelmintic (Baruah & Sharma, 1984).

Root - Stomach complaint (Karnick *et al.,* 1981); diarrhoea (Das & Sharma, 2003).

Latex - Skin diseases (Bhattacharjee *et al.,* 1980); burns (Sivakumar *et al.,* 2003); dog bite (Rajendran *et al.,* 2003); glandular swelling (Tigga *et al.,* 2003).

Bark- Severe headache (Satapathy, 1992).

Flower- Healing cracks of feet (Islam & Jha, 2003).

Fruit- Ulcer (Ganesan & Kesavan, 2003).

ASCLEPIAS CURASSAVICA L. (ASCLEPIADACEAE)

Regional and Other Names: *Bengali* – Bankarpas; *English* – Wild Ipecacunha; *Hindi* – Kauathori; *Marathi* – Kurki; *Sanskrit* – Bharadvaji.

Distribution: Throughout India.

Taxonomic description: An erect, simple or much-branched perennial undershrub, with a woody base. Flowers orange-yellow in many flowered umbels. Fruits follicles.

Medicinal parts: Whole plant, Root, Leaves, Flowers.

Taste: Bitter.

Chemical constituents: Leaves contain β-sitosterol, β-amyrin, myristic acid, palmitic acid, stearic acid, oleic acid, linoleic acid, arachidic acid, arachidonic acid, glucose, fructose, acidic mucilage, asclepine glycoside.

Medicinal properties:

भारद्वाजी हिमारूच्या व्रणशास्त्रक्षतापहा ।। (रा. नि.)

"Bhāradvājī himāruçyā vranaṣaṣṭraksatāpahā." (Rā. Ni.)

Plant- Abortifacient, anthlemintic, antipyretic, cardio tonic, emetic, expectorant, hypertensive, purgative, styptic, sudorific.

Medicinal uses: Plant- Gonorrhoea, haemorrhagic diseases, piles.

Ethno- Medicinal uses: Leaf - Abdominal pain, gonorrhoea, piles (Uniyal & Chauhan, 1973); anthelmintic (Sharma *et. al.,* 1979); antiseptic (Singh *et al.,* 1992); haemorrhage, wounds (Deokule & Magdum, 1992).

Root- Ulcer (Uniyal & Chauhan, 1973); Gonorrhoea (Bam & Bam, 1986; Singh, 1997); constipation (Jadeja *et al.,* 2006); piles (Deokule & Magdum, 1992; Deokule, 2006).

Plant juice - Anthelmintic, gonorrhoea (Banerjee & Banerjee, 1986).

Flower- Wounds (Deokule & Magdum, 1992).

ASPARAGUS ADSCENDENS Roxb. (LILIACEAE)

Syn.: *A. officinalis* L.

Regional and Other Names: *English* – Asparagus; *Gujarati* – Dholi musali; *Hindi* – Safed-musallee; *Marathi* – Safed musli; *Sanskrit* – Musali.

Distribution: Native to temperate Europe & West Asia. Cultivated in India.

Taxonomic description: Tall stout white creeping herbs with straight spines; cladodes terete corwded in tufts; flowers white in racemes.

Medicinal parts: Tuberous roots.

Taste: Sweet.

Chemical constituents: Roots contain - β-sitosterol, Sarsasapogenin & Asparagosides.

Medicinal properties:

मुशली मधुरा शीता वृष्या पुष्टिबलप्रदा ।
पिच्छिला कफदा पित्तदाहश्रमहरा परा ।। (रा. नि.)

"Muṣalī madhurā ṣītā vṛṣyā puṣtibalapṛadā
Piçchilā kaphadā piṭtadāhasṛamaharā parā." (Rā. Ni.)

Cooling, demulcent, sweet, tonic.

Medicinal uses: Diabetes, diarrhoea, dysentery, general debility, leucorrhoea, seminal debility.

Ethno- Medicinal uses: Stem- Aprodisiac (Shah & Joshi, 1971).

Leaf -Dysentery (Jain, 1984).

Root-Dyspepsia, anaemia (Gopakumar *et al.,* 1991); premature ejaculation (Sen & pradhan, 1999); snake bite & scorpion sting (Chauhan & Chauhan, 1988); diarrhoea, dysentery (Singh & Aswal, 1992; Singh, 1993; Sharma & Sharma, 1992).

AVERRHOA CARAMBOLA L. (OXALIDACEAE)

Regional and Other Names: *Bengali* – Kamranga; *English* – Carambola apple; *Gujarati* – Kamarakh; *Hindi* – Kamarakh; *Kannada* – Derehuli; *Malayalam* – Caturappuli; *Marathi* – Kamranga; *Sanskrit* – Karmarangah; *Tamil* – Tamarattai; *Telugu* – Karamonga.

Distribution: Throughout India, cultivated.

Taxonomic description: A medium sized evergreen tree; leaves compound; flowers pinikish to purplish in short racemes; fruits berries; seeds arillate.

Medicinal parts: Leaves, Fruits.

Taste : Sweet, Sour.

Chemical constituents: Fruit contains Proteins, Amino acid compounds, Vitamin-C, Oxalic acid.

Flowers contain Rutin, Quercetin-3-glucoside.

Leaves contain Oxalic acid, potassium oxalate, fluorine, glucose, sucrose, fructose, vitamins.

Medicinal properties:

कर्मरङ्ग हिमं ग्राहि स्वाद्वम्लं कफवातहृत् ।। (भा. प्र.)

"Kaṛmaraṇgam himaṃ grāhi ṣvādvaṃlaṃ kaphavātahṛṭ."(Bhā. Pṛa.)

Leaves- Anthelmintic, antipruritic, antipyretic.

Fruits - Antipyretic, constipating, febrifuge, sour, sweet, thermogenic.

Medicinal uses: Leaves - Fever, intestinal worms, pruritus, scabies.

Fruits - Diarrhoea, fever, general debility, haemorrhoids, scabies, vomiting.

Ethno-Medicinal uses: Fruits - Dysentery (Hajra & Baishya, 1981); piles (Shah *et al.*, 1981; Basak, 2006); Fever (Upadhyay & Singh, 2005); jaundice (Das *et al.*, 2006); astringent (Mukhopadhyay, 1992); burns & scalds (Singh & Singh, 2003).

BALIOSPERMUM MONTANUM (Willd.) Muell-Arg. (EUPHORBIACEAE)

Syn.: *B. polyandrum* Wight.; *B. axillare* Blume.

Regional and Other Names: *Bengali* – Danti; *Gujarati* – Dantimul; *Hindi* – Danti; *Kannada* – Kaduharalu; *Malayalam* – Nagandanti; *Marathi* – Danti; *Sanskrit* – Danti; *Tamil* – Nakatanti; *Telugu* – Adaviamudamu.

Distribution: Throughout India.

Taxonomic description: An undershrub; with herbaceous branches from roots; leaves variable in shape & size; flowers small, greenish, monoecious in axillary racemes; fruits capsules.

Medicinal parts : Roots, Leaves, Seeds.

Taste : Acrid.

Chemical constituents: Root contains 5 new phorbol esters belonging to diterpene hydrocarbotigliane skeleton viz. montain, balliospermin etc.

Leaves contain β-sitosterol, glucosides, hexacosanol.

Medicinal properties:

दन्ती तीक्ष्णोष्णकटुका कफवातोदरान् जयेत्।
अर्शोव्रणाश्मरीशूलान् हन्ति दीपनशोधनी।। (ध. नि.)

"Daṇtī tīkṣṇoṣṇakatukā kaphavātodarāṇ jayeṭ
Aṛṣovṛaṇāṣmarīṣūlāṇ haṇti dīpansodhanī" (Dha. Ni.)

Roots - Acrid, anodyne, anthelmintic, anti-inflammatory, diaphoretic, digestive, diuretic, febrifuge, purgative, rubefacient, thermogenic.

Seeds - Purgative, rubefacient, stimulant.

Medicinal uses: Roots - Anaemia, constipation, dropsy, fever, flatulence, haemorrhoids, jaundice, leprosy, leucoderma, skin diseases, strangury, wounds.

Seeds - Flatulence, inflammations.

Ethno- Medicinal uses: Root - Jaundice (Mishra & Sahu, 1984; Karnich *et al.,* 1981; Mitaliya & Bhatt, 2003); constipation (Nayak *et al.,* 2003; Mitaliya & Bhatt, 2003); anaemia (Nayak *et al.,* 2003); dropsy (Mishra & Sahu, 1984; Karnich *et al.,* 1981; Nayak *et al.,* 2003; Mitaliya & Bhatt, 2003).

Seeds - Purgative, stimulant, rubefacient (Kapoor & Kapoor, 1980; Singh & Aswal, 1992; Tirpathi *et. al.,* 1996); constipation (Ahmad, 1996); snake bite (Mishra & Sahu, 1984; Jain & Sahu, 1993; Singh, A. K., 2003); Gastric complaint, Rheumatism (Goel *et. al.,* 1984).

Seed oil - Rheumatism (Kapoor & Kapoor, 1980; Tripathi *et. al.,* 1996; Samvatsar & Diwanji, 2003).

Leaves - Headache (Hemadri & Rao, 1990); Asthma (Mishra & Sahu, 1984); cuts (Singh, A. K., 2003).

BAMBUSA ARUNDINACEA (Retz.) Willd. (BOMBUSACEAE)

Syn.: *B. bambos* Druce.

Regional and Other Names: *Bengali* – Ketua; *English* – Thorny bamboo; *Gujarati* –Wans; *Hindi* – Bans; *Kannada* – Bedru; *Malayalam* – Mula; *Marathi* – Kallak; *Sanskrit* – Vamsah; *Tamil* – Mulmunkil; *Telugu* – Vedurubiyyam.

Distribution: Throughout India.

Taxonomic description: Woody, thorny reed-bamboo, with stem-sheath hairy, cariaceous, striate. Leaves triangular-lanceolate, base rounded glandular. Spikelets pale, lanceolate, acute, glabrous. Caryopsis oblong, with persistent style-base, grooved.

Medicinal parts: Roots, leaves, sprouts, grains.

Taste: Sweet, Astringent.

Chemical constituents: Root contains Cyanogenetic glucoside.

Young shoot contains HCN, Benzoic acid, Reducing sugars & Waxes.

Medicinal properties:

कीचको मस्करो वंशी सुपर्वा षट्पदालयः ।
वंशो वेणुर्यवफलस्तृणकेतुस्तृणध्वजः ।
शतपर्वा शब्दमालः कमरिस्त्वाचिसारकः ।। (कै. नि.)

"Kīcako maṣkaro vaṃṣī suparvā saṭpadālayaḥ
Vaṃṣo veṇuṛyaphalaṣṭṛṇaketuṣtrnaḍhvajaḥ
Ṣatapaṛvā saḅdamālaḥ kamriṣtvācisārkaḥ." (Kai. Ni.)

Roots- Astringent, cooling, depurative, diuretic, laxative, sweet.

Leaves - Astringent, constipating, cooling, febrifuge, sweet.

Sprouts - Acrid, anthelmintic, anti-inflammatory, bitter, carminative, digestive, diuretic, laxative.

Grains - Acrid, alexeteric, anthelmintic, aphrodisiac, sweet.

Medicinal uses: Roots - Burning sensation, leprosy, ringworm, skin diseases.

Leaves - Diarrhoea, fever, haemorrhoids, lumbago, skin diseases, wounds.

Sprouts - Dyspepsia, flatulence, inflammations, intestinal worms, ulcers, wounds.

Grains - General debility, intestinal worms.

Ethno-Medicinal uses: Tender stem - Antifertility (Tiwari *et. al.,* 1982); eye pain (Udayan *et. al.,* 2006); cuts (Singh, A. K., 2003).

Wood oil - Eczema (Narain & Singh, 2006).

Leaves - Regulation of mensis (Mokat & Deokule, 2006); stimulate menstrual discharges (Srivastava & Singh, 2006); chest pain (Arinathan *et al.,* 2003); bone fractures (Ganesan & Kesavan, 2003).

Flower- Earache, deafness (Srivastava & Singh, 2006).

BARRINGTONIA ACUTANGULA (L.) Gaertn. (BARRINGTONIACEAE)

Syn.: *B. spicata* Bl.

Regional and Other Names: *Bengali* – Hijal; *English* – Small Indian oak; *Gujarati* – Samudarphal; *Hindi* – Samudraphal; *Kannada* – Holekavau; *Malayalam* – Nirpelu; *Marathi* – Piwar; *Sanskrit* – Samudraphalah; *Tamil* – Samuttirappalam; *Telugu* – Kanapa.

Distribution: Throughout India.

Taxonomic description: A middle sized evergreen tree. Leaves elliptic, subsessile. Flowers in long pendulous racemes.

Medicinal parts: Root, Leaves, Fruits.

Taste: Bitter, Acrid, Sweet.

Chemical constituents: Leaves contain Acutangulic acid, Barringtogenic acids, Stigmasterol, Tangulic acid, Oleanolic acid, β-amyrin, β-sitosterol, Stigmasterol, Sapogenin.

Fruits contain Triterpenoid sapogenins as Barringtogenol D, C& B, triterpenic acids as barrigenic acid, barrinic acid, barringtogenic acid.

Medicinal properties:

समुद्रनाम प्रथमं पश्चात् फलमुदाहरेत्।
समुद्रफलमित्यादि नाम वाच्यं भिषग्वरैः ।। (रा. नि.)

"Samudranāma prathamaṃ paṣcāṭ phalamudāhareṭ.
Samudraphalmityādi nāma vāçyaṃ bhisagvaraīḥ." (Rā. Ni.)

Roots - Antipyretic, aperient, bitter, cooling, emetic, stimulant.

Leaves - Bitter, constipating.

Fruits - Acrid, alexeteric, anthelmintic, bitter, cooling, depurative, diuretic, emetic, expectorant, purgative.

Medicinal uses: Root - Catarrh, constipation, fever.

Leaves - Diarrhoea, dysentery.

Fruits - Bronchitis, colic, cough, dysmenorrhoea, fever, intestinal worms, leprosy, lumbago, skin diseases, strangury, syphilis, ulcers, wounds.

Ethno-Medicinal uses: Bark-Gum trouble (Saxena *et al.,* 1931); Rheumatism (Singh *et al.,* 1987; Singh, A.K., 2003); toothache (Saxena *et al.,* 1931; Gogoi *et al.,* 2003).

Stem - Gum trouble (Hajra & Baishya, 1981); toothache (Hajra & Baishya, 1981; Gogoi *et al.,* 2003).

Seed - Liver disorders (Tribedi *et al.,* 1982).

Plant sap- Cuts (Girach *et al.,* 2003).

Root/Leaf/Fruit-Catarrh, diarrhoea, blood diseases (Nayak *et al.,* 2003).

BASELLA ALBA L. var. ***RUBRA*** (L.) Stewart (BASELLACEAE)

Syn.: *B. rubra* L.

Regional and Other Names: *Bengali* – Pui Shak; *English* – Indian spinach; *Hindi* – Poi; *Kannada* – Bansali; *Malayalam* – Vasalaccira; *Marathi* – Poi; *Sanskrit* – Upodika; *Tamil* – Vasalakkirai; *Telugu* – Baccali.

Distribution: Throughout India, cultivated.

Taxonomic description : A perennial climbing herb. Leaves broad ovate, cordate. Flowers pinkish or pale purple, sessile, in axillary, penduncled spkies. Flowers remain closed. Perianth fleshy, 5-lobed. Fruit enclosed in perianth.

Medicinal parts: Stems, Leaves.

Taste: Sour.

Chemical constituents: Plant contains Polysaccharides, organic acids, provitamin A, Carotenoids as α-carotene, β-carotene, violaxanthin, lutein, tunaxanthin & phytonene.

Medicinal properties:

पोतक्युपोदिका सा तु मालवी मृतवल्लरी ।। (भा. प्र.)

"Potaḳyupodikā sā tu mālavi mṛtavaḷlari" (Bhā. Pṛa.)

Stem & Leaves - Aphrodisiac, appetizer, cooling, demulcent, diuretic, emollient, haemostatic, laxative, sedative, sweet.

Medicinal uses: Stem & Leaves - Burning sensation, constipation, dysentery, gonorrhoea, leprosy, pruritus, strangury, ulcers, urticaria.

Ethno- Medicinal uses: Leaf - Constipation (Baruah & Sarma, 1987); piles (Subramani & Goraya, 2003); sexual debility (Bhatt *et al.,* 2003).

Plant- Bone fracture (Singh & Singh, 2003).

Tuber- Colic disorders (Muthukumarasamy *et al.,* 2003).

BAUHINIA RACEMOSA Lam. (CAESALPINIACEAE)

Syn.: *Piliostigma racemosa* (Lamk.) Bentham.

Regional and Other Names: *Bengali* – Vanraj; *English* –Downy mountain ebony; *Gujarati* – Asundro; *Hindi* – Jhinjhora; *Marathi* –Apta; *Sanskrit* – Ashmantak.

Distribution: Throughout India.

Taxonomic description : Deciduous trees.bark grey, rough. Leaves broader than longer. Flowers in terminal, leaf opposed racemes, creamy-white. Pods falcate, turgid. Seeds oval, black.

Medicinal parts: Stem bark, leaves, flowers, seeds, fruits.

Taste: Sweet.

Chemical constituents: Stem bark contains Octacosane, B-amyrin, B-sitosterol.

Seeds- Protein, pentosan, mucilage.

Medicinal properties:

कोविदारः कषायः स्यात् संग्राही व्रणरोपनः।
दीपनः कफवातध्नो मूत्रकृच्छ्रनिवारणः।। (रा. नि.)

"Kovidarah kasayah syat sangrahi vranaropanah
Dipanah kaphavataghno mutrakrcchranivaranah (Ra. ni.)

Root bark- Astringent.

Stem bark, Leaves- Antipyretic, alexipharmic, refrigerent.

Medicinal uses: Root bark- Diarrhoea, dysentery, inflammation, skin diseases, ulcers.

Stem bark, Leaves- Biliousness, diseases of blood, fistula, headache, urinary discharges.

Flowers- Cough, haemorrhages, piles.

Ethno- Medicinal uses: Stem bark – Diarrhoea, dysentry (Singh & Pandey, 1980; Sinha *et al.,* 2006; Kumar & Lal, 2003); swellings (Deshmukh *et al.,* 2003); dysentery, malaria fever (Gogoi *et al.,* 2003).

Flower- Diarrhoea (Jadeja *et al.*, 2006).

Leaves- Wounds (Sivakumar *et al.*, 2003); intestinal worms, fever, diabetes, piles, liver disorders (Kothari & Rao, 2003); headache (Deshmukh *et al.*, 2003; Kumar & Lal, 2003); dysentery, malaria fever (Gogoi *et al.*, 2003).

Gum- Diarrhoea (Deshmukh *et al.*, 2003); tonic, soothing to intestines (Kumar & Lal, 2003); malaria fever (Kumar & Lal, 2003).

Root bark- Wormicide (Deshmukh *et al.*, 2003).

BENINCASA HISPIDA (Thunb.) Cogn. (CUCURBITACEAE)

Syn.: *B. cerifera* Savi; *Cucurbita hispida* Thunb.

Regional and Other Names: *Bengali* – Kumra; *English* – White gourd melon; *Gujarati* – Koholu; *Hindi* – Petha; *Kannada* – Budikumbala; *Malayalam* – Kum palam; *Marathi* – Kohala; *Sanskrit* – Kusmandah; *Tamil* – Pusanikkai; *Telugu* – Budidagummadi.

Distribution: Cultivated throughout India.

Taxonomic description : A large climbing or trailing herb, with large, yellow, monoecious solitary flowers and large, fleshy, indehiscent fruits.

Medicinal parts: Fruits, Seeds.

Taste: Sweet.

Chemical constituents: Fruit contains β-sitosterol, asparagine, luoeol, mannitol, proline, arginine, aspartic acid, glutamic acid, glutamine, hydroxyproline, Isoleucine, cysteine, L-leucine, n-triacontanol, glucose, rhamnose, vitamins.

Medicinal properties:

कश्माण्डं स्यात्पुष्पफलं पीतपुष्पं बृहत्फलम् ।। (भा. प्र.)

"Kuṣmāṇdaṃ ṣyātpuṣpaphalaṃ pītapuṣpaṃ bṛhaṭphalaṃ"
(Bhā.Pṛa.)

Fruits - Aphrodisiac, antiperiodic, cooling, diuretic, laxative, styptic, sweet.

Seeds - Anthelmintic, cooling, sweet.

Medicinal uses: Fruits - Asthma, cough, diabetes, epilepsy, fever, haemorrhages.

Seeds - Cough, fever, syphilis.

Ethno- Medicinal uses: Fruits - Jaundice (Hemadri & Rao, 1984; Dutta *et al.*, 2006); Diabetes, epilepsy (Jha *et al.*, 1997; Nayak *et al.*, 2003); nervous disorders (Jha *et al.*, 1997); dry cough (Nayak *et al.*, 2003).

BERBERIS ARISTATA DC. (BERBERIDACEAE)

Syn.: *B. tinctoria* Leschen.; *B. chitria* Ham.

Regional and Other Names: English – Tree-turmeric; Hindi – Daaruhallada; Sanskrit – Daruharidra.

Distribution: Himalayas, Nepal.

Taxonomic description : Spinous shrubs; axillary thorns with fragrant greenish flowers in racemes and dark red-brown berries.

Medicinal parts: Fruits, Root-bark, Stem, Wood.

Taste: Bitter.

Chemical constituents: Plant contains Alkaloids: Berberine, Oxycanthine, Berbamine, Palmatine, Jatrorrhisine, Columbamine, Berberrubine, Hydrastine; Gum; Starch.

Medicinal properties:

तिक्ता दारूहरिद्रा स्याद् रूक्षोष्णा व्रणमेहनुत् ।
कर्णनेत्रमुखोद्भूतां रूजं कण्डूं च नाशयेत् ।। (ध. नि.)

"Tiḳtā dāruharidṛā ṣyāḍ ruksoṣnā vṛanamehanuṭ
Kaṛnaneṭramukhoḍbhūtāṇ rujaṃ kaṇdūṃ ca nāṣayeṭ." (Dha. Ni.)

Tonic, stomachic, astringent, antiperiodic, diaphoretic, antipyretic, alternative.

Medicinal uses: Jaundice, enlargement of spleen.

Ethno- Medicinal uses: Fruits - Haemorrhoids, laxative (Chauhan & Chauhan, 1988).

Root - Opthalmia (Chauhan & Chauhan, 1988; Singh & Aswal, 1992; Singh, 1993, 2003; Nautiyal *et al.*, 2003); antipyretic, laxative, tonic (Singh &

Aswal, 1992; Singh, 1993); malaria fever (Chauhan & Chauhan, 1998); Snake bite (Vishnu Mittre, 1981); Jaundice (Singh, 2003; Chhetri, 2005); rheumatism, diarrhoea, skin diseases (Singh, 2003); headache (Nautiyal *et al.*, 2003).

Root bark- Ophthalmic diseases (Jha *et. al.*, 1997; Tewari *et. al.*, 1990; Shah & Joshi, 1971); ulcers, wounds (Tewari *et. al.*, 1990); diarrhoea, earache (Tewari *et. al.*, 1990); Boil (Shah & Joshi, 1971).

BETA VULGARIS L. (CHENOPODIACEAE)

Regional and Other Names: *Bengali* – Palangsag; *English* – Garden Beet; *Hindi* – Cukkandar; *Kannada* – Biturutu; *Malayalam* – Bittruttu; *Marathi* – Beet; *Sanskrit* – Palakya; *Tamil* – Cencirai; *Telugu* – Bitrutu.

Distribution: Cultivated in many parts of India.

Taxonomic description: An annual or Biennial tuberous herb. Leaves ovate to oblong-ovate, passing into linear bracts in the inflorescence. Flowers in clusters, distant with narrow acute bracts.

Medicinal parts: Taproot; Leaves, Seeds.

Taste: Sweet.

Chemical constituents: Leaves contain Chlorobenzene, chloroform, phenylacetonitrile, phenylacetaldehyde.

Root contains Iodine, Folic acid, Biotin, Asparagine, Betalains, Betanins, Fluorine, Phytoalexins as 3,5-Dihydroxy-6,7-Methyl-enedioxyflavanone, 5-Hydroxy-6,7-methylenedioxyflavone.

Medicinal properties:

पालिङ्.क्या वातला शीता श्लेष्मला भेदिनी गुरुः ।
विष्टम्भिनी मदश्वासपित्तरक्तविषापहा ।। (भा. प्र.)

"Pāliṇḳyā vātalā ṣītā ṣleṣmalā bhedinī guruḥ.
Viṣtaṃbhinī madaṣvāpiṭtaraḳtavisāpahā." (Bhā. Pṛa.)

Root - Expectorant, sweet.

Leaves - Acrid, anodyne, anti-inflammatory, cooling, diuretic, purgative, Sweet.

Seeds - Aphrodisiac, bitter, carminative, diuretic, expectorant.

Medicinal uses: Root - Cough, Inflammation.

Leaves - Burns, constipation, cuts, inflammations, paralysis, strangury.

Seeds - Amenorrhoea, asthma, cough, dysmenorrhoea, flatulence, inflammations.

Ethno- Medicinal uses: Leaves - Burn healing (Ahmad, 1995; Jha *et. al.*, 1997; Deokule, 2006).

BETULA UTILIS D. Don. (BETULACEAE)

Regional and Other Names: *Bengali* – Bhurjapatri; *English* – Himalayan silver birch; *Gujarati* – Bhojpatre; *Hindi* – Bhojpatra; *Kannada* – Burjjamara; *Malayalam* – Bhurjamaram; *Marathi* – Bhojpatra; *Sanskrit* – Bhurjah; *Tamil* – Bhurjjamaram; *Telugu* – Burjapatramu.

Distribution: The plant is found in temperate Himalaya from Kashmir to Bhutan from 2300-4600 m. altitude.

Taxonomic description: A medium sized deciduous tree; stem bark silvery white, papery, soon peeling off; twigs and petioles hairy becoming glabrous; flowers in spikes.

Medicinal Parts: Bark.

Taste : Astringent, Acrid.

Chemical constituents: Bark contains Betulin, lupeol, oleanolic acid, acetyloleanolic acid, leucocyanidin, betulic acid, lupenone, methyl betulate, methyl betulonate, karachic acid.

Medicinal properties:

भूर्जपत्रः स्मृतो भूर्जश्चर्मी बहुलवल्कलः ।। (भा. प्र.)

"Bhūrjapatraḥ smṛto bhūrjaścarmī bahulavalkalaḥ." (Bhā. Pra.)

Bark - Acrid, alexeteric, antibacterial, astringent, carminative, constipating, expectorant, thermogenic.

Medicinal uses: Bark - Bacterial infections, bronchitis, cough, diarrhoea, dysentery, dyspepsia, epilepsy, haemorrhages, hysteria, jaundice, leprosy, otalgia, skin diseases, wounds.

Ethno- Medicinal uses: Resin - Contraception, burns, cuts (Shah & Joshi, 1971; Shah, 1982); cough, cold (Nautiyal *et al.*, 2003).

Bark- Antiseptic, carminative (Chauhan & Chauhan, 1988; Singh & Aswal, 1992; Malhotra & Balodi, 1984); rheumatism, hysteria (Singh & Aswal, 1992; Malhotra & Balodi, 1984); hepatistis, earache (Chauhan & Chauhan, 1988; Malhotra & Balodi, 1984); wounds (Negi *et al.*, 1985; Kala & Manjrekar, 2003); diseases of ear & blood (Kapur & Nanda, 1992); jaundice (Kapur & Nanda, 1992; Kala & Manjrekar, 2003); burns (Kala & Manjrekar, 2003); eye diseases (Singh, 2003).

BIXA ORELLANA L. (BIXACEAE)

Regional and Other Names: *Bengali* – Latkan; *English* – Arnotta plant; *Gujarati* – Sinduri; *Hindi* – Sinduriya; *Kannada* – Kappumankala; *Malayalam* – Kuppamannal; *Marathi* – Sendri; *Sanskrit* – Sinduri; *Tamil* – Sappira Virai; *Telugu* – Jaffracettu.

Distribution: Widely cultivated throughout India.

Taxonomic description : A shrub or evergreen small handsome tree, with cordate leaves and white or Rose flowers.

Medicinal parts: Roots, Bark, Seeds.

Taste: Bitter, Acrid, Astringent.

Chemical constituents: Leaf oil contain Tetracyclic sesquiterpene-ishwarane, Tomentosic acid.

Root contains Triterpenes, Tomentosic acid.

Leaves contain Essential oil which contains: Sesquiterpene, Bixaghanene.

Seeds contain Bixin.

Medicinal properties:

सिन्दूरी रक्तबीजा च रक्तपुष्पा सुकोमला ।। (भा. प्र.)

"Sindūrī raktabījā ca raktapuspā sukomalā." (Bhā. Pra.)

Root, Bark, Seeds - Antiperiodic, antipyretic, astringent.

Medicinal uses: Root, Bark, Seeds - Fever, Gonorrhoea.

Ethno- Medicinal uses: Leaf - Snake bite (Nagendra Prasad & Abraham, 1984).

Fruits - Eczema, scabies (Gopakumar *et al.,* 1991).

BLUMEA LACERA (Burm. f.) DC. (ASTERACEAE)

Syn.: *B. balsamifera* DC.; *B. densiflora* Hook. f.

Regional and Other Names: *Bengali* – Kukursunga; *English* – Blumea; *Gujarati* – Chandhadmari; *Hindi* – Kukaraunda; *Kannada* – Kukkaradru; *Malayalam* – Kukkuravrksam; *Marathi* – Burando; *Sanskrit* – Kukundarah; *Tamil* – Kattumullanki; *Telugu* – Kukundaramu.

Distribution: Throughout India.

Taxonomic description: A herbaceous erect annual with a strong odour of turpentine; flowers yellow, numerous in heads, both terminal and axillary; fruits achenes, crowned with white pappus hairs.

Medicinal parts: Whole plant.

Taste: Bitter, Astringent.

Chemical constituents: The plant contains acetylenic compounds, Diester of Coniferol alcohol, Thiophenen derivatives, Campesterol, hentriacontanc, Hentriaceontanol, α-amyrin and its acetate, Lupeol and its acetate, β-sitosterol.

Medicinal properties:

कुकुन्दरस्ताम्रचूड़ः सूक्ष्मपत्रो मृदुच्छदः ।। (भा. प्र.)

"Kukuṇdaraṣṭāmṛacūdaḥ sūkṣmapatro mṛduççhadaḥ." (Bhā. Pṛa.)

Plant - Acrid, anthelmintic, anti-inflammatory, astringent, bitter, digestive, diuretic, expectorant, febrifuge, styptic, thermogenic.

Medicinal uses: Plant - Burning sensation, bronchitis, cough, fever, inflammation, intestinal worms, leucorrhoea, liver disorders, wounds.

Ethno- Medicinal uses: Leaf - Burns, cuts, wounds (Goel *et. al.,* 1984); piles (Tarafder, 1987; Singh, 1988); urinary complaint (Joshi *et. al.,* 1980); intestinal warm (Jadeja *et al.,* 2006; Sharma & Sharma, 1992); antiseptic (Dwivedi, 2003); pneumonia, earache (Khan *et al.,* 2003).

Whole plant - Fever, bronchitis (Shah *et. al.,* 1983); piles (Srivastava *et al.,* 2003); anthelmintic, astringent, diuretic (Islam & Hasin, 2003); bronchitis, blood diseases, cholera (Nayak *et al.,* 2003).

BORASSUS FLABELLIFER L. (ARECACEAE)

Syn.: *B. flabelliformis* Roxb.

Regional and Other Names: *Bengali* – Tal; *English* – Palmyra palm; *Gujarati* – Tad; *Hindi* – Tar; *Kannada* – Talimara; *Malayalam* – Karimpana; *Marathi* – Tad; *Sanskrit* – Talah; *Tamil* – Karumpanai; *Telugu* – Tadicettu.

Distribution: Hotter parts of India.

Taxonomic description: A very tall, erect, magnificient dioecious palms; leaves 1-1.5m diam with 60-80 segments, folded along midrib; edges of petioles spinose; spadices very large; drupes large subglobose. .

Medicinal parts: Root, Leaves, Inflorescence, Fruits.

Taste: Sweet.

Chemical constituents: Stem juice contains Minerals like iron; protein, sucrose, glucose, thiamin, riboflavin, nicotinic acid, vitamin C.

Medicinal properties:

तालस्तु लेखपत्रः स्यात्तृणराजो महोन्नतः ।। (भा. प्र.)

"Tālaṣtu lekhapaṭraḥ ṣyāṭtrnarājo mahoṇnataḥ." (Bhā. Pra.)

Roots- Cooling, diuretic, stimulant.

Fruits - Anthelmintic, aphrodisiac, cooling, depurative, laxative, sedative, stomachic, styptic, sweet.

Medicinal uses: Root - Burning sensation, inflammations. Strangury.

Fruits - Burning sensation, colic, constipation, dyspepsia, flatulence, intestinal worms, leprosy, skin diseases.

Ethno- Medicinal uses: Wood pulp - Abortifacient (Maheshwari *et al.,* 1986).

Sap - Gonorrhoea (Tarafder, 1984).

Petioles – Epilepsy (Goel *et al.,* 1984; Saren *et al.,* 2003); Hysteria (Goel *et al.,* 1984, Mondal & Mukherjee, 1992; Saren *et al.,* 2003).

Inflorescence - Skin itching, boils (Upadhyay *et al.,* 1998); sores of children (Singh *et al.,* 1992).

Bark - Dysentery (Siddqui & Hussain, 1991).

Root - Bachache & Rheumatism (Hemadri & Rao, 1990); normal delivery (Thomas & Britto, 2003).

Ripe fruit- Diabetes (Ghosh & Das, 2003).

BOSWELLIA SERRATA Roxb. ex Colebr. (BURSERACEAE)

Syn.: *B. glabra* Roxb.

Regional and Other Names: *Bengali* – Salai; *English* – Indian olibanum tree; *Gujarati* –Gugali; *Hindi* – Salai; *Kannada* – Guggula; *Malayalam* – Kunturukkam; *Marathi* – Salai; *Sanskrit* – Sallaki; *Tamil* – Parankisampirani; *Telugu* – Sambrani.

Distribution: Throughout Central & Northern India on dry hills.

Taxonomic description: Deciduous tree, with bark peeling off in this flakes. Leaves imparipinnate, 7 to many-foliolate. Flowers white, bisexual. Drupes trigonous.

Medicinal parts: Bark, gum-resin.

Taste: Bitter, Sweet, Acrid, Astringent.

Chemical constituents: Bark contains Carbohydrates, Glucosides and β-sitosterol.

Gum resin contains Diterpine, alcohol, serratol, β-boswellic acid, essential oil.

Medicinal properties:

शल्लकी गजभक्षा च सुवहा सुरभी रसा।
महेरूणा कुन्दुरूकी वल्लकी च बहुस्रवा ।। (भा. प्र.)

"Ṣallaki gajabhaksā ca suvahā surabhi rasā.
Maheruṇā kuṇduruki vaḷlaki ca bahuṣravā." (Bhā. Pṛa.)

Bark - Antidysenteric, antipyretic, astringent, bitter, diaphoretic, diuretic, expectorant, stomachic, sweet.

Medicinal uses: Bark - Asthma, dysentery, skin diseases, ulcers.

Gum-resin - Arthritis, asthma, bronchitis, cough, dysentery, fevers, jaundice, stomachache, syphilis.

Ethno- Medicinal uses: Bark - Antiseptic (Gupta, 1981); cold cough (Bhatt & Sabnis, 1987; Singh & Maheshwari, 1983); diarrhoea, dysentery (Sebastian & Bhandari, 1984); snake bite (Sharma & Singh, 1988); stomach complaint (Jain, 1963); toothache (Maheshwari *et. al.,* 1986); skin eruption (Meena *et al.,* 2003); indigestion (Ravikumar & Vijaya Sankar, 2003).

Resin/Gum - Dysentery (Shah *et al.* 1981); stomach complaint (Singh & Maheshwari, 1983); skin diseases (Shah *et. al.* 1981; Kapoor & Kapoor, 1980; Tripathi *et al.,* 1996; Islam & Jha, 2003); Rheumatism (Kapoor & Kapoor, 1980; Kothari & Londhe, 2003; Samvatsar & Diwanji, 2003; Mitaliya *et al.,* 2003; Islam & Jha, 2003); leucorrhoea, blood diseases, bronchitis, cough (Tripathi *et. al.,* 1996); diarrhoea (Kapoor & Kapoor, 1980; Shah *et al.* 1981); ulcers (Dwarakan & Ansari, 1992); hair growth (Kothari & Londhe, 2003); skin diseases, general weakness, chronic rheumatism, nervous diseases (Kumar *et al.,* 2003); back pain (Mitaliya *et al.,* 2003); pneumonia, bronchial congestion (Upadhyay & Chauhan, 2003).

Fruits - Leucoderma (Tripathi *et al.,* 1996).

Leaves - Inflammation (Sebastian & Bhandari, 1984); oedema (Reddy *et. al.,* 1991).

BRASSICA JUNCEA Czern. & Coss. (BRASSICACEAE)

Regional and Other Names: *Bengali* – Rai; *English* – Indian mustard; *Hindi* – Rayi; *Kannada* – Sasive; *Malayalam* – Katuku; *Sanskrit* – Sarsapah; *Tamil* – Katugu; *Telugu* – Avalu.

Distribution: Cultivated throughout India.

Taxonomic description: A tall much-branched annual herbs. Basal leaves lyrate-pinnatipartile; middle ones obovate-oblong, pinnatilobed; upper ories lanceolate, entire-dentate. Racemes 20-40 flowered, up to 30 cm. long in fruit.

Medicinal parts : Seeds, oil.

Taste: Acrid.

Chemical constituents: Seeds contain Sinigrin, Gluconapin, sinapine base, Isothyocynates, Essential oil, Flavonol glycosides.

Medicinal properties:

राजिका कफवातघ्नी तीक्ष्णोष्णा रक्तपित्तकृत्।
किंचिद्रुक्षाग्निदा कण्डूकोष्ठकृमीहरेत् ।। (भा. प्र.)

"Rājikā kaphavātaghṇī tīkṣṇosṇā raktapittakṛaṭ.
Kiṇcidṛuksāgnidā kaṇdūkuṣthakosthakṛimīn hareṭ." (Bhā. Pṛa.)

Seeds- Acrid, anodyne, anthelmintic, anti-inflammatory, bitter, carminative, digestive, sudorific, thermogenic.

Medicinal uses: Seeds - Dyspepsia, flatulence, inflammations, intestinal worms, skin diseases.

Ethno- Medicinal uses: Seed - Ringworm (Saxena & Vyas, 1986); antirheumatic (Kumar *et al.,* 2006).

Seed oil- Rheumatism, arthritis (Mitaliya *et al.,* 2003).

Leaf- Stomach pain, diarrhoea (Rajan *et al.,* 2003).

BUCHANANIA LANZAN Spreng. (ANACARDIACEAE)

Syn.: *B. latifolia* Roxb.

Regional and Other Names: *Bengali* – Sarapappu; *English* – Buchanan's mango; *Gujarati* – Charoli; *Hindi* – Ciraumci; *Kannada* – Nurkala; *Malayalam* – Mural; *Marathi* – Narkal; *Sanskrit* – Priyalah; *Tamil* – Murvala; *Telugu* – Sara.

Distribution: Throughout India.

Taxonomic description: Tall trees, with straight trunk, leaves elliptic-oblong. Flowers greenish-white, in pyramidal panicles. Drupes obiliquely lentiform, smooth, one-seeded.

Medicinal parts: Roots, leaves, fruits.

Taste: Sweet.

Chemical constituents: Leaves contain Kaempferol glucoside, quercetain, gallic acid.

Fruit Kernel contains Proteins; minerals as Calcium, phosphorus, iron, magnessium, sodium, copper, potassium, sulpher, chlorine, thiamine, niacin, riboflavin, vitamin C.

Medicinal properties:

प्रियालस्तु खरस्कन्धश्चारारो बहुवल्कलः ।
राजादनं तापसेष्टः सन्नकर्दुर्धनुः पटः ।। (भा. प्र.)

"Pṛiyālaṣtu kharaṣkaṇdhaṣcārārō bahuvaḷkalaḥ.
Rājādanaṃ tāpaseṣtaḥ saṇnakarduṛdhanuḥ pataḥ." (Bhā. Pṛa.)

Root - Acrid, astringent, constipating, cooling, depurative.

Leaves - Aphrodisiac, cooling, depurative, digestive, expectorant, purgative.

Fruits - Anti-inflammatory, aphrodisiac, cooling, depurative, diuretic, emollient, expectorant, febrifuge, laxative, sour, stomachic, sweet.

Medicinal uses:

Roots - Diarrhoea, leprosy, skin diseases.

Leaf - Bronchitis, burning sensation, constipation, cough, dyspepsia, flatulence, leprosy, skin diseases.

Fruits - Asthma, burning sensation, cardiac debility, constipation, cough, fever, inflammations, leprosy, skin diseases, ulcers.

Ethno- Medicinal uses: Stem bark – Cuts (Goel *et. al.,* 1984); skin diseases (Roy & Chaturvedi, 1986); snake bite (Gupta, 1981; Shah & Gopal, 1986; Kumar & Pandey, 1995); menorrhagia (Heamdri, 1992); burn healing (Hemadri & Rao, 1990; Goel *et. al.,* 1984); Mouth ulcer (Pandey & Rout, 2006); wounds (Goel *et. al.,* 1984; Gopalakrishnan & Krishna Prasad,1992).

Leaf - Wound (Malhotra & Moorthy, 1973; Jain, 1963, 1965; Roy & Chaturvedi, 1986; Sharma *et. al.,* 1979; Sharma & Singh, 1988); spermatorrhoea (Singh *et. al.,* 1994); blood purifier (Tripathi *et. al.,* 1996); dysentery (Saren *et al.,* 2003); leprosy, diarrhoea, seminal weakness, ulcers (Nayak *et al.,* 2003).

Gum - Diarrhoea (Sharma *et. al.,* 1979; Mitaliya & Bhatt, 2003); Heart pain (Vijaya kumar & Pullaiah, 1998); chest pain (Deshmukh & Rothe, 2003); wound, cut, boil (Mitaliya & Bhatt, 2003).

Seeds - Pimples (Roy & Chaturvedi, 1986); Cardiotonic (Tripathi *et. al.,* 1996).

Seed oil- Eczema (Prasad *et al.,* 2003).

Fruits - Skin diseases (Gopakumar *et. al.,* 1991); aphorodisiac, laxative (Tripathi *et. al.,* 1996); leprosy, diarrhoea, seminal weakness, ulcers (Nayak *et al.,* 2003).

Flowers - Laxative, aphrodisiac (Tripathi *et. al.,* 1996).

Root - Blood diseases (Tirpathi *et. al.,* 1996); leprosy, diarrhoea, seminal weakness, ulcers (Nayak *et al.,* 2003).

CAESALPINIA SAPPAN L. (CAESALPINIACEAE)

Regional and Other Names: *Bengali* – Bakam; *English* – Sappan wood; *Gujarati* – Bakam; *Hindi* – Patang; *Kannada* – Sappange; *Malayalam* – Cappannam; *Marathi* – Patang; *Sanskrit* – Patrangah; *Tamil* – Sappamgu; *Telugu* – Bakarucakka.

Distribution: Cultivated in South India & Bengal.

Taxonomic description: A small thorny tree, with yellow flowers and woody pod.

Medicinal parts: Heart wood.

Taste: Bitter.

Chemical constituents: Heartwood contains α & β- amyrin, glucoside, monosaccharides, fatty acid, protosappanins A,B & C, amino acid, β-sitosterol, quercetin, rhamnetin, embuin.

Medicinal properties:

पतङ्.गं मधुरं शीतं पित्तश्लेष्मव्रणास्रनुत् ।
हरिचन्दनवद्वेद्यं विशेषात् दाहनाशनम् ।। (भा. प्र.)

"Patangaṃ madhuraṃ sītaṃ piṭtaṣleṣmāvṛanāsṛanuṭ
Haricaṇdanavadvẹdyaṃ visesāṭ dāhanāsanaṃ." (Bhā. Pra.)

Heart wood - Acrid, astringent, bitter, constipating, depurative, refrigerant, sedative, sweet, vulnerary.

Medicinal uses: Heart wood - Burning sensation, diabetes, diarrhoea, dysentery, epilepsy, leprosy, leucorrhoea, skin diseases, ulcers, wounds.

CALLICARPA MACROPHYLLA Vahl. (VERBENACEAE)

Syn.: *C. nudiflora* Hook. & A.; *C. revesii* Wall. ex Schaucer.; *C. acuminata* Roxb.; *C. incana* Roxb.; *C. roxburghii* Wall.

Regional and Other Names: *Bengali* – Mathara; *English* – Calicarpa; *Hindi* – Priyangu; *Kannada* – Priyangu; *Malayalam* – Nalal; *Marathi* – Gahula; *Sanskrit* – Priyangu; *Tamil* – Nalal; *Telugu* – Priyangu.

Distribution: Bengal, Assam & Sub-Himalayan tracts.

Taxonomic description : An erect shrubs, with straggling branches, leaves 15-25 cm. long; cyme axillary, compounds. Flowers small, pale rose-coloured; drupe white.

Medicinal parts: Flowers, Fruits.

Taste : Bitter, Astringent.

Chemical constituents: Leaves contain 2-tetracyclic diterpenoid, B-sitosterol, calliterpenone, luteolin, apigenin, ursolic acid, crategolic acid.

Medicinal properties:

प्रियङ्.गुः शीतला तिक्ता मोहदाहविनाशिनी ।
ज्वरवान्तिहरा रक्तमुद्रिक्तं च प्रसादयेत् ।। (ध. नि.)

"Priyaṇguḥ ṣītalā tiķtā mohadāhavināṣinī
Jvaravāṇtiharā raķtamudriķtaṃ ca prasādayeṭ." (Dha. Ni.)

Flowers & Fruits - Acrid, alexeteric, anodyne, astringent, bitter, cooling, constipating, depurative, digestive, febrifuge, styptic, sweet.

Medicinal uses: Flowers & Fruits - Burning sensation, colic, diabetes, diarrhoea, dysentery, dyspepsia, fever, flatulence, skin diseases, vomiting.

Ethno- Medicinal uses: Fruits - Blisters (Maheshwari *et. al.,* 1980, 1981); boils, blisters on the tongue (Singh, 2003).

Leaf - Headache (Tiwari *et. al.,* 1979); rheumatism (Sharma *et. al.,* 1979; Nautiyal, 1981); wounds (Gaur *et. al.,* 1980).

Bark - Cuts, wounds (megoneitso & Rao, 1983).

Seed - Ulcers (Uniyal, 1968).

CALOPHYLLUM INOPHYLLUM L. (CLUSIACEAE)

Regional and Other Names: *Bengali* – Punnag; *English* – Alexandrian laureal; *Gujarati* – Punnag; *Hindi* – Sultan campa; *Kannada* – Uma; *Malayalam* – Punna; *Marathi* – Surangi; *Sanskrit* – Punnagah; *Tamil* – Punnai; *Telugu* – Ponnavittulu.

Distribution: East & West coasts, along river banks in certain localities.

Taxonomic description : A medium sized evergreen glabrous tree, with pure white fragrant flowers and drupe fruits.

Medicinal parts: Bark, Leaves, Seeds.

Taste : Sweet, Astringent.

Chemical constituents: Seeds contain Friedelin, β-sitosterol, β-amyrin, canophyllol, 4-phenylcoumarins-calophylloide, inophylloie, calloph-yllic acid.

Leaves contain Saponin & hydrocyanic acid.

Bark contains Inophyssloidic acid, tanin, resin.

Medicinal properties:

पुन्नागस्तुवरः शीतो स्वादु पित्तकफास्रजित्।। (कै. नि.)

"Puṇnāgaṣtuvaraḥ ṣīto ṣvādu piṭtakaphāsṛajiṭ." (Kaī. Ni.)

Bark - Anodyne, astringent, cooling, demulcent, diuretic, emetic, emollient, purgative, sweet.

Seed oil - Anodyne, demulcent, diuretic.

Medicinal uses: Bark - Pruritus, skin diseases, strangury, wounds.

Seed oil - Gonorrhoea, leprosy, scabies, skin diseases.

Ethno- Medicinal uses: Seed - Gonorrhoea (Shah, 1984); wound, gonorrhoea, scabies (Nayak *et al.,* 2003).

Bark- Minor wounds (Gopalakrishnan & Krishna Prasad,1992); wound, gonorrhoea, scabies (Nayak *et al.,* 2003).

Seed oil- Rheumatic pains, skin diseases (Kothari & Rao, 2003).

Leaf- wound, gonorrhoea, scabies (Nayak *et al.,* 2003).

CALYCOPTERIS FLORIBUNDA Lam. (COMBRETACEAE)

Syn.: *Getonia floribunda* Roxb.

Regional and Other Names: *English* – Kokkarai; *Hindi* – Marsadabaguli; *Kannada* – Bagule; *Malayalam* – Pullani; *Marathi* – Ukshi; *Sanskrit* – Susavi; *Tamil* – Minnarkoti; *Telugu* – Bandimurududu.

Distribution: Throughout India.

Taxonomic description: A scandent woody shrub with slender brown streaked diffuse branches. Calyx persistent, petals absent.

Medicinal parts : Leaves, Fruits.

Taste : Bitter.

Chemical constituents: Leaves contain n-octacosanal, sitosterol, calycopterin, ellagic acid, quercetin, proanthocynadinin, tanin.

Medicinal properties:

कारवेल्लं तु जलजं कृमिपित्तकफे हितम् ।। (कै. नि.)

"Kāravellaṃ tu jalajaṃ kṛamipittakaphe hitaṃ" (Kaī. Ni.)

Leaves - Anthelmintic, astringent, bitter, depurative, diaphoretic, febrifuge, laxative.

Medicinal uses: Leaf - Colic, dysentery, fever, intestinal worms, leprosy, ulcers, vomiting.

Fruits - Jaundice, pruritus, skin diseases, ulcers.

Ethno- Medicinal uses: Leaf - Wounds, Cuts (Ramachandran & Nair, 1981); malaria fever, jaundice (Nayak *et al.,* 2003).

Fruit- Jaundice (Kothari & Rao, 2003); malaria fever, jaundice (Nayak *et al.,* 2003).

Tender branches- Snake bite (Kothari & Rao, 2003).

CAMELLIA SINENSIS (L.) O. Kuntze (THEACEAE)

Syn.: *C. thea* Link.; *C. theifera* Griff.

Regional and Other Names: *Bengali* – Cha; *English* – Tea plant; Hindi – Cay; *Kannada* – Teyaku; *Malayalam* – Teyila; *Marathi* – Cha; *Sanskrit* – Syamaparni; *Tamil* – Teyilai; *Telugu* – Teyaku.

Distribution: Throughout India, cultivated at high altitudes.

Taxonomic description: An evergreen shrub or tree, with white fragrant flowers and capsule fruits.

Medicinal parts : Leaves.

Taste : Bitter, Astringent.

Medicinal properties:

तीक्ष्णोष्णा तुवरा चाहा दीपनी पाचनी लघुः ।
कफपित्तहरी चैव किंचिद्वातप्रकोपनी।। (शा. नि.)

"Tīkṣṇoṣṇā turvarā cāhā dīpanī pācanī laghuḥ
Kaphapiṭtaharī caīva kiṇcidvātapṛakopanī." (Ṣa. Ni.)

Leaves - Appetizer, astringent, bitter, carminative, detergent, digestive, diuretic.

Medicinal uses: Leaves - Abdominal disorders, fatigue, fever, inflammations, strangury.

Ethno- Medicinal uses: Leaf - Abortifacient, Cuts, Injury (Rao & Jamir, 1982); Diabetes (Ghosh, 2006); To make smooth and silky hair (External application) (Jadeja *et al.,* 2006).

CAPPARIS DECIDUA (Forsk.) Edgew. (CAPPARACEAE)

Regional and Other Names: *English* – Caper plant; *Gujarati* – Kera; *Hindi* – Karil; *Kannada* – Nispatige; *Malayalam* – Karimulli; *Marathi* – Karil; *Sanskrit* – Karirah; *Tamil* – Senkam; *Telugu* – Enugadanta.

Distribution: Throughout India, in dry areas.

Taxonomic description: Leafless spiny shrubs or small trees, with red or Orange-Red flowers in corymbose racemes or fascicles. Berries subglobose, scarlet when ripe.

Medicinal parts: Roots, Fruits.

Taste : Bitter, Acrid.

Chemical constituents: Isothiocyanate glucoside, glucocapparin, stachydrine, n-triaconate, β-carotene, β-sitotsterol, n-triacontanol, n-pentacosane, phthalic acid.

Medicinal properties:

करीरः कटुकस्तिक्तः स्वेद्युष्णो भेदनः स्मृतः ।
दुर्नामकफवातामगरशोफव्रणप्रणुत् ।। (भा. प्र.)

"Karīraḥ katukaṣtiktah ṣveḍyuṣṇo bhedanaḥ ṣmṛtaḥ.
Duṛnāmakaphavātāmagaraṣophavṛanapṛanuṭ." (Bhā. Pṛa.)

Roots - Acrid, alexeteric, anodyne, anthelmintic, bitter, carminative, digestive, expectorant, purgative, sudorific, thermogenic, vulnerary.

Fruits - Acrid, aphrodisiac, astringent, bitter, stimulant, sweet, thermogenic.

Medicinal uses: Root - Amenorrhoea, arthritis, asthma, boils, constipation, cough, dysmenorrhoea, dyspepsia, cruptions, flatulence, gout, hiccough, intestinal worms, lumbago, swelling, vomiting.

Fruits - Cardiac disorders.

Ethno- Medicinal uses: Leaf - Cardiac problems (Shah *et. al.,* 1981); tooth troubles (Bhatt & Sabnis, 1987); flatulence, cough, cold (Kumar *et al.,* 2003).

Fruits - Intestinal worms (Saxena & Vyas, 1981).

Stem - Rheumatism, tooth troubles (Saxena & Vyas, 1983); asthma, swelling, cough (Deokule, 2006); flatulence, sough, cold (Kumar *et al.,* 2003).

Whole plant- Asthma, swelling, cough (Deokule & Magdum, 1992).

Root bark- flatulence, sough, cold (Kumar *et al.,* 2003).

CAPSICUM ANNUUM L. (SOLANACEAE)

Syn.: *C. longum* DC.; *C. grossum* Willd.; *C. condiforme* Mill.

Regional and Other Names: *Bengali* – Morich; *English* – Chillies; *Gujarati* – Marcha; *Hindi* – Lalmirca; *Kannada* – Kempumenasu; *Malayalam* – Mulaku; *Marathi* – Mirchi; *Sanskrit* – Katuvirah; *Tamil* – Milagai; *Telugu* – Mivapakaya.

Distribution: Throughout India, cultivated.

Taxonomic description: Perennial herbs, with lanceolate leaves, white flowers & slender, Green red or orange fruits.

Medicinal parts: Fruits.

Taste : Acrid.

Chemical constituents: Fruits contain A volatile alkaloid-capsicin; a crystalline substance-capsacin; a volatile oil-solanine; fatty acid, resin.

Medicinal properties:

लंका तीक्ष्णा कटुष्णातिलालास्त्रावकरी मता।
विदोहजननी पित्तकारिणी कफवातहृत् ।। (द्रव्यगुण विज्ञान)

"Laṇkā tīkṣṇā katuṣṇātillālāṣṭrāvakarī matā
Vidahajananī pịttakāriṇı kaphavātahṛṭ." *(Ḍravyaguṇa)*

Fruits - Acrid, antiperiodic, bitter, carminative, digestive, expectorant, laxative, rubefacient, stimulant, sudorific, thermogenic.

Medicinal uses: Fruits - Arthritis, cholera, cough, dropsy, dyspepsia, fever, flatulence, gout, hoarseness, sciatica.

Ethno- Medicinal uses: Fruits - Gout (Jadeja *et al.,* 2006); snake bite (Rai *et al.,* 1992); bee & wasp sting (Singh & Singh, 2003).

CARDIOSPERMUM HALICACABUM L. (SAPINDACEAE)

Regional and Other Names: *Bengali* – Shibjhul; *English* – Ballon vine; *Gujarati* –Karolio; *Hindi* – Kanphuti; *Kannada* – Kanakayya; *Malayalam* – Ulinna; *Marathi* – Kanphuti; *Sanskrit* – Sakralata; *Tamil* – Mudukkottan; *Telugu* – Vekkudutiga.

Distribution: Throughout India.

Taxonomic description: Herbaceous climbers, with 5-fid axillary tendrils and bi-or trinate leaves. Flowers white, in cymes on terminal tendrils.

Medicinal parts : Roots, Leaves, Seeds.

Taste : Bitter, Acrid.

Chemical constituents: Seed - Cyanogenic glycoside, essential oil.

Medicinal properties:

दाहप्रदा दीपनकृश्च मेध्या ।
प्रज्ञांच पुष्णाति तथा तेजोवती ।। (रा. नि.)

"Dāhap̣radā dīpanakṛṣca meḍḥyā
P̣rajnāṇca puṣṇāti tathā tejovatī." (Rā. Ni.)

Root - Diaphoretic, diuretic, emetic, laxative.

Leaves - Rubefacient.

Seeds - Diaphoretic.

Medicinal uses: Root-Menorrhoea, arthritis, fever, lumbago, strangury.

Leaves - Arthritis.

Seeds - Arthritis, fever.

Ethno- Medicinal uses: Leaf - Earache (Janardhanan, 1963; Deokule, 2006); wounds (Malhotra & Moorthy, 1973; Sharma *et. al.,* 1979); Gas trouble (Ganesan *et. al.,* 2006); leucorrhoea (Srivastava *et al.,* 1992); Rheumatism (Samvatsar & Diwanji, 2003); inflammation, swelling, dysentery (Rosakutty *et al.,* 2003); skin diseases, general weakness, chronic rheumatism, nervous diseases (Kumar *et al.,* 2003); arthritis, amenorrhoea, otalgia (Nayak *et al.,* 2003); asthma (Arinathan *et al.,* 2003); joint pain (Ravikumar & Vijaya Sankar, 2003; Ganesan & Kesavan, 2003).

Stem - Fever (Jain *et. al.,* 1973; Banerjee *et. al.,* 1977); skin diseases, general weakness, chronic rheumatism, nervous diseases (Kumar *et al.,* 2003).

Leaf juice - Earache (Shubhangi & Patil, 2006; Tomar & Singh, 2005); dysentery (Subramanian *et al.,* 2003).

Root - Diuretic, diaphoretic (Tomar & Singh, 2005); skin diseases, general weakness, chronic rheumatism (Kumar *et al.,* 2003); lumbago, rheumatism (Kumar & Lal, 2003); nervous diseases (Kumar *et al.,* 2003; Kumar & Lal, 2003); arthritis, amenorrhoea, otalgia (Nayak *et al.,* 2003); heart trouble (Gopal & Chandra, 2003); urinary stone (Ganesan & Kesavan, 2003).

Seed - Fever (Kadaval & Jisha, 2006).

Whole plant - Snake bite (Basak, 2006); stifness of limbs, decay of teeth/jaws (Sharma & Sharma, 1992); rheumatism (Deokule & Magdum, 1992; Sharma & Sharma, 1992; Basak, 2006; Gogoi & Das, 2003); earache (Deokule & Magdum, 1992); bone fractures (Dwarakan & Ansari, 1992); diuretic (Gogoi *et al.,* 2003); earache (Prasad *et al.,* 2003).

Fruit- Boils (Girach *et al.,* 2003).

CAREYA ARBOREA Roxb. (BARRINGTONIACEAE)

Regional and Other Names: Bengali – Kumbh; English – Kumbi; Gujrati –Kumbi; Hindi – Kumbi; Kannada –Gudda; Malayalam – Pelu; Marathi – Kuba; Sanskrit – Kumbhi; Tamil – Kumbi; Telugu – Duddipi.

Distribution: Throughout India.

Taxonomic description: A small to medium sized deciduous tree with yellowish-white flowers and berries fruit.

Medicinal parts : Bark, leaves, flowers, fruits.

Taste : Acrid.

Medicinal properties:

कटम्भरः कटुः सोष्णो नाडीव्रणविशोधनः ।
निहन्ति कफकुष्ठास्रमेदोमेह विषकृमीन् ।। (कै. नि)

Kataṃbharaḥ katuḥ soṣṇo nādīvṛaṇaviṣodhanaḥ
Nihaṇti kaphakuṣthāṣramedomeh visakṛmīṇ (Kaī. ni.)

Bark - Acrid, alexeteric, anthelmintic, astringent, bitter, expectoranr, thermogenic.

Fruit - Acrid, astringent, aromatic, anaphrodisiac.

Medicinal uses: Bark - Bronchitis, catarrh, colic, cough,dysentery, dyspepsia, leucoderma, tumours.

Fruit - Dyspepsia.

Ethno- Medicinal uses: Bark - Dysentery (Saxena & Dutta, 1975; Joshi *et al.,* 1980); cuts, wounds (Chaudhury *et al.,* 1975); diarrhoea, eye diseases (Jain, 1965); skin diseases (Malhotra & Moorthy, 1973; Sharma *et al.,* 1979); snake bite (Roy & Chaturvedi, 1986); asthma, burnings, dental diseases, snake bite (Kothari & Londhe, 2003); indigestion flatulence (Islam & Jha, 2003).

Leaves - Intestinal trouble (Mokat & Deokule, 2006).

Flower- Cough, cold (Kumar & Lal, 2003); dysentery, indigestion, colic, flatulence, worms (Mitaliya & Bhatt, 2003).

Gum- Antiseptic (Kumar & Lal, 2003).

Bark fibres- Eczema (Sahoo & Bahali, 2003).

CARICA PAPAYA L. (CARICACEAE)

Regional and Other Names: *Bengali* – Papeya; *English* – Papaya; *Gujarati* – Chibda; *Hindi* – Pappita; *Kannada* – Pappaya; *Malayalam* – Pappaya; *Marathi* – Papaya; *Sanskrit* – Erandakarkati; *Tamil* – Pappali; *Telugu* – Bobbasi.

Distribution: Throughout India.

Taxonomic description: A rapidly growing tree, up to 7 m. tall, with milky sap. Leaves palmately-lobed and flowers creamy yellow; female flowers in short clusters and males in long drooping panicles.

Medicinal parts : Fruits, Latex.

Taste : Sweet.

Chemical constituents: Fruits pulp contains Sucrose, invert sugar, papain, malic acid, salts of tartaric acid & citric acid, pectins, carotenoid, vitamins.

Latex contains Enzymes papain & chymopapain.

Medicinal properties:

पारीशं शीतलं रूच्यम् दीपनं पाचनं सरम् ।
मधुरं रक्तपित्तघ्न विषेशादर्शसे हितम् ।। (द्र. वि.)

"Pārīsaṃ ṣītalaṃ ruçyaṃ dīpanaṃ pācanaṃ saraṃ
Madhuraṃ raḳtapiṭtaghnaṃ viṣesādaṛṣase hitaṃ." (Dṛavyaguna)

Fruits - Acrid, anodyne, anthelmintic, anti-inflammatory, antifungal, aphrodisiac, appetizer, bitter, carminative, demulcent, digestive, stomachic, thermogenic.

Latex - Anodyne, anthelmintic, febrifuge, sudorific.

Medicinal uses: Fruits - Bronchitis, cough, dyspepsia, inflammations, intestinal worms, psoriasis, ringworm, skin diseases.

Latex - Amenorrhoea, constipation, dysmenorrhoea, dyspepsia, leprosy, skin diseases.

Ethno- Medicinal uses: Leaf - Bone fractures (Pal & Srivastava, 1976); constipation (Megoneitso & Rao, 1983); toothache (Das *et al.,* 2006); malaria fever (Das & Sharma, 2003); dermatitis (Thomas & Britto, 2003).

Fruit - Gastric trouble (Rao & Jamir, 1982); urine bladder complaint (Rao & Jamir, 1982); abortifacient (Tarafder, 1983); gout (Jadeja *et al.,* 2006); hepatitis (Dutta *et al.,* 2006); dysentery (Das *et al.,* 2006; Das & Sharma, 2003); constipation (Deokule & Magdum, 1992; Deokule, 2006); skin diseases, digestive troubles (Mukhopadhyay, 1992); stomachic (Bhuyan, 2003; Rajan *et al.,* 2003); abortion (Singh & Singh, 2003); improve eyesight (Kumar *et al.,* 2003).

Latex - Abortifacient (Ramachandran & Nair, 1981); ringworm (Shah *et. al.,* 1981; Maheshwari & Singh, 1984; Tigga *et al.,* 2003); skin diseases (Megoneitso & Rao, 1983); toothache (Singh *et. al.,* 1985; Maheswhari & Singh, 1984); rickets (Kshirsagar & Singh, 2003); eczema, infected wounds, malignant tumours, bleeding haemorrhoids (Tigga *et al.,* 2003); indigestion (Kumar *et al.,* 2003).

Root - Abortifacient (Bhatacharjee *et. al.,* 1980; Tiwari *et. al.,* 1982).

Flower - Earache (Das *et al.,* 2006).

Buds- Giddiness (Bora, 2003).

Seed- Abortion (Singh & Singh, 2003).

CARTHAMUS TINCTORIUS L. (ASTERACEAE)

Regional and Other Names: *Bengali* – Kusum; *English* – Safflower; *Gujarati* –Karada ; *Hindi* – Kusum; *Kannada* – Kusubbi; *Malayalam* – Kuyimpu; *Marathi* – Kardi; *Sanskrit* – Kusumbah; *Tamil* – Senturakam; *Telugu* – Kusumbha.

Distribution: Cultivated throughout India.

Taxonomic description: An erect branching annual herb, with yellow or orange-red flowers and achene fruits.

Medicinal parts: Leaves, Flowers, Seeds.

Taste : Sweet, Astringent.

Chemical constituents: Seeds - Matairesinol monoglucoside.

Flowers - Safflomin pigment, cathamin, neocarthamin, kaempferol glucoside.

Leaves - Acetylene compounds.

Medicinal properties:

कुसुंभबीजं वरटा स वै प्रोक्ता वराटिका ।। (भा. प्र.)

"Kusuṃbhabījaṃ varatā sa vaī p̣roḳtā varātika." (Bhā. P̣ra.)

Leaves - Appetizer, Bitter, diuretic, laxative, sweet.

Flowers - Bitter, diuretic, expectorant, laxative, sedative.

Seeds - Bitter, carminative, diuretic, purgative, aphrodisiac.

Medicinal uses: Flowers - Boils, bronchitis, inflammations, leprosy, lurcoderma, ringworm, scabies.

Seeds - Arthritis, catarrh, constipation, leucoderma, scabies.

Ethno- Medicinal uses: Root - Purgative, diuretic (Sinha *et al.,* 2006).

Seed - Purgative, diuretic (Sinha *et al.,* 2006).

Flower- Jaundice (Islam & Hasin, 2003).

Seed oil- Rheumatic pain (Islam & Hasin, 2003).

CARYOTA URENS L. (ARECACEAE)

Regional and Other Names: *Bengali* – Golsabu; *English* – Fish-tail palm; *Gujarati* – Shankarjata; *Hindi* – Mari; *Kannada* – Kondapana; *Malayalam* – Anappana; *Marathi* – Berli; *Sanskrit* – Sritalah; *Tamil* – Kuntarpanai; *Telugu* – Kondajilugu.

Distribution: Throughout India.

Taxonomic description: A tall, feather-leaved palm, with smooth shiny trunk and pendulous spadix inflorescence.

Medicinal parts: Tender bud, leaves & nuts.

Taste : Sweet.

Chemical constituents: Leaves contain Epicatechin, Gallo-catechin and epicatechingallate.

Medicinal properties:

श्रीतालो मधुतालश्च लक्ष्मीतालो मृदुच्छदः ।। (रा. नि.)

"Ṣrītālo madhutālaṣca lakṣmītālo mrduçchadaḥ." (Rā. Ni.)

Tender leaves - Cooling, sweet.

Medicinal uses: Fruits - Fatigue, hyperdisia.

Ethno- Medicinal uses: Root - Dysentery (Kumar *et. al.*, 1987).

Fruit- Headache (Kothari & Rao, 2003).

Spadices & Nuts- Aphrodisiac, laxative (Gogoi *et al.,* 2003).

CEIBA PENTANDRA (L.) Gaertn. (BOMBACACEAE)

Syn.: *Eriodendron anfractuosum* DC.; *Bombax pentandrum* L.

Regional and Other Names: *Bengali* – Shwetsimul; *English* – True kapok tree; *Hindi* – Saphed simal; *Kannada* – Bili buruga; *Malayalam* – Pannimaram; *Marathi* – Salmali; *Sanskrit* – Svetasalmali; *Tamil* – Pancu; *Telugu* – Buruga sauna.

Distribution: Throughout India.

Taxonomic description: A medium sized to tall deciduous tree, trunk prickly when young and smooth when old, branches green; leaves digitately compound, leaflet lanceolate, entire; flowers white or yellowish appearing at the ends of the branches along with the leaves; fruits capsules, lined with long silky white hairs.

Medicinal parts: Root, bark.

Taste: Bitter, Acrid.

Medicinal properties:

कुत्सितः शाल्मलिः प्रोक्तो रोचनः कूटशाल्मलिः ।। (भा. प्र.)

"Kutsiṭaḥ ṣāḷmaliḥ pṛoḳto rōcanaḥ kūtaṣāḷmaliḥ." (Bhā. Pṛa.)

Roots - Aphrodisiac, antipyretic, diuretic.

Bark - Acrid, bitter, diuretic, emetic, febrifuge, purgative, thermogenic.

Medicinal uses: Roots - Dysuria, fever, gonorrhoea.

Bark - Abdominal complaint, colic, flatulence, strangury, tumours.

Ethno- Medicinal uses: Plant- Leucorrhoea (Basu, 2003).

Root- Diabetes (Ghosh & Das, 2003).

Seed- Diabetes (Ghosh & Das, 2003).

CICER ARIETINUM L.(PAPILIONACEAE)

Regional and Other Names: *Bengali* – Chola; *English* – Bengal gram; *Gujarati* –Chana ; *Hindi* – Cana; *Kannada* – Kadale; *Malayalam* – Katala; *Marathi* – Harbara; *Sanskrit* – Canakah; *Tamil* – Katalai; *Telugu* – Canakamula.

Distribution: Cultivated throughout India.

Taxonomic description: Much branched herbs, with pinnate leaves and turgid-oblong fruits.

Medicinal parts : Leaves, Seeds.

Taste : Sweet.

Chemical constituents: Leaves contain Vanillic, P-hydroxybenzoic acid; oxalic acid, malic acid, arginine, tryosine, lycine, cystine, tryptophane; carotenoids & vitamins.

Medicinal properties:

कफास्त्रपित्तपुस्त्वघ्नाष्चणका वातला हिमाः ।
लघवो भृष्टचणका आमक्लमहराः पराः ।
छर्दिघ्ना रोचनाः शुष्कास्तेजोवीर्यबलप्रदाः ।। (ध. नि.)

"Kaphāṣrapiṭtapuṃṣtvaghnāṣcaṇakā vātalā himāḥ.
Laghavo bhṛstacaṇakā āmaḳlamaharāḥ parāḥ.
Chaṛdighnā rocanāḥ ṣuṣkāṣtejovīṛyabalapṛadāḥ." (Dha. Ni.)

Leaves - Abortifacient, purgative.

Seed - Aphrodisiac, cooling, expectorant.

Medicinal uses: Leaves - Bronchitis, Dyspepsia.

Seed - Bronchitis, burning sensation, inflammations, leprosy, skin diseases.

Ethno- Medicinal uses: Seed - Jaundice (Lal & Yadav, 1983; Jadhav, 2006); To make silky hair (External application) (Jadeja *et al.,* 2006).

Leaf- Stomach disorders (Deokule & Magdum, 1992).

CINCHONA OFFICINALIS L. (RUBIACEAE)

Syn.: *C. condaminea* Humb.

Regional and Other Names: *English* – Quinine bark; *Hindi* – Kunain; *Kannada* – Sinkona; *Malayalam* – Sinkona; *Marathi* –; *Sanskrit* – Sinkona; *Tamil* – Cinkona; *Telugu* – Cinkona.

Distribution: Cultivated in India in Nilgriris at an elevation of 1800-2400 m.

Taxonomic description : A slender tree, with Pink or Purple flowers and capsule fruits.

Medicinal parts : Bark.

Taste : Bitter.

Chemical constituents: Stem bark contain Quinoline alkaloids – Quinine, cinchonidine, cinchonine, quinidine. Others- Hydroqunine, hydrocinchonidine, quiniamine, cinchotine, homocinchonidine, cinchotannic acid, quinic acid, bitter amorphous glycoside quinovin.

Medicinal properties:

लघुरूक्षश्चोष्णः सपदि कफपित्तप्रशमनः ।
ज्वरोच्छ्रायं तिक्तो हरति विषमाख्यं कुनयनः ।। (द्र. गु. वि.)

"Laghuruksaṣcoṣṇaḥ sapadi kaphapịttapṛaṣamanaḥ
Ḍvaroc̣chṛāyaṃ tịkto harati visamāḳḥyaṃ kunayanaḥ." (Dṛa.Gu.Vi.)

Quinine - Acrid, anodyne, anthelmintic, anti-inflammatory, antipyretic, astringent, bitter, constipating, depurative, digestive, expectorant, febrifuge, thermogenic.

Medicinal uses: Quinine - Amenorrhoea, bronchitis, cardiac debility, cough, dysentery, dysmenorrhoea. dyspepsia, fevers, lumbago, sciatica, skin diseases.

Ethno-Medicinal uses: Bark-Intermittent fever, Toothache (Rajan, 1992).

CINNAMOMUM CAMPHORA (L.) Presl (LAURACEAE)

Syn.: *Laurus camphora* L.; *Camphora officinarum* Nees.

Regional and Other Names: *Bengali* – Karpur; *English* – Camphor tree; *Hindi* – Kapur; *Kannada* – Karpura; *Malayalam* – Karpuram; *Marathi* – Kapur; *Sanskrit* – Karpurah; *Tamil* – Karpuram; *Telugu* – Karpuramu.

Distribution: A native of India, China & Formosa; now cultivated in India.

Taxonomic description: A large handsome evergreen tree; Leaves leathery, shining, 5-10 cm. long, aromatic; fruits dark green, ovoid.

Medicinal parts : Deposits in the oil cells (Camphor).

Taste : Bitter, Acrid, Sweet.

Chemical constituents: Essential oil sesquiterpenes, camphorenone, campherenol.

Roots contain Alkaloids, laurolistsine, Reticuliene.

Leaves contain Palmitone.

Heartwood contain Cyclopentenone.

Medicinal properties:

ईशावासश्च कर्पूरो भेदी वृष्यो मदापहः ।। (नि. र.)

"Ēṣāvāsaṣca karpūro bhedi vṛṣyo madāpahaḥ." (Ni. Ra.)

Camphor - Antiseptic, anodyne, aphrodisiac, aromatic, bitter, diaphoretic, emollient, expectorant, thermogenic.

Medicinal uses: Camphor - Asthma, cardiac debility, cough, diarrhoea, dysentery, dyspepsia, flatulence, inflammations.

Ethno- Medicinal uses: Stem bark - Gout (Jadeja *et al.,* 2006).

Leaves - Gout (Jadeja *et al.,* 2006).

Fruit powder & Camphor - Toothache (Mokat & Deokule, 2006).

CINNAMOMUM TAMALA (Buch.-Ham.) Nees. (LAURACEAE)

Regional and Other Names: *Bengali* – Tejpata; *English* – Indian cassia lignea; *Gujarati* – Taj; *Hindi* – Tejpatt; *Kannada* – Kadu lavanga patte; *Malayalam* – Paccila; *Marathi* – Tamal; *Sanskrit* – Tamalapatram; *Tamil* – Tamalapattiri; *Telugu* – Talisa patri.

Distribution: Himalayas in area of 900-2400 m elevation.

Taxonomic description : A medium sized, evergreen, scented, about 25 feet high, flowers yellowish in panicles.

Medicinal parts : Leaves.

Taste : Sweet, Aromatic.

Chemical constituents: Leaves contain - Essential oil, eugenol and isoeugenol.

Medicinal properties:

पत्रकं मधुरं किंचित्तीक्ष्णोष्णं पिच्छिलं लघु ।
निहन्ति कफवातार्शोहृल्लासारुचिपीनसान् ।! (भा. प्र.)

"Paṭrakaṃ madhuraṃ kiṇciṭtikṣṇoṣṇaṃ piçchilaṃ laghu
Nihaṇti kaphavātāṛṣohṛ̣llāsārucipīnasāṇ." (Bhā. Pṛa.)

Bark - Acrid, alexeteric, aphrodisiac, aromatic, astringent, bitter, carminative, diuretic, expectorant, febrifuge, stimulant, sweet.

Medicinal uses: Bark - Asthma, bronchitis, diarrhoea, fever, flatulence, nausea, vomiting.

Ethno- Medicinal uses: Bark - Cough (Kharkongor & Joseph, 1981); toothache (Saikh & Nath, 2003; Das *et al.,* 2006); mumps (Nath & Maiti, 2003).

Leaves - Toothache (Baruah *et al.,* 2006; Das *et al.,* 2006).

CINNAMOMUM VERUM L. Presl (LAURACEAE)

Syn.: *C. zeylanicum* Blume.

Regional and Other Names: *English* – Cinnamon; *Gujarati* – Dalchini; *Hindi* – Dalcini; *Kannada* – Dalcini; *Malayalam* – Karuva; *Marathi* – Dalchini; *Sanskrit* – Cocam; *Tamil* – Karuva; *Telugu* – Dalcini.

Distribution: China, Ceylon, Cultivated in South India.

Taxonomic description: A small sized evergreen tree, with reddish brown soft bark and having numerous small warts; leaves ovate or elliptic-ovate, flowers small in axillary or sub-terminal cymes or panicles; fruits ovoid berry.

Medicinal parts : Bark, Oil.

Taste : Bitter, Sweet, Acrid.

Chemical constituents: Bark contains - Essential oil, cinnamon oil, eugenol, volatile oil, cinnamaldehyde, camphor, cinnzeylamine, tannin & gum.

Medicinal properties:

त्वचं तु कटुकं शीतं कफकासविनाशनम् ।
शुक्लामशमनं चैव कण्ठशुद्धिकरं लघु ।। (रा. नि.)

"Ṭvacaṃ tu katukaṃ ṣītaṃ kaphakāsavināsanaṃ
Ṣuķlāmasamanaṃ caīva kaṇthaṣuddḥikaraṃ laghu." (Rā. Ni.)

Bark - Acrid, alexeteric, aphrodisiac, aromatic, astringent, bitter, carminative, diuretic, expectorant, febrifuge, stimulant, sweet.

Cinnamon oil - Carminative, stomachic, styptic.

Medicinal uses: Bark - Asthma, bronchitis, cardiac diseases, diarrhoea, fever, flatulence, nausea, vomiting.

Cinnamon oil - Inflammations, vomiting.

Ethno- Medicinal uses: Leaf - Cough (Kharkongor & Joseph , 1981).

Bark - Diarrhoea, nausea, vomiting (Nautiyal, 1981); dysentery, flatulence, gout (Jadeja *et al.,* 2006); Diabetes (Ghosh, 2006); Toothache (Saikh & Nath, 2003).

CITRUS LIMON (L.) Burm. f. (RUTACEAE)

Regional and Other Names: *Bengali* – Baranebu; *English* – Lime; *Hindi* – Jamiri nimbu; *Kannada* – Limbe; *Malayalam* – Cerunarakam; *Marathi* – Limbu; *Sanskrit* – Jambirah; *Tamil* – Elumiccai; *Telugu* – Nimma.

Distribution: Cultivated all over India.

Taxonomic description: Thorny trees, with ovate-elliptic leaves, white flowers tinged with pink-purple and oval or oblong fruits.

Medicinal parts : Fruits.

Taste : Sour.

Chemical constituents: Oil from peel contains d-limonene, camphene, linalool.

Peel contains Bitter principle, essential oil, hesperidin, citronellal, bergamotine, eriocitrin, apigenin, luteolin, chrysoseriol, quercetin, isorhamnetin, limocitin, limocitriol.

Seeds contain Bitter principles, obacunone, limonin.

Roots contain Xanthyletin, stigmasterol, β-sitosterol.

Medicinal properties:

जम्बीरो जम्भलो जम्भो प्रोक्तो दन्तशठस्तथा ।
जम्भीरो वत्क्रशोधी च रोचनो दन्तहर्षणः ।। (ध. नि.)

"Jaṃbīro jaṃbhalo jaṃbho p̣roḳto daṇtaṣathaṣtathā
Jaṃbhīro vaṭkṛaṣodhī ca rōcano daṇtahaṛsaṇaḥ." (Dha. Ni.)

Fruits - Anthelmintic, antiseptic. carminative, digestive, laxative, stimulant, sour, stomachic, thermogenic.

Medicinal uses: Fruits - Bronchitis, colic, constipation, cough, dyspepsia, fatigue, flatulence, helminthiasis, scabies, vomiting.

Ethno- Medicinal uses: Leaves - Eye diseases (Jadhav, 2006).

Fruit - Gout, dandruff (Jadeja *et al.*, 2006); malaria (Deka *et al.*, 2006).

CITRUS MEDICA L. (RUTACEAE)

Regional and Other Names: *Bengali* – Bara nimbu; *English* – Citron; *Gujarati* – Bijora; *Hindi* – Baranimbu; *Kannada* – Madala; *Malayalam* – Ganapatinarakam; *Sanskrit* – Matulungah; *Tamil* – Kadaranarattai; *Telugu* – Madia.

Distribution: Throughout India.

Taxonomic description: Large shrubs or small trees, with axillary spines, white flowers and globose fruits.

Medicinal parts : Whole plant.

Taste : Sweet, Acidic.

Chemical constituents: α-pinene, β-pinene, myrcene, camphene, limonene, α-phellandrene, 3-carene, P-cymene, γ-terpinene, terpinolence, nonylaldehyde, citronellal oil.

Medicinal properties:

बीजपूरफलं स्वादु सरेऽम्लं दीपनं लघु ।
रक्तपित्तहरं कण्ठजिह्वाहृदयशोधनम् ।
श्वासकासारुचिहरं हृदयं तृष्णाहरं स्मृतम् ।। (भा. प्र.)

"Bījapuraphalaṃ ṣvādu rasemlaṃ dīpanaṃ laghu
Raḳtapiṭlaharaṃ kaṇthajihvāhṛdayaṣodhanaṃ
Ṣvāsakāsāruciharaṃ hṛdyaṃ ṭṛṣṇāharaṃ ṣmṛtaṃ." (Bhā. Pṛa.)

Roots - Anthlemintic, diuretic, laxative.

Buds & Flowers - Astringent, antiemetic, appestiser. stimulant.

Fruits - Anthelmintic, astringent, carminative, digestive, emollient, refrigerant, sour, stimulant, sweet.

Seeds - Anti-inflammatory, stimulant.

Medicinal uses: Root - Colic, constipation, flatulence, helminthiasis, strangury, tumours, vomiting.

Buds & Flowers - Abdominal disorders, dysmenorrhoea, flatulence, leprosy, tumours, vomiting.

Seeds - Amenorrhoea, dysmenorrhoea, inflammations, skin diseases.

Ethno- Medicinal uses: Root - Juandice (Krishna & Singh, 1987).

Bark - Pimples (Purohit *et. al.,* 1985); To make strong and healthy hair (External application) (Jadeja *et al.,* 2006).

Fruit - Urinary disorders, kidney disorders (Rao & Jamir, 1982); malaria (Megoneitso & Rao, 1983); ringworm (Purohit *et. al.,* 1985).

Leaf juice- Headache (Kumar *et al.,* 2003).

CITRUS RETICULATA Blanco (RUTACEAE)

Syn.: *C. aurantium* var. *aurantinum* Pro Parte.; *C. auratinum* L. var. *bigaradia* Hook. f.; *Citrus vugaris* Risso., *C. nobilis* Lour.; *C. chrysocarpa* Lushington.

Regional and Other Names: *Bengali* – Kamla lebu; *English* – Loose-skinned orange; *Hindi* – Narangi, Santara; *Kannada* – Dorale; *Malayalam* – Madhuranaranna; *Sanskrit* – Narangah; *Tamil* – Narangam; *Telugu* – Narinja.

Distribution: Cultivated throughout India.

Taxonomic description : An evergreen bushy moderate sized tree with greenish-white glabrous branches and white fragrant flowers.

Medicinal parts : Flowers, Fruits.

Taste: Sweet, Acidic.

Chemical constituents: Leaves-Essential oil contains 7-hydroxycoumarin geranyl ether.

Dried peels - Pectin, glucosides, nobilitin, citrantin.

Flowers - Glycosides neopesperidin.

Roots - Xanthyletin.

Medicinal properties:

नारंगोनागरंगः स्यात् त्वक्सुगन्धो मुखप्रियः ।। (भा. प्र.)

"Nāraṇgo nāgaraṇgaḥ ṣyāṭ ṭvaḳsugaṇdho mukhapṛiyaḥ." (Bhā.Pṛa.)

Flowers - Anodyne, diuretic, febrifuge, sedative, stimulant.

Fruit rind - Anthlemintic, antidiarrhoeal, stomachic.

Fruits - Alexeteric, aphrodisiac, appetizer, cooling, digestive, sour, sweet.

Medicinal uses:

Flowers - Fever, lumbago, strangury.

Fruits rind-Dyspepsia, flatulence, helminthiasis, skin diseases, vomiting.

Fruits - Cardiac disorders, dyspepsia, seminal weakness.

Ethno- Medicinal uses:

Fruit pericarp - Intestinal warm, flatulence (Jadeja *et al.,* 2006).

Fruit-Appetizer, antiseptic (Basak, 2006); Diabetes (Ghosh & Das, 2003).

COCHLOSPERMUM RELIGIOSUM (L.) Alston. (COCHLOSPERMACEAE)

Regional and Other Names: *Bengali* – Kanta palash; *English*– Yellow flowered cotton tree; *Gujarati* –Kadachogund; *Hindi* – Galgal; *Kannada* – Arasina buruga; *Malayalam* – Appakkutukka; *Marathi* – Ganeri; *Sanskrit* – Girisalmalika; *Tamil* – Kattupparutti; *Telugu* – Kongu.

Distribution: Throughout India.

Taxonomic description : A small deciduous tree; Leaves crowded at the ends of branches, palmately 3-5 lobed; flowers golden-yellow in terminal corymbose. Panicles when plant leafless; fruits capsule; seeds covered with brown silky wool.

Medicinal parts: Leaves, Flowers, Gum.

Taste: Sweet.

Medicinal properties:

कासश्वासहरः त्वच्यो वृष्यो वस्त्यामयान् जयेत् ।।

"Kāsaṣvāsaharaḥ tvacyo vṛṣyo vaṣtyāmayāṇ jayeṭ"

Leaves & Flowers - Stimulant.

Gum - Anodyne, sedative, sweet, thermogenic.

Medicinal uses: Gum - Cough, diarrhoea, dysentery, gonorrhoea, syphilis.

Ethno- Medicinal uses: Bark - Jaundice (Goel *et al.,* 1984).

Root - Urinary diseases (Jain & De, 1966).

Fruit- Cough, cold (Mondal & Mukherjee, 1992).

Gum- Cough, gonorrhoea (Kumar & Lal, 2003); gastric trouble (Upadhyay & Chauhan, 2003); bone fractures (Subramani & Goraya, 2003); diarrhoea, dysentery, cough (Mitaliya & Bhatt, 2003).

COCUS NUCIFERA L. (ARECACEAE)

Regional and Other Names: *Bengali* – Narikel; *English* – Coconut tree; *Gujarati* – Nariel; *Hindi* – Nariyal; *Kannada* – Tengu; *Malayalam* – Tennu; *Marathi* – Narel; *Sanskrit* – Narikelah; *Tamil* – Tenkai; *Telugu* – Tenkaya.

Distribution: Cultivated throughout South India, especially along the coast.

Taxonomic description: A tall palm tree, with subglobose drupe. Drupe Green or Yellowish; pericarp fibrous; endocarp bony; albumen lining the endocarp, the large cavity filled with a sweet fluid.

Medicinal parts : Roots, Inflorescence, Seeds (Shell, kernel, water, oil).

Taste : Sweet.

Chemical constituents: Kernel contain Mannan, galactomannan, enzymes, amino-acids, proteins.

Medicinal properties:

नारिकेलं गुरुस्निग्धं पित्तकृत् स्वादु शीतलम् ।
बलमांसप्रदं वृष्यं बृहणं वस्तिशोधनम् ।। (ध. नि.)

"Nārikelaṃ guruṣnigdhaṃ piṭtakṛt ṣvādu ṣītalaṃ
Balamāṃsapṛadaṃ vṛṣyaṃ bṛmhaṇaṃ vaṣtiṣodhanaṃ." (Dha. Ni.)

Root - Anthlemintic, astringent, diuretic.

Juice of the young spadix - Aperient, aphrodisiac, diuretic, intoxicating, refrigerant, sweet.

Shell - Cooling, diuretic.

Kernel - Aphrodisiac, appetizer, cooling, laxative, sweet.

Water - Anthlemintic, aperient, aphrodisiac, cooling, digestive, diuretic, sweet.

Oil - Aphrodisiac, appetiser, digestive, sweet.

Medicinal uses: Root - Bronchitis, helminthiasis, strangury.

Juice of the young spadix - Diarrhoea, dysentery, dyspepsia, diabetes, leprosy.

Shell - Strangury.

Kernel - Bronchitis, Skin diseases, Tumours.

Water - Diarrhoea, Dyspepsia, Strangury.

Oil - Bronchitis, cough, diabetes, strangury.

Ethno- Medicinal uses: Coconut water - Blood purifier, fever, urin disorders (Bhalla *et. al.,* 1982).

Root - Bronchitis, dysentery, liver complaint, uterine disorders (Bhalla *et. al.,* 1982); toothache, promotes flow of urine (Rosakutty *et al.,* 2003).

Coconut oil- Migraine (Upadhay *et al.* 2006); gout (Jadeja *et al.,* 2006); To make strong and healthy hair (External application) (Jadeja *et al.,* 2006).

Kernel - Diabetes (Ghosh, 2006).

Flower- Diabetes, diseases of the uterus (Rosakutty *et al.,* 2003).

Endocarp- Scratching, inflammation of skin (Singh & Singh, 2003).

COFFEA ARABICA L. (RUBIACEAE)

Regional and Other Names: *Bengali* – Kafi; *English* – Coffee; *Gujarati* – Bundadana; *Hindi* – Caphi; *Kannada* – Kafi; *Malayalam* – Kappi; Marathi – Bundadana; *Sanskrit* – Rajapiluh; *Tamil* – Kappi; *Telugu* – Kaphi.

Distribution: Cultivated in shade on hills.

Taxonomic description: A glabrous large shrub, with white flowers and berry fruits.

Medicinal parts : Seeds

Taste : Bitter.

Chemical constituents: Seed contain 2-Methyl-3-furanthiol, 2-furfurylthiol, prenylmerceptan, β-galactosidase, tocopherols, theobromine, theophylline, trigonelline, chlorogenic acid, caffeine, cafestol, isochlorgenic acid, neochlorogenic acid, 3-feruloylquinic acid, palmitic acid, stearic acid, oleic acid, linoleic acid, cafaryloside, atractyligenin glycoside, stigmasterol, campesterol, sitosterol, cholesterol, cafestol.

Medicinal properties:

काफी तिक्ता कटुः पाके हृद्योष्णा कफवानुवत् ।
स्फुर्त्तिदा श्वासकासघ्नी परं निन्द्रानिवारणी ।। (द्र. वि.)

"Kāphi tiḳtā katuḥ pāke hṛḍyoṣṇā kaphavānuvaṭ
Ṣphuṛttidā ṣvāsakāsagḥnī paraṃ niṇḍṛānivāraṇī." (Dṛa. Vi.)

Seeds - Antipyretic, bitter, diuretic, stimulant.

Medicinal uses: Unripe seeds - Fever, gout, migraine.

Ripe roasted seeds - Diarrhoea.

Ethno- Medicinal uses: Leaf - Hair dye (Jadeja *et al.,* 2006); injury in eyes (Thomas & Britto, 2003).

COPTIS TEETA Wall. (RANUNCULACEAE)

Regional and Other Names: Bengali – Tita; English – Coptis; Hindi – Mamiran; Malayalam – Pitarohini; Sanskrit – Pita; Tamil – Pitarohini; Telugu – Mismitita.

Distribution: Northern frontier of Assam, in damp places.

Taxonomic description: A rhizomatous, herbaceous perennial with golden yellow woody rhizome.

Medicinal parts: Rhizomes.

Taste: Bitter.

Chemical constituents: Root contain Berberine.

Medicinal properties:

ममीरा तिक्तमूला स्यात् कामरूपसमुद्भवा ।
स्निग्धखण्डितपत्रा च सितपुष्पाऽतितिक्तका ।। (द्र. वि.)

"Mamīrā tiķtamulā şyāt kāmarupasamuḍbhavā.
Şnigdhakhaṇḍitapaṭrā ca sitapuṣpāatitiķtakā." (Dṛa. Vi.)

Rhizomes - Anthlemintic, antipyretic, carminative, cooling, depurative, diuretic, expectorant, laxative, stomachic.

Medicinal uses: Rhizomes - Bronchitis, cough, diabetes, dropsy helminthiasis, leprosy leucoderma, strangury.

Ethno- Medicinal uses: Rhizomes - Backache, malaria fever (Mudgal & Jain, 1980).

CORIANDRUM SATIVUM L. (APIACEAE)

Regional and Other Names: *Bengali* – Dhoney; *English* – Coriander; *Gujarati* –Konphir ; *Hindi* – Dhaniya; *Kannada* – Kottambri; *Malayalam* – Kottamalli; *Marathi* – Dhanya; *Sanskrit* – Dhanaka; *Tamil* – Kottamalli; *Telugu* – Kotimira.

Distribution: Cultivated throughout India.

Taxonomic description: An annual glaberous herbs, with a strong smell; lower leaves palmatipartite, upper leaves ternately decompound; flowers white, dull purplish in the centre; fruits elliptic-orbicular, glabrous.

Medicinal parts: Leaves, Fruits.

Taste: Bitter, Sweet, Acrid, Astringent.

Chemical constituents: Leaves - Oxalic acid, calcium, vitamin-C.

Fruits - β-sitosterol, chlorogenic acid, caffic acid, umbelliferone, scopoletin.

Seeds - Quercetin 3-0-caffeyl glucoside, kaempferol 3-glucoside, fatty oil, essential oil.

Medicinal properties:

धान्यकं धानकं धान्यं धाना धानेयकं तथा ।
कुलटी धेनुका छत्रा कुस्तुम्बुरू वितुन्नकम् ।। (भा. प्र.)

"Dhāṇyakaṃ dhānakaṃ dhānyaṃ dhānā dhāneyakaṃ tathā
Kulatī dhenukā chaṭrā kuṣthuṃburu vituṇnakaṃ." (Bhā. Pra.)

Leaves - Acrid, anti-inflammatory, aromatic, astringent, styptic.

Fruits - Acrid, anit-inflammtory, appetizer, aromatic, astringent, bitter, carminative, digestive, diuretic, emollient, stimulant, sweet, thermogenic.

Medicinal uses: Leaves - Hiccough, Inflammations, Jaundice.

Fruits - Bronchitis, burning sensation, cough, diarrhoea, dropsy, dysentery, erysipelas, helminthiasis, scrofula.

Ethno- Medicinal uses: Leaf - Colic, piles, flatulence (Bhalla et. al., 1982); Rheumatism (Mitaliya *et al.,* 2003).

Seed- Stomachache, chicken pox (Negendra & Abraham, 1984); Headache (Jadhav, 2006); Ulcers, carbuncles (Tomar & Singh, 2005).

Fruit - Flatulence (Jadeja *et al.,* 2006); fever (Deokule, 2006).

Whole plant - Gout, dandruff (Jadeja *et al.,* 2006).

CRESSA CRITICA L. (CONVOLVULACEAE)

Regional and Other Names: *Gujarati* – Paliyo; *Hindi* – Rudravanti; *Kannada* – Kharda; *Malayalam* – Alukanni; *Marathi* – Rudanti; *Sanskrit* – Rudanti; *Tamil* – Uppumarikkoluntu; *Telugu* – Uppusanga.

Distribution: The plant is found in coastal regions of India.

Taxonomic description : Dwarf, hairy herbs, with apparently crowded, ovate leaves. Flowers Pink, axillary, stamens exsected, capsules ovoid.

Medicinal parts: Whole plant.

Taste : Bitter, Acrid.

Chemical constituents: Plant contains n-octacosanol, β-sitosterol, n-octacosanoic acid, scopaletin, umbelliferone, isopimpinellin, D-glucoside, quercetin.

Medicinal properties:

चणपत्रसमं पत्रं क्षुपंचैव तथाऽम्लकम् ।
शिशिरे जलबिन्दुनां स्त्रवन्तीति रूदन्दिका ।। (रा. नि.)

"Caṇapatrasamaṃ patraṃ ksupaṇcaiva tathāamlakaṃ
Ṣiṣire jalabiṇdunaṃ ṣravaṇtiti rudaṇdikā." (Ra. Ni.)

Plant - Acrid, alterant, anthlemintic, aphrodisiac, bitter, carminative, digestive, expectorant, stomachic, thermogenic.

Medicinal uses: Plant - Anaemia, asthma, bronchitis, colic, diabetes, dyspepsia, flatulence, Helminthiasis, leprosy.

Ethno- Medicinal uses: Whole plant- Health tonic for Children (Singh & Pandey, 1998); diabetes, cough, bronchitis, tuberculosis, eye diseases (Kothari & Rao, 2003).

CROCUS SATIVUS L. (IRIDACEAE)

Syn.: *C. orsinii* Parl.

Regional and Other Names: *Bengali* – Jafran; *English* – Saffron; *Hindi* – Kesar; *Kannada* – Kunkumakesari; *Malayalam* – Kunkumappuvu; *Marathi* – Keshara; *Sanskrit* – Kunkumam; *Tamil* – Kunkumappu; *Telugu* – Kunkuma puvvu.

Distribution: Cultivated in Kashmir & Jammu.

Taxonomic description: A small bulbous perennial herb with Blue flowers and capsule fruits.

Medicinal parts: Dried stigmas.

Taste : Bitter, Acrid.

Chemical constituents: Glucoside-crocin, crocetin, picrocrocin, essential oil.

Medicinal properties:

कुंकुमं घुसृणं रक्तं काश्मीरं पीतकं वरम् ।
संकोचं पिशुनं धीरं वाह्निकं शोणिताभिधम् ।। (भा. प्र.)

"Kuṇkuṃaṃ ghusṛnaṃ raktaṃ kāṣmīraṃ pītakaṃ varaṃ
Saṇkocaṃ piṣanaṃ dhīraṃ vāhnikaṃ ṣoṇitābhidhaṃ." (Bhā. Pṛa.)

Dried stigmas - Acrid, anodyne, aphrodisiac, bitter, diuretic, fragrant, laxative, stimulant, stomachic.

Medicinal uses: Dried stigmas - Bronchitis, epilepsy, fever, inflammtions, skin diseases, vomiting.

Ethno- Medicinal uses: Style - Flatulence, piles (Jadeja *et al.*, 2006).

Dried stamen- Headache, fever (Nautiyal *et al.*, 2003).

CROTON TIGLIUM L. (EUPHORBIACEAE)

Syn.: *Tiglium officinale* Klotch.; *Croton jamalgota* f. Hamn.

Regional and Other Names: *Bengali* – Joypal; *English* – Croton oil plant; *Gujarati*– Nepal; *Hindi* – Jamalgota; *Kannada* – Jayapala; *Malayalam* – Nirvalam; *Marathi* – Jeyapal; *Sanskrit* – Dantibijah; *Tamil* – Nervalam; *Telugu* – Nepalamu.

Distribution: Naturalized & cultivated in Bengal, Assam & South India.

Taxonomic description: A small evergreen tree, with ash-coloured smooth bark and young shoots sprinkled with stellate hairs; leaves oblong to ovate lanceolate, yellowish, green minutely toothed; flowers small unisexual; fruits ovoid capsules.

Medicinal parts: Seeds, oil.

Taste : Acrid.

Chemical constituents: Seeds contain β-sitosterol, 2 toxic proteins-croton globulin & croton albumin, sucrose, glycoside crotonoside.

Medicinal properties:

जयपालो दन्तिबीजं विख्यातं तिन्तिडीफलम् ।। (भा. प्र.)

"Jayapālo daṇtibījaṃ vikḥyataṃ tiṇtidīphalaṃ." (Bhā. Pṛa.)

Seeds & oil - Acrid, anthlemintic, anti-inflammatory, bitter, carminative, detergent, digestive, emollient, expectorant, thermogenic.

Medicinal uses: Seed oil-Abdominal disorders, bronchitis, catarrh, constipation, cough, dyspepsia, fever, helminthiasis, inflammations, leucoderma.

Ethno-Medicinal uses: Plant - Stomach disorders (Khakongor & Joseph, 1981).

CUMINUM CYMINUM L. (APIACEAE)

Regional and Other Names: *Bengali* – Jira; *English* – Cumin; *Gujarati* – Jiru; *Hindi* – Jira; *Kannada* – Jirige; *Malayalam* – Jirakam; *Marathi* – Jira; *Sanskrit* – Jiraka; *Tamil* – Jirakam; *Telugu* – Jila karra.

Distribution: Cultivated throughout India.

Taxonomic description: Glabrous, annual herbs, with Rose-coloured flowers. Fruits setulose, narrowly oblong.

Medicinal parts: Fruits.

Taste: Bitter, Acrid.

Chemical constituents: Fruits contain Apigenin-7-O-glucoside, Luteolin-7-O-glucoside, essential oil.

Medicinal properties:

जीरको जरणोऽजाजी कणा स्याद् दीर्घजीरकः ।। (भा. प्र.)

"Jīrako jaraṇoajājī kaṇā ṣyād dīṛghajīrakaḥ." (Bhā. Pṛa.)

Fruits - Acrid, anaphrodisiac, anodyne, anthelmintic, anti-inflammatory, astringent, carminative, constipating, cooling, depurative, digestive, febrifuge, stomachic, sweet.

Medicinal uses: Fruits - Asthma, colic, dyspepsia, fever, flatulence, helminthiasis, inflammations, leprosy, leucorrhoea, skin diseases, strangury, vomiting.

Ethno- Medicinal uses: Fruits - Diarrhoea, dyspepsia (Bhalla *et. al.*, 1982); stomachache (Nagendra Prasad & Abraham, 1984); Indigestion (Ganesan *et. al.,* 2006); flatulence (Jadeja *et al.,* 2006); Diabetes (Ghosh, 2006).

CURCUMA AROMATICA Salisb. (ZINGIBERACEAE)

Regional and Other Names: *Bengali* – Ban halud; *English* – Wild turmeric; *Gujarati* –Kapurkachali; *Hindi* – Jangli-haldi; *Kannada* – Kasturi-arisina; *Malayalam* – Kattumanna; *Marathi* – Ran haladu; *Sanskrit* – Vanaharidra; *Tamil* – Kattumanjal; *Telugu* – Kasturi pasupu.

Distribution: Wild throughout India.

Taxonomic description: An erect herbs; rhizomes strongly aromatic, whitish inside; leaves long petioled; spikes 15 cm. long; lower bracts green, upper Pink-tipped.

Medicinal parts : Rhizomes.

Taste: Bitter, Acrid.

Chemical constituents: Volatile oil, resin, starch, mucilage, sugar, gum, albuminoids, curcumin.

Medicinal properties:

आरण्यहलदीकन्दः कुष्ठवातास्त्रनाशनः ।। (भा. प्र.)

"Āraṇyahaladīkandaḥ kuṣthavātāṣṛanāṣanaḥ." (Bhā. Pṛa.)

Rhizomes - Appetizer, bitter, carminative.

Medicinal uses: Rhizomes - Bronchitis, cough, hiccough, leucoderma, skin diseases, sprains.

Ethno- Medicinal uses: Rhizomes - Indigestion, rheumatism, child birth (Rao, 1981); pain, fever (Tarafder, 1986); intestinal worms (Rao & Jamir, 1982); anthelmintic, dysentery (Singh *et al.*, 1992); scabies, headache, leucoderma, skin diseases, diseases of blood (Saikia & Nath, 2003); sprains (Behura & Rout, 2003); skin care (Thomas & Britto, 2003).

Root - Menstrual problems (Pereira, 2006).

CYMBOPOGON CITRATUS (DC.) Stapf. (POACEAE)

Syn.: *Andropogon citratus* DC.

Regional and Other Names: *Bengali* – Gandhabena; *English* – West Indian lemon grass; *Gujarati* – Hiravacha; *Hindi* – Gandhatrun; *Kannada* – Majjigahullu; *Malayalam* – Cennanampullu; *Marathi* – Hiravacha; *Sanskrit* – Bhustrnah; *Tamil* – Vasanapillu; *Telugu* – Nimmagaddi.

Distribution: Cultivated throughout India.

Taxonomic description: A tall perennial herbaceous grass about 6-7 feet high; leaves 3-4 feet long, fragrant; spikelets paired, decompound, enclosed in spathaceous bracts.

Medicinal parts : Whole plant.

Taste : Bitter.

Chemical constituents: Plant contains- Volatile aromatic oil (Indian Melissa oil), Citronela or Indian oil of Verbena which contains: Citral Citronellal, Geraniol, Citronellal, Tespene and Nevol.

Medicinal properties:

भूस्तृणो लघुरूष्णश्च रूक्षः श्लेष्मामयापहः ।
अस्य प्रयोगः सहसा हन्ति जन्तून् समुद्धतान् ।। (ध. नि.)

"Bhūṣṭṛṇo laghuruṣṇaṣca ruksaḥ ṣleṣmāmayāpahaḥ
Aṣya pṛayogaḥ sahasā haṇti jaṇtūṇ samuddhatāṇ." (Dha. Ni.)

Plant - Acrid, anthelmintic, appetizer, aromatic, bitter, laxative, thermogenic.

Medicinal uses: Plant - Bronchitis, cholera, fever, epilepsy, flatulence, helminthiasis, leprosy, skin diseases, sprains.

Ethno- Medicinal uses: Leaf - Headache (Rao & Jamir, 1982); cold, fever (Deokule & Magdum, 1992); measles (Srivastava & Singh, 2006); abortion (Ganesan & Kesavan, 2003).

Leaf oil- Headache, fever, cholera (Srivastava & Singh, 2006).

CYPERUS ESCULENTUS L. (CYPERACEAE)

Regional and Other Names: *English* – Rush nut; *Hindi* – Cicada; *Kannada* – Konnarigadde; *Malayalam* – Kalimuttanna; *Sanskrit* – Bhandra-musta; *Telugu* – Musta.

Distribution: In Punjab & Nilgiri hills.

Taxonomic description: An erect perennial glabrous grass-like sedge, upto 50 cm. in height with slender subterranean stolons ending in ovoid or cylindrical brown edible tubers; leaf blades shorter than stems; spikelets in umbellate peduncled spikes, flowering glumes boat shaped; Fruit abovoid-ellipsoid nut with 3-sharp angles.

Medicinal parts: Tubers.

Taste : Bitter, Astringent.

Medicinal properties:

भद्रमुस्तं च गुन्द्रा च तथा नागरमुस्तकः ।। (भा. प्र.)

"Bhadṛamuṣtaṃ ca guṇdṛā ca tathā nāgaramuṣtakaḥ." (Bhā. Pṛa.)

Tubers - Acrid, anthelmintic, aphrodisiac, astringent, bitter, carminative, cooling, digestive, febrifuge.

Medicinal uses: Tubers - Colic, diarrhoea, dysentery, dyspepsia, flatulence, helminthiasis, leprosy.

Ethno-Medicinal uses: Tubers- Stimulant, Aphrodisiac (Singh & Srivastava, 2003).

DAUCUS CAROTA L. (APIACEAE)

Regional and Other Names: *Bengali* – Gajar; *English* – Carrot; *Gujarati* – Gajar; *Hindi* – Gajar; *Kannada* – Gajjari; *Malayalam* – Karattu; *Marathi* – Gajara; *Sanskrit* – Garjarah; *Tamil* – Gajjarakkilangu; *Telugu* – Gajjaragadda.

Distribution: Throughout India, cultivated.

Taxonomic description: Annual herbs, with conical fleshy roots and yellow, white or light purple flowers.

Medicinal parts : Roots, Seeds.

Taste : Sweet.

Chemical constituents: Root contains Carotin, hydrocarotin, sugar, pectin, malic acid, lignin, albumin, salts & volatile oil; β-carotene, daucic acid, pyrrolidine.

Medicinal properties:

गाजरं मधुरं तीक्ष्णं तिक्तोष्णं दीपनं लघु ।
संग्राहि रक्तपित्तार्शोग्रहणीकफवातजित् ।। (भा. प्र.)

"Gājaraṃ madhuraṃ tīkṣṇaṃ tiktoṣṇaṃ dīpanaṃ laghu
Saṃgrāhi raktapittārṣograhaṇīkaphavātajit." (Bhā. Pra.)

Tap root - Anthlemintic, aphrodisiac, appetizer, carminative, constipating, digestive, diuretic, expectorant, stimulant, sweet, thermogenic.

Medicinal uses: Tap root - Asthma, bronchitis, burns, cough, diabetes, dyspepsia, flatulence, hyperacidity, inflammations, jaundice, leprosy, myopia, strangury, tumours.

Ethno- Medicinal uses: Leaf - Toothache (Dar *et. al.*, 1984).

Root - Diabetes (Ghosh, 2006).

DESMOSTACHYS BIPINNATA (L.) Stapf. (POACEAE)

Syn.: *D. cynosuroides* Stapf.; *Eragrostis cynosuroides* Beauv.

Regional and Other Names: *Bengali* – Darbha; *English* – Sacrificial grass; *Gujarati* –Dabha ; *Hindi* – Dab; *Kannada* – Darbha; *Malayalam* – Darbha; *Marathi* – Darbha; *Sanskrit* – Darbha; *Tamil* – Darbhaipul; *Telugu* – Dharbha.

Distribution: Throughout India.

Taxonomic description: Tufted, rhizomatous, perennial grass. Leaf-sheaths glabrous, densely flabellate. Spikelets terminating axis of inflorescence, falling entire at maturity. Glumes 1-nerved.

Medicinal parts : Whole plant.

Taste : Sweet, Astringent.

Medicinal properties:

दर्भः स्निग्धो हिमः स्वादुः कशायः कफपित्तहा ।
विसर्पदाहकृच्छाश्मतृष्णावस्तिविकारनुत् ।। (कै. नि.)

"Daṛbhaḥ ṣnigdho himaḥ ṣvāduḥ kasāyaḥ kaphapiṭtahā
Visaṛpadāhakṛçchrāṣmaṭṛṣṇāvaṣtvikāranuṭ." (Kaī. Ni.)

Roots - Astringent, bitter, cooling, diuretic, emollient, sweet.

Leaves - Acrid, aphrodisiac, diuretic, stimulant, sweet.

Medicinal uses: Roots - Asthma, Jaundice.

Leaves - Asthma, dysentery, jaundice, menorrhoea, strangury.

Ethno-Medicinal uses: Culms - Dysentery (Malhotra & Moorthy, 1973).

Root- Asthma, jaundice, biliousness (Mukhopadhyay, 1992); for relieving labour-pain (Satapathy, 1992); abdominal pain, colic pain (Sattapathy & Brahmam, 2003).

DILLENIA INDICA L. (DILLENIACEAE)

Syn.: *D. speciosa* Thunb.

Regional and Other Names: *Bengali* – Chanta; *English* – Elephant apple; *Gujarati* – Karmbal; *Hindi* – Chanta; *Kannada* – Betta kanigala; *Malayalam* – Chalita; *Marathi* – Karambel; *Tamil* – Akku; *Telugu* – Kalinga.

Distribution: From Nepal to Assam and South to Ceylone, Malay Peninsula.

Taxonomic description : Large trees; flowers white, solitary; fruits fleshy globose.

Medicinal parts : Fruits, Leaves, Bark.

Taste : Acrid, Sour.

Chemical constituents: Betalin, betalinaldehyde, betulic acid, hydroxylaceton, myricetin, kaempferol, isorrhamnetin, dillentin, naringenin, malic acid, glucose, tannin, sitosterol.

Medicinal properties:

भव्यं स्वादु कशायाम्लं रूक्षं गुर्वास्यशोथनम् ।
विशदं रोचनं हृदयं शीतलं ग्राहि वातलम् ।। (कै. नि.)

"Bhaẏyaṃ ṣvādu kasāyāṃlaṃ ruksaṃ guṛvāṣyaṣothnaṃ
Viṣdaṃ rocnaṃ hṛdyaṃ ṣitalaṃ g̣rāhi vātalaṃ" (Bhā. Pra.)

Appetizer, astringent, cardiac tonic, laxative.

Medicinal uses: Fruit - Abdominal pain, Colic.

Leaves & Bark - Conception.

Ethno- Medicinal uses: Leaf - Dysentery (Tiwari *et. al.,* 1987).

Whole plant - Fever (Puri, 1983).

Fruits - Weakness (Hajra & Baishya, 1981); to check bleeding from cuts (Bora, 2003); appetiser, astringent (Gogoi *et al.,* 2003).

DIOSPYROS MALABARICA (Desr.) Kostel. (EBENACEAE)

Syn.: *D. peregrina* auct. non (Gaertn.) Guerke.; *D. embryopteris* Pers.

Regional and Other Names: *Bengali* – Gab, tendu; *English* – Indian persimon; *Gujarati* – Zeeberwo; *Hindi* – Tedu; *Kannada* – Kusarta; *Malayalam* – Panacca; *Marathi* – Timburi; *Sanskrit* – Tinduki; *Tamil* – Panicika; *Telugu* – Gabu.

Distribution: Throughout India.

Taxonomic description: A middle sized evergreen trees; leaves reddish; flowers cream coloured; fruits yellow berries.

Medicinal parts: Bark, Leaves, Flowers, Fruits.

Taste: Astringent.

Chemical constituents: Fruit pulp contains β-sitosterol & its glucoside, Betulin, a monohydroxy triterpene ketone, betulinic acid, gallic acid, hexacosane, hexacosanol. Oleanolic acid, myricyl alcohol from leaves. Saponin from Bark.

Medicinal properties:

तिन्दुकः स्फूर्जकः कालस्कन्धश्च शितिसारकः ।। (भा. प्र.)

"Tiṇdukaḥ ṣphūrjakaḥ kālaṣkaṇdhaṣca ṣitisārakaḥ." (Bhā.Pṛa.)

Bark - Acrid, anti-inflammatory, astringent, constipating, cooling, depurative, febrifuge.

Leaves - Carminative, diuretic, laxative, styptic.

Flowers - Aphrodisiac, diuretic.

Fruits - Acrid, bitter, carminative, cooling, digestive.

Medicinal uses: Bark - Burning sensation, burns, diabetes, dysentery, dyspepsia, fever, inflammations, leprosy, pruritus, skin diseases, spermatorrhoea.

Leaves - Burns, dyspepsia, flatulence, scabies, strangury, wounds,

Flowers - Anaemia, leucorrhoea, scabies.

Ethno-Medicinal uses: Fruits - Diarrhoea, Blisters of mouth (Jain, 1965); severe headache (Satapathy, 1992).

Bark/Leaf/Flower-Burn, diabetes, anaemia, scabies (Nayak *et al.,* 2003).

ELAEOCARPUS SPHAERICUS (Gaertn.) K. Schum. (ELAEOCARPACEAE)

Syn.: *E. ganitrus* Roxb.

Regional and Other Names: *Bengali* – Rudraksa; *English* – Utrasum-bead tree; *Hindi* – Rudraks; *Kannada* – Rudraksa; *Malayalam* – Rudraksam; *Marathi* – Rudraksh; *Sanskrit* – Rudraksah; *Tamil* – Ruttiratcam; *Telugu* – Rudraksi.

Distribution: Bihar, Bengal, Assam, Maharashtra & Madhya Pradesh.

Taxonomic description: A medium sized evergreen tree with a spreading handsome crown; leaf simple, oblong-lanceolate; flowers white in dense racemes in old leaf axils; fruits globose, or somewhat obovoid purple drupes, stone tubercled, longitudinally grooved, generally 5-celled and 5-seeded.

Medicinal parts : Fruits, Seed, Kernel.

Taste : Sour.

Chemical constituents: Fruit contains Rudrakine alkaloid; Elaeocarpidine, elaeocarpine, isoelaeocarapine.

Seed oil contains Palmitic acid, isopalmitic acid, linoleic acid.

Medicinal properties:

रूद्राक्षमम्लमुष्णं च वातघ्नं कफनाशनम् ।
शिरोऽर्त्तिशमनं रूच्यं भूतग्रहविनाशनम् ।। (रा. नि.)

"Rudṛaksamaṃlamuṣṇam ca vātaghnaṃ kaphanaṣanaṃ
Ṣiroaṛttiṣamanaṃ ruçyaṃ bhūtagṛahavināṣanaṃ." (Rā. Ni.)

Fruits - Appetizer, sedative, sour, thermogenic.

Medicinal uses: Fruits - Brain disorders, bronchitis, cough.

Ethno- Medicinal uses: Fruits- Mental stability (Bhatt *et al.,* 2003).

ELETTARIA CARDAMOMUM (L.) Maton. (ZINGIBERACEAE)

Syn.: *Amomum repens* Sonnt.; *A. cardamomum* White non L.; *Alpine cardamomum* Roxb.

Regional and Other Names: Bengali – Chhota elach; English – Cardamom; Gujarati – Elchi; Hindi – Elaci; Kannada – Elakki; Malayalam – Elam; Marathi – Veldode; Sanskrit – Ela; Tamil – Elam; Telugu – Elakkayalu.

Distribution: Throughout India.

Taxonomic description: A tall herbaceous perennial with branching subterranean rootstock; leaves subsessile, elliptic or lanceolate with sheathing base; flowers in panicles; fruits capsules.

Medicinal parts: Seeds, Oil.

Taste: Sweet, Acrid.

Chemical constituents: Seed contains - Volatile oil, limonene, borneol, L-terpineol, potassium salts, starch, nitrogenous mucilage, α-pinene, sabiene, myrcene, limonene, cineol, cymane, linalool, linalys acetate etc. from essential oil.

Medicinal properties:

रसे तु कटुका शीता लघ्वी वातहरी मता।
एलासूक्ष्मा कुफश्वासकासार्शोमूत्रकृच्छहृत् ।। (भा. प्र.)

"Rase tu katukā ṣītā laghvī vātaharī matā
Elāsukṣmā kaphaṣvāsakāsāṛṣomūṭrakṛçchrahṛṭ." (Bhā. Pṛa.)

Seeds - Abortifacient, acrid, aromatic, carminative, cooling, digestive, diuretic, sweet, stimulant, stomachic.

Medicinal uses: Seeds - Asthma, bronchitis, burning sensation, dyspepsia, strangury.

Ethno- Medicinal uses: Fruit - Diarrhoea, To make black hair (External application) (Jadeja *et al.,* 2006).

Seeds- Urinary obstruction (Thomas & Britto, 2003).

ELEUSINE CORACANA (L.) Gaertn. (POACEAE)

Syn.: *Cynosurus coracanus* L.; *Ochthochloa coranaca* Edgew.

Regional and Other Names: *Bengali* – Madua; *English* – Ragi; *Gujarati* –Navtonagli; *Hindi* – Maruva; *Kannada* – Ragi; *Malayalam* – Ragi; *Marathi* – Nachoni; *Sanskrit* – Ragi, Narttakah; Tamil – Ragi; *Telugu* – Ragulu.

Distribution: Cultivated throughout South India in areas upto 1500 m elevation.

Taxonomic description: An erect annual grass, 60-120 cm in height; spikes 4-7 spikelets awnless, 3-6 flowered; each spikelet containing 4-7 seeds; seeds varying in colour from dark reddish brown to nearly white.

Medicinal parts: Grains.

Taste: Bitter, Astringent, Sweet, Acrid.

Chemical constituents: Grains contain Prolamines, glycine, glutelins, globulins, albumins, protein, calcium, phosphorus, iron, copper.

Medicinal properties:

मलिंजको नृत्यकुण्डो नर्तको नर्तकुण्टकः ।। (कै. नि.)

"Maliṇjako nṛtyakuṇdo naṛtako naṛtakuṇdakaḥ." (Kaī. Ni.)

Grains - Acrid, astringent, bitter, cooling, depurative, diuretic, sweet.

Medicinal uses: Grains - Burning sensation, leprosy, skin diseases, strangury.

Ethno- Medicinal uses: Grain - Skin eruption (Purohit *et. al.,* 1985); liver tonic (Srivastava & Singh, 2006); diarrhoea (Rajan *et al.,* 2003).

EUCALYPTUS GLOBULUS Labill. (MYRTACEAE)

Regional and Other Names: *English* – Blue gum; *Hindi* – Yukeliptus; *Malayalam* – Yukkalimaram; *Sanskrit* – Tailpaparnah; *Tamil* – Yukkalimaram.

Distribution: Introduced and Cultivated in India.

Taxonomic description: A tall tree with smooth bark; branchlets 4-angular. Leaves lanceolate-falcate, thick. Flowers axillary 2-3-nate or usually solitary, sessile. Fruit angular and warty capsule.

Medicinal parts: Oil.

Taste : Bitter, Astringent, Acrid.

Chemical constituents: Leaves contain Cis & Trans pinocarveol derivatives, α-pinene & unsaturated α-ketone.

Fruits contain Cystein, ornithine, asparagine, glutamic acid, threonine, α & β alanine, norvaline.

Medicinal properties:

तैलपर्णः सुगंधाढ्यपत्रो हरितपर्णकः ।
सृजति क्षतमात्रेण नीलनिर्यास इत्यसौ ।। (द्र. वि.)

"Taīlapaṛṇaḥ sugaṇdhāḍhyapaṭro haritapaṛnakaḥ
Sṛjati ksatamāṭreṇa nilaniṛyāsa iṭyasaū." (Dṛa. Vi.)

Oil - Acrid, anodyne, anthelmintic, antiseptic, astringent, bitter, carminative, digestive, diuretic, expectorant, rubefacient. Stimulant, sudorific, thermogenic.

Medicinal uses: Oil - Asthma, bronchitis, burns, dyspepsia, flatulence, hoarseness, skin diseases, strangury, tuberculosis.

Ethno- Medicinal uses: Leaf - Malaria, swelling (Megoneitso & Rao, 1983); antiseptic (Basak, 2006).

EUPATORIUM TRIPLINERVE Vahl. (ASTERACEAE)

Syn.: *E. ayapana* Vent.; *E. perfpliatum* L.; *E. ayapana* Vent.; *E. cannabinum* L.

Regional and Other Names: *English* – Gravel root; *Gujarati* – Alleppa; *Hindi* – Aayaapaan; *Kannada* – Ayapanam; *Malayalam* – Ayyappana; *Marathi* – Ayapana; *Sanskrit* – Ayapana; *Tamil* – Ayappani; *Telugu* – Ayaparni.

Distribution: A native of Brazil, now found throughout India.

Taxonomic description: A profusely branching prostrate undershrub; leaves simple, opposite, subsessile, lanceolate, 3-nerved, acuminate; flowers slaty blue; fruits achenes.

Medicinal parts: Whole plant.

Taste : Bitter, Astringent.

Chemical constituents: Eupatorin, inulin & a resin.

Medicinal properties:

अजपर्णं तु तुवरं तिक्तं वीर्योष्णमेव च ।
कफपित्तहरं हृदयं ज्वरघ्नं रक्तरोधकम् ।। (द्र. वि.)

"Ajaparṇaṃ tu tuvaraṃ tiktaṃ vīryoṣṇameva ca
Kaphapittaharaṃ hṛdyaṃ jvaraghnaṃ raktarodhakaṃ." (Dra. Vi.)

Plant - Acrid, alexeteric, antipyretic, astringent, bitter, carminative, detergent, digestive, emetic, expectorant, stimulant, sudorific, thermogenic.

Medicinal uses: Plant - Asthma, cardiac debility, cough, dyspepsia, fevers, haematemesis, haemorrhoids, inflammations, menorrhagia, pruritus, scabies, skin eruptions, ulcers, wounds.

EURYALE FEROX Salsb. (NYMPHAEACEAE)

Regional and Other Names: *Bengali* – Makhna; *English* – Fox nut; *Hindi* – Machana; *Marathi* – Padmakant; *Sanskrit* – Makhannum; *Telugu* – Mellunipadmanu.

Distribution: Kashmir, E. Bengal.

Taxonomic description: Prickly aquatic herbs, with bright red flowers and prickly fruits.

Medicinal parts: Fruits.

Taste: Sweet.

Chemical constituents: Seed contains Protein, carbohydrates, iron, phosphorus, carotene.

Medicinal properties:

मखान्नं पद्मबीजाभं पानीयफलमित्यपि ।
मखान्नं पद्मबीजस्य गुणैस्तुल्यं विनिर्दिशेत् ।। (भा. प्र.)

"Makhāṇnaṃ paḍmabījābhaṃ pānīyaphalamiṭyapi
Makhāṇnaṃ paḍmabījaṣya guṇeṣṭuḷyaṃ viniṛdiṣheṭ." (Bhā. Pṛa.)

Aphrodisiac, astringent, styptic, tonic.

Medicinal uses: Seeds - Asthma, cardiac diseases, cough, spermatorrheoa.

Ethno- Medicinal uses: Leaves- Tonic, Astringent (Gogoi *et al.,* 2003); dysentery, rheumatism (Gogoi & Das, 2003).

Seeds- Tonic, Astringent (Gogoi *et al.,* 2003; Gogoi & Das, 2003).

FERULA ASAFOETIDA L. (APIACEAE)

Syn.: *F. foetida* Regel.

Regional and Other Names: *Bengali* – Hing; *English* – Asafoetida; *Hindi* – Hing; *Kannada* – Hingu; *Malayalam* – Kāyam; *Marathi* – Hing; *Sanskrit* – Hingu; *Tamil* – Kayam; *Telugu* – Inguva.

Distribution : Wild in Punjab, Kashmir, Iran & Afganistan. Cultivated in North-West parts of India.

Taxonomic description: A small shrubby tree 5-9 feet high; Leaves hairy, ovate, decurrent, multifid, 1-2 feet long; flowers in terminal umbel of yellow colour.

Medicinal parts: Root, Stem, Leaves and Gum-resin.

Taste: Bitter, Acrid.

Chemical constituents: Luteolin & its compound. Essential oil, ferulic acid, organic sulphur compound, pinene, isobutyl propanyl disulphide and umbeliferone.

Medicinal properties:

सहस्रवेधि जतुकं बाह्लीकं हिंगु रामठम् ।। (भा. प्र.)

"Sahasṛavedhi Jatukaṃ bāḥlīkaṃ hiṇgu rāmathaṃ." (Bhā. Pṛa.)

Oleo resin - Acrid, anthelmintic, antispasmodic, bitter, carminative, digestive, diuretic, expectorant, laxative, sedative.

Medicinal uses: Oleo resin - Asthma, chronic bronchitis, colic, constipation, dyspepsia, epilepsy, hysteria, whooping cough.

Ethno- Medicinal uses: Root extract (Gum-resin) - Toothache (Jadhav, 2006); Flatulence, stomachache, dysentery (Jadeja *et al.*, 2006).

FICUS HISPIDA L. f. (MORACEAE)

Syn.: *F. oppositifolia* Will.; *F. promineus* Wall.; *F. doemonum* Koen.

Regional and Other Names: *Bengali* – Kakodumar; *Gujarati* – Dhedaumaro; *Hindi* – Katguleriya; *Kannada* – Kaduatti; *Malayalam* – Parakam; *Marathi* – Bhokada; *Sanskrit* – Malayu, Kakodumbarika; *Tamil* – Kattatti; *Telugu* – Adaviatti.

Distribution: Throughout India.

Taxonomic description: A moderate sized weak tree with hollow internodes, hispid parts, rough grey bark and without aerial roots; leaves opposite, 3-5 ribbed; receptacles facicled on the stem or leafless branchlets; obovoid, hispid, and yellow when ripe.

Medicinal parts: Bark, Fruits.

Taste : Bitter, Astringent.

Chemical constituents: β-amyrin, β-sitosterol, gluacolacetate, hispidine, n-tri-acontanylacetate.

Medicinal Properties:

काकोदुम्बरिका फल्गुर्मलयूर्जघने फला ।
मलयूः स्तंभकृत्तिका शीतला तुवरा जयेत् ।
कफपित्तव्रणश्वित्रकुष्ठपाण्ड्वर्शकामलाः ।। (भा प्र.)

"Kākodumbarikā phalgurmalyūrjaghne falā
Malayuḥ stambhkruttikā shītlā tuvarā jayet
Kaphapittavranswitrakusthapāndvarshkāmlāḥ ." (Bhā. Pra.)

Bark - Emetic, laxative.

Fruits - Acrid, antidysenteric, anti-inflammatory, astringent, bitter, depurative, refrigerant.

Medicinal uses: Fruits - Anaemia, fevers, inflammations, jaundice, leucoderma, psoriasis, ulcers.

Ethno- Medicinal uses: Fruits - Purgative (Das *et al.,* 1983); emetic (Rajwar, 1983); diarrhoea (Nath & Maiti, 2003).

Latex - Ulcers in mouth (Singh *et. al.,* 1987).

Leaf- Earache, ear infection (Singh & Singh, 2003).

Aerial roots- Paralysis (Tigga *et al.,* 2003).

FICUS MICROCARPA L. f. (MORACEAE)

Syn. **:** *F. retusa* Auct. non. L.

Regional and Other Names: *Bengali* – Kamrup; *Hindi* – Kamarup; *Kannada* – Itti; *Malayalam* – Itti; *Marathi* –Nandruk; *Sanskrit* – Plaksah; *Tamil* – Icci; *Telugu* – Plaksa.

Distribution: Throughout India.

Taxonomic description: A large glabrous evergreen tree with few aerial roots; leaves short petioled, stipules lanceolate; fruit receptacles sessile and globose in axillary pairs, yellowish when ripe.

Medicinal parts: Root, Bark, Leaves.

Taste- Acrid, Astringent.

Medicinal Properties:

प्लक्षो जटी पर्कटी च कर्पटी च स्त्रियामपि ।। (भा प्र.)

"Ṗlakso jati paṛkati ca kaṛpati ca ṣṭṛiyāmapi." (Bhā. Pṛa.)

Bark & Leaves - Acrid, astringent, refrigerant, stomachic.

Medicinal uses: Bark & Leaves - Burning sensation, diabetes, diarrhoea, dropsy, dysentery, erysipelas, leucorrhoea, ulcers, wounds.

Ethno-Medicinal uses: Leaf - Bone fracture (Appranantham & Chellachurai, 1986).

Juice- Liver disorders (Tigga *et al.,* 2003).

FLACOURTIA INDICA (Burm. f.) Merr. (FLACOURTIACEAE)

Syn.: *F. ramantchi* L. Herit.; *F. ramontchi* L. Herit.; *F. intermis* auct. (non Roxb.); *F. latifolia* Cooke; *F. occidentalis* Blatter; *F. cataphracta*; *F. sapida* Roxb.; *F. sepiaria* Roxb.

Regional and Other Names: *Bengali* – Bainchi; *English* – Madagascar plum; *Gujarati* –Kankod; *Hindi* – Kancu, Bilangra; *Kannada* – Nakkeharagu; *Malayalam* – Aghori; *Marathi* – Bhekal; *Sanskrit* – Aghori; *Tamil* – Sottaikala; *Telugu* – Putikatada.

Distribution: Throughout India.

Taxonomic description: Deciduous thorny trees, with ovate-elliptic or suborbicular leaves and greenish-yellow flowers.

Medicinal parts : Root, Leaves, Fruits.

Taste: Sweet.

Chemical constituents: Bark contains Tannin & flacourtin (A Phenolic glucoside ester).

Medicinal properties:

विकंकतफलं पक्वं मधुरं सर्वदोषजित्।। (भा. प्र.)

"Vikaṇkataphalaṃ pakvaṃ madhuraṃ saṛvadosajiṭ." (Bhā. Pṛa.)

Roots - Alexipharmic, depurative, diuretic, refrigerant, sweet.

Fruits - Appetizer, digestive, diuretic, sweet.

Medicinal uses: Roots - Erysipelas, poisonous bites, pruritus, skin diseases, strangury.

Leaves - Pruritus, scabies.

Fruits - Jaundice, strangury.

Ethno- Medicinal uses: Leaf - Sanke bite (Shah *et al.,* 1981); Dysentery (Ramachandran & Nair, 1981); conjunctivitis (Srivastava *et al.,* 1992); poisonous bites, scabies, jaundice (Nayak *et al.,* 2003).

Bark - Dog bite (Joshi *et al.,* 1980); dysentery (Bhalla *et al.,* 1982); Eczema (Jain, 1963; 1965; 1981); Rheumatism (Samvatsar & Diwanji, 2003); given after delivery as tonic (Jain *et al.,* 2003).

Fruit - Child birth (Tarafder, 1984); rheumatism (Shah *et. al.,* 1981); jaundice (Sharma *et. al.,* 1979; Bhatt *et al.,* 2003); liver disorders (Maheshwari & Singh, 1987; Bhatt *et al.,* 2003); poisonous bites, scabies, jaundice (Nayak *et al.,* 2003).

Root - Skin diseases (Maheshwari *et. al.,* 1986); poisonous bites, scabies, jaundice (Nayak *et al.,* 2003).

FOENICULUM VULGARE Mill. (APIACEAE)

Syn.: *F. capillaceus* Gilb.; *Anethum foeniculum* L.; *A. officinale* All.

Regional and Other Names: *Bengali* – Mauri; *English* – Fennel; *Gujarati* –Variari; *Hindi* – Sounph; *Kannada* – Badhesoppu; *Malayalam* – Perumjirakam; *Marathi* – Shepu; *Sanskrit* – Madhurika; *Tamil* – Sompu; *Telugu* – Peddajilakarra.

Distribution: Cultivated throughout India.

Taxonomic description: A large annual herb, pinnately compound leaves; Flowers yellow in compound umbels; cremocarp of 2 carples or mericarp, each one in 5-ridged furrowed.

Medicinal parts: Fruits.

Taste: Aromatic sweet.

Chemical constituents: Constituents of plant are Fatty oil, protein, anethose, fenchone, anisalehyde, feniculin, nelumboside; Flavons, abscisic acid. Essential oil from fruit anethole, xanthotoxin, bergapten, psoralen, scoparone, vanillin, α-pinene, camphene, limonene, α-phellandrene, fenchone, methylchavicol.

Medicinal properties:

तालपर्णी मधुरिका मिश्रेया श्वबला मिशी।
शाली शालेयशालिन्यौ तिक्ता शीतशिवा मता ।। (कै.नि.)

"Tālparṇī madhurikā misṛeyā ṣvabalā miṣī
Ṣālī ṣāleyaṣāliṇyau tiḳtā ṣītaṣivā matā." (Kaī. Ni.)

Fruits - Acrid, alexipharmic, anthelmintic, antiemetic, aphrodisiac, bitter, carminative, digestive, diuretic, emollient, expectorant, febrifuge, haematinic, ophthalmic, refrigerant, stomachic, sudorific, sweet.

Medicinal uses: Fruits - Anaemia, bruning sensation, bronchitis, cardiac diseases, colic, cough, dysentery, dyspepsia, dysuria, fever, flatulence, inflammation, skin diseases, vomiting.

Ethno-Medicinal uses: Seed - Headache, Kidney complaints, Spleen complaints, Dysentery, Wounds, Fever (Bhalla *et al.,* 1982); Toothache (Dar *et al.,* 1984); menstrual disorders (Bhalla *et al.,* 1982; Manandhav, 2003).

Leaves - Colic (Bhalla *et al.,* 1982); Cough (Bhalla *et al.,* 1982; Manandhav, 2003).

Fruits - Flatulence, gout (Jadeja *et al.,* 2006); toothache, headache, wound, burns, diarrhoea (Manandhav, 2003).

FRITILLARIA ROYLEI Hook. f. (LILIACEAE)

Regional and Other Names: *Bengali* – ; *English* – Fritillary; *Hindi* – Kakoli; *Kannada* – Kakoli; *Malayalam* – Kakoli; *Sanskrit* – Kakoli; *Tamil* – Kakoli; *Telugu* – Kakoli.

Distribution: In the Himalayas from 2400 to 3900 m.

Taxonomic description: A glabrous bulbous unbranched herbs; leaves opposite or whorled, linear-lanceolate; flowers yellowish green, solitary and terminal; fruits obovoid capsules; seeds many, winged.

Medicinal parts : Bulbs.

Taste : Bitter, Sweet

Medicinal properties:

काकोली वायसोली च वीरा कायस्थिका तथा ।। (भा प्र.)

"Kākolī vāyasolī ca vīrā kāyaṣthikā tathā." (Bhā. Pṛa.)

Bulbs - Antipyretic, aphrodisiac, bitter, diuretic, expectorant, refrigerant, sweet.

Medicinal uses: Bulbs - Bronchitis, burning sensation, cough, fevers, seminal weakenss, strangury.

Ethno- Medicinal uses: Bulbs - Asthma, bronchitis (Gaur *et al.,* 1983); burns, stomach disorders (Koul, 1941).

Whole plant- Tonic, asthma, tuberculosis (Kapur & Nanda, 1992).

GARCINIA GUMMI-GUTTA (L.) Robs. (CLUSIACEAE)

Regional and Other Names: *Hindi* – Bilatti-amli; *Kannada* – Punarpuli; *Malayalam* – Kutappuli; *Sanskrit* – Vrksamlah; *Tamil* – Kodukkappuli; *Telugu* – Vrksamla.

Distribution: Throughout the Western ghats.

Taxonomic description: A moderate sized handsome evergreen tree with rounded crown & horizontal or drooping branches; flowers tetramerous; fruits ovoid, yellow or red when ripe; seeds arillate.

Medicinal parts: Leaves, dried fruits.

Taste: Astringent, Sour.

Chemical constituents: Hydroxycitric acid, hydroxycitric acid lactone, citric acid, tartaric acid.

Medicinal properties:

वृक्षाम्लं तिन्तिडीकं च चुक्रं स्यादम्लवृक्षकम् ।। (भा. प्र.)

"Vṛksāṃlaṃ tiṇtidikaṃ ca cukṛaṃ ṣyādaṃlavṛksakaṃ." (Bhā. Pṛa.)

Leaves & Fruits - Astringent, constipating, digestive, sour, thermogenic.

Medicinal uses: Leaves & Fruits - Diarrhoea, dysentery, dyspepsia, inflammations, ulcers.

Ethno- Medicinal uses: Fruits – Obesity (Kumar *et al.,* 2003).

GARCINIA MORELLA (Gaertn.) Desr. (CLUSIACEAE)

Syn.: *G. hanburyi* Hook. f.

Regional and Other Names: *Bengali* – Tamal; *English* – Indian gamboge tree; *Hindi* – Tamal; *Kannada* – Jirigehuli; *Malayalam* – Iravi; *Marathi* –Tamil; *Sanskrit* – Hiravi; *Tamil* – Makki, Iravalsinni; *Telugu* – Karukkampuli.

Distribution: Throughout the evergreen forests of western Ghats and Assam & Khasi hills.

Taxonomic description: A small or middle sized evergreen tree; leaves thick & coriaceous, elliptic-ovate to ovate-lanceolate; flowers unisexual, males axillary in fascicles; female flowers large, solitary & axillary; fruits Berries.

Medicinal parts : Gamboge, stem.

Taste : Bitter, Acrid.

Chemical constituents: Plant contains - Morellin, α- & β-guttiferins (Antibiotics).

Medicinal properties:

तमालः शालवद् वेधो दाहविस्फोटहृद् पुनः ।। (भा. प्र.)

"Tamālaḥ ṣālavaḍ vedyo dāha viṣphotahṛḍ punaḥ." (Bhā.-Pṛa.)

Gamboge - Aborifacient, anthelmintic, antibacterial, aphrodisiac, astringent, cathartic, sweet, tonic.

Stem - Antibacterial.

Medicinal uses: Gamboges - Inflammation with burning sensation, ulcers.

Stem - Pimples & Boils (external application).

GARDENIA GUMMIFERA L. f. (RUBIACEAE)

Syn.: *G. lucida* Roxb.

Regional and Other Names: *Bengali* – Dikamali; *English* – Cumbi-gum tree; *Gujarati* –Dikamalli; *Hindi* – Dikamali; *Kannada* – Bikkegidha; *Malayalam* – Gandhrajan; *Marathi* – Dikamali; *Sanskrit* – Nadihingu; *Tamil* – Dikkamalli; *Telugu* – Bikki.

Distribution: Throughout India.

Taxonomic description: A small compact tree; leaves simple smooth & bright; flowers white during early period but yellow later on; 1-3 in cluster, gum is secreted from tender branches and buds during winter.

Medicinal parts: Gum.

Taste: Acrid-Pungent.

Chemical constituents: Oleanonic aldehyde, sitosterol, D-mannitol, erythrodiol, 5-flavons, gardenin, de-me-tangeretin nevadensin.

Fruits contain Nonacosane, β-sitosterol, d-mannitol.

Medicinal properties:

वंशपत्री वेणुपत्री पिङ्.गा हिंङ्.गु शिवाटिका।। (भा. प्र.)

"Vaṇṣapaṭrī veṇupaṭrī piṇgā hiṇgu ṣivātikā." (Bhā. Pra.)

Resin - Acrid, anodyne, anthelmintic, antispasmodic, appetiser, bitter, carminative, depurative. diaphoretic, digestive, expectorant, thermogenic, vulnerary.

Medicinal uses: Resin - Bronchitis, cardiac debility, colic, constipation, cough, dyspepsia, fever, flatulence, hiccough, intestinal worms, leprosy, skin diseases, wounds.

Ethno- Medicinal uses: Gum - Antiseptic (Ramachandran & Niar, 1981); Constipation (Tribedi *et. al.,* 1982); diarrhoea, ulcers, nervous disorders (Kumar & Lal, 2003); foul ulcers, intestinal worms, obesity (Nayak *et al.,* 2003); pneumonia (Upadhyay & Chauhan, 2003).

Whole plant- Bone fractures (Mondal & Mukherjee, 1992).

GLYCOMIS ARBOREA (Roxb.) DC. (RUTACEAE)

Syn.: *G. pentaphylla* Correa.; *G. cochinchinensis* Pierre. ex Engler.

Regional and Other Names: *Bengali* – Ashshoura; *English* – Ash sheora; *Hindi* – Potali; *Kannada* – Kasarkana; *Malayalam* – Panal; *Marathi* – Kirmira; *Sanskrit* – Asvasakhotah; *Tamil* – Konci.

Distribution: Throughout India.

Taxonomic description: An aromatic shrub; leaves, alternate, imparipinnately compound, leaflets glossy, gland dotted; flowers small, white in axillary panicles; fruits pulpy yellowish white or pinkish berry.

Medicinal parts : Whole plant.

Taste: Bitter, Astringent.

Chemical constituents: Stem & Leaves - Alkaloids-arborinine, arborinone.

Root bark - Skimmianine, γ-fagarine & dictamine.

Medicinal properties:

वदद्रुश्चास्यशाखोटः सपित्तकफनाशनः ।
वातलश्च क्रिर्मान् हन्ति पाण्डुताज्वरकामलाः ।। (द्रव्यगुण)

"Vadadṛuṣcāṣyaṣākhotaḥ sapiṭtakaphanāṣanaḥ
Vātalaṣca kṛiṛmaṇ hanti pāṇdutājvarakāmalāḥ." (Dṛa. Vi.)

Plant - Anti-inflammatory, astringent, bitter, expectorant, febrifuge, vermifuge.

Fruits - Sweet.

Medicinal uses: Plant - Bronchitis, cough, fever, helminthiasis, inflammations.

Root - Anaemia, jaundice, rheumatism.

Leaves - Eczema, erysipelas, fever, helminthiasis, skin diseases, wounds.

Fruits - Bronchitis, cough.

Ethno- Medicinal uses: Fruits - Dysentery (Ramachandran & Nair, 1981).

Root - Fever (Karnick *et. al.,* 1981; Sharma *et. al.*, 1979); labour pain (Tarafder, 1981; Chaudhuri *et. al.,* 1975); snake bite (Rao & Neogi, 1980); worms (Jain *et. al.,* 1973); toothache (Gogoi *et al.,* 2003); headache (Thomas & Britto, 2003).

Bark - Gastric trouble (Rao & Neogi, 1980); Jaundice (Gogoi & Boissya, 1984).

Leaves - Skin diseases (Das *et al.,* 2006); toothache (Gogoi *et al.,* 2003); intestinal worms (Nath & Maiti, 2003).

GOSSYPIUM ARBOREUM L. (MALVACEAE)

Syn.: *G. indicum* Tod.; *G. neglectum* Tod.; *G. intermedium* Tod.; *G. cernuum* Tod.; *G. nanking* Meyen.

Regional and Other Names: *Bengali* – Kapas; *English* – Tree Cotton; *Hindi* – Kapas; *Kannada* – Jade-hatti-gida; *Malayalam* – Kattuparutti; *Marathi* – Kapas; *Sanskrit* – Raksatika; *Tamil* – Semparutti; *Telugu* – Karpasamu.

Distribution: Throughout India, wild as well as cultivated.

Taxonomic description: A large perennial shrub or small tree; leaves simple, alternate, ovate-cordate, palmately 3-7 lobed; flowers purple with darker coloured claws; fruits capsules.

Medicinal parts: Leaves.

Taste: Sweet.

Chemical constituents: Alcoholic extract of aerial parts is CNS depressant.

Medicinal properties:

भरद्वाजी महावीर्या कुष्ठला कुष्ठनाशिनी ।। (वाचस्पति)

"Bharadvājī mahāvīryā kuṣthalā kuṣthanāṣinī." (Vācaṣpati)

Leaves - Anti-inflammatory, astringent, bitter, demulcent, depurative, diuretic, febrifuge, thermogenic, vulnerary.

Medicinal uses: Leaves - Amenorrhoea, dysmenorrhoea, erysipelas, fever, inflammations, leprosy, otalgia, pruritus, skin diseases, strangury, ulcers, wounds.

Ethno- Medicinal uses: Earache, Labour complaints (Jain & Tarafder, 1970).

GOSSYPIUM HERBACEUM L. (MALVACEAE)

Syn.: *G. obtusifolium* L.; *G. wightianum* Tod.

Regional and Other Names: *Bengali* – Yula; *English* – Indian cotton; *Gujarati* – Kapas; *Hindi* – Kapas; *Kannada* – Janivara-hatti-mara; *Malayalam* – Parutti; *Marathi* –Kapas; *Sanskrit* – Karpasah; *Tamil* – Karpasam; *Telugu* – Pratti.

Distribution: Throughout India, cultivated.

Taxonomic description: A small shrub; leaves simple, alternate, clefts upto half into 3-7 lobes, lobes broad, ovate, leathery, gland dotted; flowers yellow with purple centre; fruits rounded beaked capsules, 3-4 locular.

Medicinal parts: Roots, leaves, flowers, seeds.

Taste : Sweet.

Chemical constituents: Betaline, choline, salicylic acid, gossypol, gossyfulvin, gossypurpurin, gossycaerulin, gossypin, gossipetin, gossipitrin herbacitrin, quercitin, carotenoids, vitamin- E, methyl & higher alcohols, peptone.

Medicinal properties:

कर्पासी तुण्डिकेरी च समुद्रान्ता च कथ्यते।। (शा. नि.)

"Karpāsi tuṇdikeri ca samudrāntā ca kaṭhyate." (Ṣā. Ni.)

Root - Abortiacient, acrid, antidysenteric, astringent, depurative, diuretic, emollient.

Leaves - Constipating, cooling, diuretic, haematinic.

Flowers - Diuretic, refrigerent, sweet.

Seeds - Anodyne, aphrodisiac, diuretic, emollient, expectorant, laxative, refrigerant, sweet.

Medicinal uses: Root - Amenorrhoea, diarrhoea, dysentery, dysmenorrhoea, fever, flatulence, leprosy, skin diseases, strangury,

Leaves - Anaemia, diarrhoea, dysentery, otalgia, rheumatism, strangury.

Flowers - Amenorrhoea, burns, dysmenorrhoea, jaundice, scabies, strangury.

Seeds - Amentia, bronchitis, cough, dizziness, dysentery, dyspepsia, epilepsy, fever, gout, inflammation, otalgia, ulcers, wounds.

Ethno- Medicinal uses: Root - Abortifacient (Tarafder, 1983).

Bark - Abortifacient (Tarafder, 1983).

Epicalyx - Proper regulation of mensus (Jadhav, 2006).

Leaves - Snake bite (Basak, 2006); headache (Deokule, 2006).

Seed- Diabetes (Ghosh & Das, 2003); earache, ear infection (Singh & Singh, 2003).

Flower- Diabetes (Bhatt *et al.*, 2003).

Fruit- Diabetes (Bhatt *et al.*, 2003).

HELIANTHUS ANNUS L. (ASTERACEAE)

Regional and Other Names: *Bengali* – Surjamukhi; *English* – Sunflower; *Gujarati* – Surajmukhi; *Hindi* – Surajmukhi; *Kannada* – Adityabhakti; *Malayalam* – Suryakanti; *Marathi* –Surayphul; *Sanskrit* – Adityabhakta, Suryamukhi; *Tamil* – Curiyakanti; *Telugu* – Suryakanti.

Distribution: Throughout India, cultivated.

Taxonomic description: A small annual herb of about 4-8 feet high; leaves hairy, serrate; flowers in large heads, yellow; fruits cypsella without pappus.

Medicinal parts: Roots, leaves, flowers, seeds.

Taste: Bitter, Acrid.

Chemical constituents: Seed contains - Protein, fats, carbohydrates, fibres, oil which contains- Liolenic acid.

Leaves contain - Malonic, lactic, succinic, aconitic, fumaric acid.

Medicinal properties:

सुवर्चला सूर्यभक्ता वरदा वरदापि च।
सूर्यावर्ता रविप्रिता परा ब्रह्मसुवर्चला ।। (भा. प्र.)

"Suvaṛcalā sūṛyabhaktā varadā varadāpi ca
Sūṛyāvartā ravipṛitā parā bṛahmasuvaṛcalā." (Bhā. Pṛa.)

Roots - Anodyne.

Leaves - Emetic.

Flowers - Acrid, anthelmintic, antiperiodic, aphrodisiac, bitter, refrigerant.

Seeds - Diuretic, expectorant.

Medicinal uses: Roots - Toothache.

Leaves - Burning sensation, fever, lumbago, malaria ulcers, wounds.

Flowers - Anaemica, asthama, bronchitis, buring sensation, fevers, helminthiasis, hysteria, inflammation, leprosy, pruritus, skin diseases, ulcers.

Seeds - Catarrh, cough, strangury.

Ethno- Medicinal uses: Bone fractures, colic, diarrhoea, dysentery, fever, menorrhoea, snake bite, scorpion sting, wounds (Jain & Tarafder, 1970).

Seeds - Gout (Jadeja *et al.,* 2006); cough, cold, scorpion sting (Islam & Hasin, 2003).

HIPTAGE BENGHALENSIS (L.) Kurz (MALPIGHIACEAE)

Syn.: *H. madablota* Gaertn.; *H. parvifolia* W. & A.

Regional and Other Names: *Bengali* – Madhabhlata; *English* – Clustered hiptage; *Gujarati* –Madhavi; *Hindi* – Madhumalati; *Kannada* – Madhavivasantadhuti; *Malayalam* – Sitampu; *Marathi* – Madhavi; *Sanskrit* – Madhavi; *Tamil* – Madhavi; *Telugu* – Madavi Tige.

Distribution: Throughout India.

Taxonomic description: A large woody evergreen climbing shrub with silky young parts; leaves simple, opposite, coriaceous, elliptic-oblong, ovate-lanceolate; flowers yellowish-white, fragrant in racemes; fruits samara.

Medicinal parts: Bark, leaves, flowers.

Taste: Acrid.

Chemical constituents: Root contain - Glucoside hiptagin.

Root bark - Mangiferin.

Medicinal properties:

माधवी मधुरा शीता लध्वी दोषत्रयापहा ।। (भा. प्र.)

"Mādhavī madhurā ṣītā laghvī dosaṭrayāpahā." (Bhā. Pra.)

Bark- Acrid, anti-inflammatory, aromatic, astringent, bitter, expectorant, refrigerant, vulnerary.

Leaves- Acrid, anti-inflammatory, aromatic, astringent, bitter, expectorant, refrigerant, vulnerary.

Flowers - Acrid, anti-inflammatory, aromatic, astringent, bitter, expectorant, refrigerant, vulnerary.

Medicinal uses: Bark - Asthma, burning sensation, cardiac debility, cough, leprosy, rheumatism. scabies, skin diseases, ulcers, wounds.

Leaves - Asthma, burning sensation, cardiac debility, cough, leprosy, rheumatism. scabies, skin diseases, ulcers, wounds.

Flowers - Asthma, burning sensation, cardiac debility, cough, leprosy, rheumatism. scabies, skin diseases, ulcers, wounds.

Ethno- Medicinal uses: Leaf - Rheumatism, Skin diseases, Asthma (Sharma *et al.,* 1979); rheumatism (Sebastian & Bhandari, 1984); body pain (Sasidharan & Augustine, 2006); cough, rheumatism, hyperdispia (Nayak *et al.,* 2003).

Bark- cough, rheumatism, hyperdispia (Nayak *et al.,* 2003).

Plant sap- To reduce body heat (Ravikumar & Vijaya Sankar, 2003).

HORDEUM VULGARE L. (POACEAE)

Syn.: *H. sativum* Pers.

Regional and Other Names: *Bengali* – Job; *English* – Barley; *Gujarati* – Jav; *Hindi* – Jau; *Kannada* – Yava; *Malayalam* – Yavam; *Marathi* – Jau; *Sanskrit* – Yavah; *Tamil* – Barliarisi; *Telugu* – Yava.

Distribution: Throughout North India, cultivated.

Taxonomic description: Erect, glabrous annuals, spikes emerging from the leaf-sheaths; spikelets 2-ranked.

Medicinal parts: Grains.

Taste : Sweet.

Chemical constituents: Fat, starch, protein. Alkaloid hordenine. Luteolin glucoside, orientoside, orientin. Hordenine and its methyl ether.

Medicinal properties:

यवस्तु शीतशूकः स्यान्निशूकोऽतियवः स्मृतः ।
तोक्यस्तद्वत्सहरितस्ततः स्वल्पश्च कीर्त्तितः ।। (भा. प्र.)

"Yavaṣtu ṣītaṣūkaḥ ṣyāṇniṣukōatiyavaḥ ṣmṛtaḥ
Toḳyaṣtadvatsaharitaṣtataḥ ṣvaḷpaṣca kīṛttitaḥ." (Bhā. Pṛa.)

Grains - Acrid, aphrodisiac, astringent, digestive. diuretic, emollient, refrigerant, sweet.

Medicinal uses: Grains - Anaemia, asthma, bronchiotitis, burns cough, dyspepsia, fever, stranguary, ulcers.

Ethno- Medicinal uses: Grains - Pimples (Purohit *et. al.,* 1985); Urine complaint (Dar *et. al.,* 1984; Beigh *et al.,* 2003); diarrhoea, dysentery (Kataria & Gauchan, 2006); indigestion (Srivastava & Singh, 2006).

HYDNOCARPUS LAURIFOLIA (Dennst.) Sleumer (FLACOURTIACEAE)

Syn.: *H. pentandra* Oken.; *H. wightiana* Blume.; *H. inebrians* Wall.; *H. venenata* Gaertn.

Regional and Other Names: *English* – Chaulmurga; *Hindi* – Calmogara; *Kannada* – Surti; *Malayalam* – Marotti; *Marathi* –Kantel; *Sanskrit* – Tuvarakah; *Tamil* – Maravattai; *Telugu* – Adisadamu.

Distribution: Western Peninsula, Konkan and South India.

Taxonomic description: A medium sized to large dioecious evergreen tree; leaves simple, ovate, oblong, lanceolate or elliptic; flowers greenish white, unisexual; fruits berries.

Medicinal parts: Seeds, Oil.

Taste: Bitter, Acrid, Astringent.

Chemical constituents: Seeds - Hydrocarpin.

Seed hulls - Flavonolignan, hydrocarpin, isohydrocarpin, methoxyhydrocarpin, apigenin, luteolin, chrysoeriol.

Seed coat - Flavonolinans hydnowightin, neohydnocarpin.

Seed oil – Hydnocarpic, chaulmogric, gorlic, oleic, palmitic acids.

Medicinal properties:

आरूष्करं तौवरकं कषायं कटुपाकि च।
उष्णं कृमिज्वरानाहमेहोदावर्त्तनाशनम् ।। (सु. सू.)

"Āruṣkaraṃ taūvarakaṃ kasāyaṃ katupāki ca
Uṣnaṃ kṛmijvarānāhamehodāvaṛttanāṣnaṃ." (Su. Sū.)

Seeds & Oil - Acrid, alterant, anodyne, astringent, bitter, carminative, depurative, emetic, emollient, haematinic, purgative, stomachic, vermifuge.

Medicinal uses: Seeds & Oil - Colic, diabetes, dyspepsia, eczema, flatulence, leprosy, leucoderma, pruritus, skin diseases, sprains, ulcers, wounds.

HYOSCYAMUS NIGER L. (SOLANACEAE)

Syn.: *H. agrestis* Kit.; *H. pallidus* Kit.

Regional and Other Names: *Bengali* – Khurosanivaya-mani; *English* – henbane; *Gujarati* –Khorasaniajmo; *Hindi* – Khurasani ajavayan; *Kannada* – Khurasani ajavayan; *Malayalam* – Kurassani; *Marathi* – Khorasanivova; *Sanskrit* – Parasikayavani; *Tamil* – Kurassaniyomam; *Telugu* – Kurasani-omam.

Distribution: Kashmir to Garhwal.

Taxonomic description: An erect hairy annual or biennial; flowers yellow-green, veined with purple, darker in the centre; fruits capsules; seeds kidney shaped, brown.

Medicinal parts: Leaves, Seeds.

Taste: Bitter, Acrid, Astringent.

Chemical constituents: Leaves & Seeds - Alkaloids-hyoscyamine, hyoscine, scopalamine.

Medicinal properties:

यवानी यवानी तीव्रा तुरूष्को मदकारिणी ।। (ध. नि.)

"Yavānī yavānī tīvṛā turuṣko madakāriṇī." (Dha. Ni.)

Leaves & Seeds - Acrid, anodyne, anthelmintic, anti-inflammatory, antispasmodic, bitter, expectorant, narcotic, stomachic.

Medicinal uses: Leaves & Seeds - Asthma, bronchitis, cardiac debility, colic, dysmenorrhoea, epilepsy, fever, flatulence, rheumatism, scabies, spermatorrhoea, whooping cough.

Ethno- Medicinal uses: Leaf- Whooping cough (Gaur *et. al.,* 1985; Gupta *et. al.,* 1981; Ara & Naqshi, 1992); Sedative (Gupta *et. al.,* 1981); asthma (Ara & Naqshi, 1992).

Seeds - Toothache (Koelz, 1979; Ganai & Nawchoo, 2003); astringent (Gupta *et. al.,* 1981).

Fruit tops- Whooping cough, asthma (Ara & Naqshi, 1992).

Fruit- Toothache (Kala & Manjrekar, 2003).

Plant- Dysentery, indigestion, intestinal worms (Kapur & Nanda, 1992).

ICHNOCARPUS FRUTESCENS (L.) R. Br. (APOCYNACEAE)

Syn.: *Apocynum frutescens* L.

Regional and Other Names: *Bengali* – Shyamalata; *English* – Black creeper; *Hindi* – Kalidudhi; *Kannada* – Kappunamadaberu; *Malayalam* – Parvalli; *Marathi* – Kantebhouri; *Sanskrit* – Palindi; *Tamil* – Udarkkoti; *Telugu* – Nallatiga.

Distribution: Throughout India.

Taxonomic description: Twining shrubs, with elliptic-oblong or ovate-lanceolate leaves. Corolla greenish-white or Rose-coloured, lobes overlapping to the right. Follicles cylindric.

Medicinal parts: Roots.

Taste: Sweet.

Chemical constituents: Leaves - Flavons & Phenolic acids.

Stem - Triterpen glucoside.

Medicinal properties:

सारिवा द्वे तु मधुरा कफवातास्त्रनाशिनी।
कुष्ठकण्डूज्वरहरो मेहदुर्गन्धीनाशने।। (रा. नि.)

"Sārivā dve tu madhurā kaphavātāṣ̣ranāṣinī.
Kuṣthakaṇdūjvarahara mehadurgandhīnāṣane." (Ra. Ni.)

Root - Aphrodisiac, alterant, demulcent. depurative, diaphoretic, diuretic, febrifuge, refrigerant, sweet.

Medicinal uses: Root - Burning sensation, diabetes, dyspepsia, fever, leprosy, pruritus, seminal weakness, skin diseases, strangury, vomiting.

Ethno- Medicinal uses: Root - Blood purifier (Sudhakar & Rolla, 1985; Goel & Mudgal, 1988); fever (Maheshwari *et. al.,* 1986; Nayak *et al.,* 2003); rheumatism (Singh & Pandey, 1980); skin diseases (Sharma *et. al.,* 1979; Malhotra & Moorthy, 1973); scorpion sting (Gaur *et. al.,* 1980); tongue sore (Singh *et al.,* 1992); seminal weakness, diabetes (Nayak *et al.,* 2003).

Whole plant - Bone fractures (Hajra & Baishya, 1981).

Stem - Gum trouble, toothache (Goel *et. al.,* 1984); rickets (Mondal & Mukherjee, 1992).

Leaf - Fever (Rajwar, 1983; Kumar *et. al.,* 1980); stomachache (Srivastava & Varma, 1981).

INDIGOFERA TINCTORIA L. (PAPILIONACEAE)

Regional and Other Names: *Bengali* – Nil; *English* – Indian indigo; *Gujarati* –Nil; *Hindi* – Nil; *Kannada* – Nili; *Malayalam* – Nilamari; *Marathi* – Neeli; *Sanskrit* – Nilini; *Tamil* – Nili; *Telugu* – Nili.

Distribution: Throughout India.

Taxonomic description: Grey-pubescent undershrubs, with 7-13, obovate or oblanceolate leaflets. Racemes shorter than leaves. Pods deflexed, 8 to 10 seeded.

Medicinal parts: Whole plant.

Taste : Bitter.

Chemical constituents: Inorganic salts of Nitrogen, phosphoric acid, lime, potash, apigenin, kaempferol, luteolin, quercetin.

Seeds contain Galactomannan, galactose & mannose.

Medicinal properties:

नीली तिक्ता रसे चोष्णा कटिवातकफापहा।
केश्या विषोदरं हन्ति वातासृक्कृमिनाशिनी ।। (ध. नि.)

"Nīlī tiktā rase coṣṇā kativātakaphāpahā.
Keṣya visodaraṃ haṇti vātāsṛkkṛmināṣinī." (Dha. Ni.)

Root, Leaves & Stem - Anthelmintic, bitter, diuretic, expectorant, laxative.

Medicinal uses: Root, Stem & Leaves - Asthma, bronchitis, skin diseases, ulcers.

Ethno- Medicinal uses: Leaf - Eye diseases (Tribedi *et. al.,* 1985); hair growth (Shekhawat & Sunil anand, 1984); liver disorders (Gopal & Shah, 1985; Rajwar, 1983); nervous disorders (Rajwar, 1983); jaundice, spleen swelling, snake bite (Thomas & Britto, 2003); boils (Rosakutty *et al.,* 2003).

Root - Fever (Joshi *et. al.,* 1980); wounds (Dam & Hajra, 1981); antidote for poisoning (Rosakutty *et al.,* 2003).

Whole plant- Growth of hair, asthma, hydrophobia (Nayak *et al.,* 2003); scorpion sting (Thomas & Britto, 2003).

Juice- Leucorrhoea (Subramanian *et al.,* 2003).

INULA RACEMOSA Hook. f. (ASTERACEAE)

Syn.: *I. helenium* L.; *Corvisartia helenium* Mer.

Regional and Other Names: *Hindi* – Puskarmul; *Kannada* – Rasnabheda; *Malayalam* – Puskkaramulam; *Sanskrit* – Pauskaram; *Tamil* – Puskkaramulam; *Telugu* – Puskaramu.

Distribution: Indigenous to Iran, Afganistan & Baluchistan, Europe.

Taxonomic description : A herb with rough grooved stem; leaves simple, leathery, rough above, densely hairy beneath; flowers yellow, many in heads; fruits achenes with reddish pappus.

Medicinal parts : Roots.

Taste: Bitter, Acrid.

Chemical constituents: Root contain-Essential oil, resin, inulin, inulenin, pseudo-Inulin, alantolactone, isoalantolactone, dihydroalantolactone.

Medicinal properties:

उक्तं पुष्करमूलन्तु पौष्करं पुष्करं च तत्।
पद्मपत्रं च काश्मीरं कुष्ठभेदमिमं जगुः।। (भा. प्र.)

"Uktaṃ puṣkaramūlaṇtu paūṣkaraṃ puṣkaraṃ ca taṭ.
Paḍmapatraṃ ca kāṣmīraṃ kuṣthabhedamiaṃ jaguḥ." (Bhā. Pṛa.)

Root- Acrid, alexipharmic, anodyne, anti-inflammatory, antiseptic, aphrodisiac, bitter, carminative, digestive, diuretic, expectorant, stimulant, stomachic, sudorific.

Medicinal uses: Root - Amenorrhoea, asthma, bronchitis, cardiac debility, colic, cough, dysmenorrhoea, dyspepsia, fever, flatulence, hiccough, inflammations, skin diseases, ulcers, wounds.

Ethno- Medicinal uses: Root - Rheumatism, Gastro-intestinal problems (Gupta *et. al.,* 1981).

Seed- Heart ailments (Ara & Naqshi, 1992).

IPOMOEA BATATAS (Linn.) Lam. (CONVOLVULACEAE)

Syn.: *Convolvulus batalas* L.

Regional and Other Names: *Bengali* – Ranga alu; *English* – Sweet potato; *Gujarati* –Sakaria; *Hindi* – Mitha alu, Sakkarkand; *Kannada* – Sihigenasu; *Malayalam* – Madhurakkilannu; *Marathi* – Ratalu; *Sanskrit* – Pindaluh; *Tamil* – Cakkaravallikkilanku; *Telugu* – Genusu.

Distribution: Throughout India, cultivated.

Taxonomic description: A prostrate vine with tuberous roots which may be red or white in colour; simple, ovate-cordate; flowers purple, corolla funnel-shaped; fruits capsules.

Medicinal parts: Tuberous roots.

Taste: Sweet.

Chemical constituents: Tubers - Hydrocyanic acid, oxalic acid, phytic acid, starch, vitamins, enzymes, β-sitosterol, oalmitic acid, NaCl.

Medicinal properties:

मुखालुकः स्यान्मधुरः शिशिरः पित्तनाषनः ।
रूचिकृद्वातकृच्चैव दाहशोषतृषापहः ।। (रा. नि.)

"Mukhālukaḥ ṣyāṇmadhuraḥ ṣiṣirah piṭtanāṣanaḥ.
Rucikṛdvātakṛccaiva dāhaṣosatṛsāpahaḥ." (Rā. Ni.)

Roots - Aphrodisiac, diuretic, laxative, refrigerant, sweet.

Medicinal uses: Roots Burning sensation, constipation, renal & Diabetes, vesical calculi, strangury.

Ethno- Medicinal uses: Leaves- Expelling thorn from foot (Kshirsagar & Singh, 2003).

IPOMOEA MAURITIANA Jacq.(CONVOLVULACEAE)

Syn.: *I digitata* L.; *I. paniculata* R. Br.; *Convolvulus paniculata* L.

Regional and Other Names: *Bengali* – Bilaikand; *English* – Giant potato; *Hindi* – Bhilaykand; *Kannada* – Nadakumbala; *Malayalam* – Palmutukku; *Marathi* –Vidarikand; *Sanskrit* – Ksiravidari; *Tamil* – Palmudamgi; *Telugu* – Nelagummudu.

Distribution: Throughout India.

Taxonomic description: A much branched perennial climber with large tuberous roots; leaves palmately lobed, ovate-lanceolate; flowers purple; fruits capsule; seeds clothed with cottony hairs.

Medicinal parts : Tuberous roots.

Taste : Sweet.

Chemical constituents: Tuber - Fixed oil from tubers contained Palmitic, stearic, oleic, linoleic, linolenic acids.

Medicinal properties:

पयस्या कुसुमं वृष्यं मधुरं रसपाकयोः।
पित्तघ्नं शीतवीर्यं च वातश्लेष्मकरं गुरूः ।। (कै. नि.)

"Payaṣyā kusumaṃ vṛṣyaṃ madhuraṃ rasapākayoḥ.
Pịttaghanaṃ ṣītavīṛyaṃ ca vātaṣleṣmakaraṃ guruḥ." (Kaī. Ni.)

Root - Acrid, anthelmintic, aphrodisiac, appetiser, astringent, carminative, cooling, depurative, diuretic, emollient, expectorant. sour, stimulant, sweet.

Medicinal uses: Root - Bronchitis, burning sensation, colic, dyspepsia, fever, flatulence, gonorrhoea, inflammation, leprosy, skin diseases, strangury, syphilis, vomiting.

Ethno- Medicinal uses: Tuber- Diabetes (Sarkar *et al.,* 2003).

IPOMOEA NIL (Linn.) Roth. (CONVOLVULACEAE)

Syn.: *I. headeracea* auct. non (L.) Jacq.; *Convolvulus nil* L.; *C. bilobatus* Roxb.

Regional and Other Names: *Bengali* – Nil-Kalmi; *English* – Morning glory; *Gujarati* – Kaladana; *Hindi* – Kaladana; *Kannada* – Gouribija; *Malayalam* – Taliyari; *Marathi* –Nilyel; *Sanskrit* – Krsnabijah; *Tamil* – Kakkattan; *Telugu* – Kollivittulu.

Distribution: Throughout India.

Taxonomic description: Twining herbs, with ovate-cordate leaves and purple flowers in axillary cymes. Capsules 3-valved; seeds glabrous.

Medicinal parts : Seeds.

Taste: Acrid, Sweet.

Chemical constituents: Seeds contain - Alkaloids: Lysergol, chanoclavine, penniclavine, isopeniclavine, elymoclavine; Resin, Glucosides.

Medicinal properties:

कृष्णबीजं श्यामबीजं स्मृतं श्यामलबीजकम् ।। (शा. नि.)

"Kṛṣṇabījaṃ ṣyāmabījaṃ ṣmṛtaṃ ṣyāmalabījakaṃ." (Sā. Ni.)

Seeds - Acrid, anti-inflammatory, carminative. depurative, purgative, sweet.

Medicinal uses: Seeds - Brochitis, constipation, fever, flatulence, gout, inflammation, leucoderma, scabies, skin diseases.

Ethno- Medicinal uses: Seeds - Purgative (Sharma *et. al.,* 1979; Shah & Joshi, 1971; Singh & Pandey, 1980; Shah *et. al.,* 1983; Basak, 2006); colic, constipation (Bhatt *et al.,* 2003).

Fruit- Blood purifier, improve eye sight (Srivastava *et al.,* 1992)

Leaf- Blood purifier, improve eye sight (Srivastava *et al.,* 1992)

JASMINUM GRANDIFLORUM L. (OLEACEAE)

Syn.: *J. officinale* L.

Regional and Other Names: *Bengali* – Chameli; *English* – Common Jasmine; *Gujarati* – Chambeli; *Hindi* – Cameli; *Kannada* – Mallige; *Malayalam* – Piccakam; *Sanskrit* – Malati; *Tamil* – Kotimalligi; *Telugu* – Malati.

Distribution: Throughout India.

Taxonomic description: Scandent or climbing shrubs, with imparipinnate leaves and white flowers in lax panicles.

Medicinal parts : Root, Leaves, Flowers.

Taste : Bitter, Astringent.

Chemical constituents: Leaves - Salicylic acid.

Flowers - Essential oil in flowers contains lactone, pyridine & nicotinate derivatives.

Medicinal properties:

जातिर्जाती च सुमना मालती राजपुत्रिका।
चेतिका हृद्यगन्धा च सा पीता स्वर्णजातिका।। (भा. प्र.)

"Jātịrjātī ca sumanā mālatī rājaputṛikā
Cetikā hṛḍyagaṇdhā ca sā pītā svarṇajātiktā." (Bhā. Pṛa.)

Root & Leaves - Acrid, anodyne, anthelmintic, antiseptic, aphrodisiac, astringent, bitter, depurative, diuretic, emollient.

Flowers - Ophthalmic, refrigerant.

Medicinal uses: Root - Amenorrhoea, constipation, dysmenorrhoea, flatulence, leprosy, mental debility, paralysis, ringworm, skin diseases. sterility, strangury.

Leaves - Corns, dysmenorrhoea, leprosy, otalgia, skin diseases, strangury, ulcers, wounds.

Flowers - Dysmenorrhoea, leprosy, pruritus, skin diseases, strangury, ulcers.

Ethno- Medicinal uses: Flower- Stimulate hair growth (External application) (Jadeja *et al.,* 2006).

Bark - Burns, Skin diseases (Sinha *et al.,* 2006).

Leaf- Toothache, skin diseases (Deokule & Magdum, 1992).

JASMINM SAMBAC (Linn.) Ait. (OLEACEAE)

Regional and Other Names: *Bengali* – Motia; *English* – Arabian Jasmine; *Gujarati* –Mogro; *Hindi* – Mogra, Bel; *Kannada* – Dundumallige; *Malayalam* – Mulla; *Marathi* –Mogra; *Sanskrit* – Mallika; *Tamil* – Malligai; *Telugu* – Malli.

Distribution: Throughout India.

Taxonomic description: Scandent or climbing shrubs, with simple leaves and white flowers.

Medicinal parts : Roots, Leaves, Flowers.

Taste : Bitter, Astringent.

Chemical constituents: Flowers contain Pyridine, nicotinate derivatives.

Medicinal properties:

मल्लिका मदयन्ती च शीतभीरूश्च भूपदी ।। (भा. प्र.)

"Maḷlikā madayaṇtī ca ṣītabhīruṣca bhūpadī." (Bhā. Pṛa.)

Flowers - Acrid, alexipharmic, bitter, ophthalmic, purgative, refrigerant.

Medicinal uses: Leaves - Fever, skin diseases, ulcers.

Flowers - Fever, leprosy, hiccough, insanity, pruritus, ulcers, vomiting.

Ethno- Medicinal uses: Leaves - Boils & wounds (Jadhav, 2006).

JUGLANS REGIA L. (JUGLANDACEAE)

Regional and Other Names: *Bengali* – Akhrot; *English* – Common walnut; *Gujarati* – Akhrot; *Hindi* – Akhrot; *Kannada* – Akrodu; *Malayalam* – Akrottu; *Marathi* –Akroda; *Sanskrit* – Aksotah; *Tamil* – Akrottu; *Telugu* – Akrotu.

Distribution: Cultivated in the Himalayas & Khasia hills.

Taxonomic description: A large deciduous monoecious tree; leaves imparipinnately compound, aromatic; flowers yellowish-green, small and in catkins; fruits drupes with leathery exocarp, woody, wrinkled, hard endocarp enclosing 4-lobed, oily seed.

Medicinal parts: Leaves, Fruits, Bark.

Taste : Sweet.

Chemical constituents: Leaves & Fruits - Cysteine, tryptophane, thiamin, riboflavin, nicotinic acid, pantothenic acid, folic acid, vitamin-B_6 , biotin, vitamin-A, ascorbic acid, essential oil, oxalic acid.

Bark & Roots - Juglone, bernerine, cyclotrisjuglone, β-sitosterol.

Medicinal properties:

पीलुः शैलभवोऽक्षोटः कन्दरालश्च कीर्त्तितः ।। (भा. प्र.)

"Pīluḥ Ṣaīlabhavoaksotaḥ kaṇdarālaṣca kīṛttitaḥ." (Bhā. Pṛa.)

Leaf - Anthelminitic, astringent, detergent.

Bark - Antiscorbutic, detergent.

Fruits - Aphrodisiac, carminative, emollient, sweet.

Medicinal uses: Leaves & Bark - Eczema, scrofula, syphilis.

Fruits - Rheumatism.

Ethno- Medicinal uses: Bark - Anthelmintic (Sharma *et al.,* 1979); toothache (Negi *et al.,*1985; Singh, 2003); rheumatic pain, joint pain (Singh, 2003).

Leaf - Astringent (Sharma *et al.,* 1979); Skin diseases (Chhetri, 2005).

Seed oil- Rheumatic pain (Ara & Naqshi, 1992; Singh, 2003).

Root epidermis- Cleaning teeth (Ara & Naqshi, 1992; Sharma *et al.*, 2003).

Fruit- Cleaning teeth (Sharma *et al.*, 2003).

JUSTICIA GENDARUSSA Burm. f. (ACANTHACEAE)

Syn.: *J. vulgaris* Nees.

Regional and Other Names: *Bengali* – Jagat madan; *Hindi* – Nīlīnirgundī; *Malayalam* – Vatamkolli; *Marathi* –Bakas; *Sanskrit* – Vataghni; *Tamil* – Vataikkutti; *Telugu* – Addasaramu.

Distribution: Throughout India.

Taxonomic description: An erect undershrub; leaves simple, linear-lanceolate or lanceolate; flowers white, spotted purple within, clustered in the interrupted spikes; fruits capsules.

Medicinal parts: Root, Leaves.

Taste: Bitter, Astringent.

Chemical constituents: Root - ß-Sitosterol.

Leaves - β-Sitosterol, Alkaloid.

Medicinal properties:

नीलानिर्गुडिका तिक्ता रूक्षा चोष्णा कटुः स्मृता।
आध्मानवानं प्रदरं क्रासंशोथं कफं हरेत्।
वातनाश करीप्रोक्तामुनिभिर्गुणपार गैः।। (नि. र.)

"Nīlānirgudikā tiḳtā ruksā coṣṇā katuḥ ṣmṛtā.
Āḍḥmānavānaṃ p̣radaraṃ krāsaṃṣothaṃ kaphaṃ hareṭ
Vātanāṣa karīp̣roḳtā munibhiṛguṇapāra gaīḥ." (Ni. Ra.)

Roots & Leaves - Acrid, anodyne, anti-inflammatory, antiperoidic, bitter, diaphoretic, emetic, expectorant, insecticidal.

Medicinal uses: Roots & Leaves - Amenorrhoea, Arthritis, bronchitis, cough, dysmenorrhoea, fevers, otalgia, rheumatism.

Ethno- Medicinal uses: Leaf - Bone fractures (Rao, 1981); paralysis (Nagendre Prasad & Abraham, 1984); small pox, measles (Singh *et al.*, 1992); facial paralysia, arthritis, ascites (Nayak *et al.*, 2003); body pain, snake bite

(Sivakumar *et al.,* 2003); headache (Arinathan *et al.,* 2003); increase strength (Nath & Maiti, 2003).

Whole plant - Paralysis (Nagendre Prasad & Abraham, 1984); rheumatic pain (Udayan *et al.,* 2006).

KAEMPFERIA ROTUNDA L. (ZINGIBERACEAE)

Regional and Other Names: *Bengali* – Bhuichampa; *English* – Indian crocus; *Gujarati* – Bhuichampo; *Hindi* – Bhuyicampa; *Kannada* – Nelasampige; *Malayalam* – Cennalinirkuva; *Marathi* – Bhuichampa; *Sanskrit* –Bhumicampaka; *Tamil* – Nerppicin; *Telugu* – Bhucampakamu.

Distribution: Throughout India.

Taxonomic description: An aromatic herb with tuberous root-stak and very short stem; leaves simple, few, oblong, ovate-lanceolate, acuminate; flowers white or liliac in spikes.

Medicinal parts: Tubers.

Taste : Bitter, Acrid.

Chemical constituents: Tubers contain Crotepoxide, benzoic acid.

Medicinal properties:

भूमिजश्चम्पकश्चोश्णः कटुः शोफरूजापहः।
गलगण्डं व्रणं चैव नाशयेदिति कीर्त्तितम्।। (नि. र.)

"Bhūmijaṣcaṃpakaṣcoṣṇaḥ katuḥ ṣopharujāpahaḥ.
Galagaṇdaṃ vṛanaṃ caiva nāṣayediti kīṛttitaṃ." (Ni. Ra.)

Tubers - Acrid, anti-inflammatory, aromatic, emetic, stomachic, vulnerary.

Medicinal uses: Tubers - Blood clots, cancerous swellings, dropsy, inflammations, tumours, ulcers, wound.

Ethno- Medicinal uses: Tubers - Eye diseases (Rao, 1981); gastric complaints, tumours, swellings, wounds (Behura & Rout, 2003).

KYLLINGA NEMORALIS (Forster) Dandy. ex Hutch. (CYPERACEAE)

Syn.: *K. monocephala* Rottb.; *Cyperus kyllingia* Endl.

Regional and Other Names: *Bengali* – Nirbishi; *Hindi* – Nirbisi; *Malayalam* –Palnirvasi; *Marathi* –Mustu; *Sanskrit* –Svetanirvisa; *Tamil* – Velutta nirbasi; *Telugu* –Gandala.

Distribution: Throughout India.

Taxonomic description: An erect glabrous sedge with elongate creeping rhizome; flowers minute in spike, solitary or 2-3 togethere, the rachis naked when spikelets fall off; spikelets one-flowered; fruits nuts.

Medicinal parts: Tubers.

Taste : Sweet, Astringent.

Medicinal properties:

श्वेतनिर्विषा मधुरा शीता तिक्ता श्लेष्मानिलापहा ।।

"Ṣvetanirvisā madhurā ṣītā tiktā ṣleṣmānilāpaha"

Tuber - Aromatic, astringent, bitter, demulcent, diuretic, expectorant, febrifuge, fragrant, sweet.

Medicinal uses: Tuber - Bronchitis, cough, diabetes, diarrhoea, dysentery, fever, stangury, tumours.

Ethno- Medicinal uses: Tuber - Diabetes, Snake bite (Basak, 2006); Tumour (Jain & Tarafder, 1970); fever (Mukhopadhyay, 1992; Gogoi & Das, 2003).

LABLAB PURPUREUS L. (PAPILIONACEAE)

Syn.: *Dolichos lablab* L.

Regional and Other Names: *Bengali* – Shim; *English* – Lablab bean; *Gujarati* – Val; *Hindi* – Sem; *Kannada* – Capparada-avare; *Malayalam* – Amara; *Marathi* – Papta; *Sanskrit* – Nispavah; *Tamil* – Avarai; *Telugu* – Cikkkudu.

Distribution: Throughout India, cultivated.

Taxonomic description : A tall, glabrous twining perennial herb, with white or pink flowers & white pods.

Medicinal parts : Leaves, Seeds.

Taste : Sweet, Astringent.

Chemical constituents: Seeds - Hydrocarbons, proteins, lipids, amino acids, tryptophan, arginine, tyrosinase, hydrocyanic acid, calcium, phosphorus, iron, vitamins-A,B, B_2, C.

Pods - L-pipecolic acid, galactusonic acid, galactose, glucose & arabinose.

Medicinal properties:

निष्पावो राजशिम्बीस्यात् वेल्लकः श्वेतशिम्बकः ।। (भा. प्र.)

"Niṣpāvo rājaṣiṃbī ṣyāṭ veḷlakaḥ ṣvetaṣiṃbikaḥ." (Bhā. Pṛa.)

Leaves - Alexipharmic.

Seed - Aphrodisiac, astringent, diuretic, laxative, sour, stomachic, sweet.

Medicinal uses: Leaves - Colic.

Seed - Inflammations, stranugry.

Ethno- Medicinal uses: Root - Antifertility (Majumdar *et. al.,* 1978); cough (Singh, 2003); leucorrhoea (Shukla *et al.,* 2003).

Leaf - Cough (Singh *et. al.,* 1987); ringworm (Purohit *et. al.,* 1985; Manandhav, 2003); earache (Saren *et al.,* 2003).

Fruit- Diabetes (Manandhav, 2003).

LAGENARIA SICERARIA (Mol.) Standley. (CUCURBITACEAE)

Syn.: *L. leucantha* (Duchesne) Rusby.

Regional and Other Names: *Bengali* – Bitter bottle gourd; *English* – Bitter bottle gourd; *Hindi* – Kadvilauki; *Kannada* – Kadusore; *Malayalam* – Kattucura; *Sanskrit* – Katutumbi; *Tamil* – Sorakkai; *Telugu* – Sorakkaya.

Distribution: Throughout India.

Taxonomic description : Climbing herbs, with angular or shortly 3-lobed, white flowers & bottle shaped fruits.

Medicinal parts: Whole plant.

Taste : Bitter.

Chemical constituents: Fruits - Pectin, cucurbitacins, triterpenoids.

Seed - Rhamnose, glucose, fructose, galactose, sucrose, raffinose, stachyose.

Seed oil - Saponin, fatty oil, palmitic, palmitoleic, oleic, stearic & linoleic acids.

Medicinal properties:

अलाबुः कथिता तुम्बी द्विधा दीर्घा च वर्त्तुला।। (भा. प्र.)

"Alābuḥ kathitā tuṃbī dvidhā dirghā ca vaṛttulā." (Bhā. Pṛa.)

Root - Anti-inflammatory, emetic, purgative.

Leaves - Anodyne, bitter, depurative, emetic, expectorant, febriuge, purgative, refrigerant.

Flowers - Cooling.

Fruits - Acrid, anti-inlammatory, bitter, depurative, diuretic, emetic, expectorant, febrifuge, purgative, refrigerant.

Seeds - Brain tonic, cooling, diuretic, purgative.

Medicinal uses: Root - Constipation, Inflammations.

Leaves - Asthma, bronchitis, constipation, cough, fever, flatulance, inflammations, jaundice, leprosy, skin diseases.

Flowers - Useful in Odontalgia & Ophthalmia.

Fruits - Bronchitis, cough, fever, inflammations, leprosy, skin diseases.

Seed - Cough, dropsy, fever, inflammations.

Ethno- Medicinal uses: Fruits - Cracks in sole (Singh *et al.,* 1980); Purgative (Singh *et al.,* 1980); To make black and silky hair (External application) (Jadeja *et al.,* 2006).

Leaf - Jaundice (Singh *et al.,* 1980; Kothari & Londhe, 2003).

Root - Jaundice (Hemadri & Rao, 1984); abortion (Barua *et al.,* 2003).

LENS CULINARIS Med. (PAPILIONACEAE)

Regional and Other Names: *English* – Lentil; *Hindi* – Masur; *Kannada* – Kesaribele; *Malayalam* – Vattupparippu; *Marathi* – ; *Sanskrit* – Masurah; *Tamil* – Misur paruppu; *Telugu* – Misuri pappu.

Distribution: Throughout the colder parts of India, cultivated.

Taxonomic description : A small erect soft pubescent herb, with white Rose, Red or Violet flowers & pod fruits.

Medicinal parts : Seeds.

Taste: Sweet.

Chemical constituents: Seeds contain - Proteins, vitamin-B, tricetin, luteolin, kaempferol glycoside, 3, 4, 7 – trihydroxyflavone, proanthocyanidins, diglycosyldelphinidin.

Chemical constituents:

मङ्गल्यको मसूरः स्यात् मङ्गल्या च मसूरिका ।। (भा प्र.)

"Maṇgalyako masūraḥ ṣyāṭ maṇgạlyā ca masūrikā." (Bhā. Pra.)

Seeds - Astringent, constipating, diuretic, sweet.

Medicinal uses: Seeds - Anaemia, diarrhoea, dysentery, skin diseases, strangury, tumours.

Ethno- Medicinal uses: Seeds - Boil (Baruah *et al.,* 2006).

LEPIDIUM SATIVUM L. (BRASSICACEAE)

Regional and Other Names: *Bengali* – Halim; *English* – Water cress; *Gujarati* – Asahio; *Hindi* – Halim, Candsur; *Kannada* – Alavibija; *Malayalam* – Asali; *Marathi* –Ahliva; *Sanskrit* – Asalika; *Tamil* – Aliviral; *Telugu* – Aditya.

Distribution: Cultivated throughout India as a culinary vegetable.

Taxonomic description: Erect annual herbs, with pinnatifid leaves & white flowers fruits pod.

Medicinal parts: Roots, Leaves, Seeds.

Taste : Bitter, Acrid.

Chemical constituents: Glucotropoeoline, sinapine, sinapic acid, β-sitosterol, benzylcyanide, vitamins, essential oil.

Medicinal properties:

चंद्रशूरं हितं हिक्कावातश्लेश्मातिसारिणाम्।
असृग्वातगदद्वेषी बलपुष्टि विवर्धनम्।। (भा. प्र.)

"Caṇḍraṣuraṃ hitaṃ hikkāvataṣleṣmātisāriṇāṃ.
Asṛgvatagadadvesī balapuṣtivivaṛdhanaṃ." (Bhā. Pṛa.)

Root - Acrid, bitter.

Leaves - Antibacterial, diuretic, stimulant.

Seeds - Aphrodisiac, bitter, depurative, diuretic, rubefacient.

Medicinal uses: Seeds - Asthma, cough, diarrhoea, dysentery, dyspepsia, hiccough, leucorrhoea, lumbago, scurvy, seminal weakness, skin diseases.

Ethno- Medicinal uses: Plant - Asthma, bronchitis, colic, dysentery, pain, stomachache (Jain & Tarafder, 1970); Diabetes (Bhatt *et al.,* 2003).

Fruit - Gout (Jadeja *et al.,* 2006).

Seed oil- Rheumatism (Mitaliya *et al.,* 2003).

Leaves- Sciatica, backache (Mitaliya *et al.,* 2003).

Seed- sexual debility (Bhatt *et al.,* 2003).

LINUM USITATISSIMUM L. (LINACEAE)

Regional and Other Names: *Bengali* – Tishi; *English* – Linseed, Flax plant; *Gujarati* – Alshi; *Hindi* – Alsi; *Kannada* – Alasibija; *Malayalam* – Akasi; *Marathi* – Javas; *Sanskrit* – Atasi; *Tamil* – Alivirai; *Telugu* – Avisi.

Distribution: Cultivated throughout India.

Taxonomic description: An annual herb; leaves linear-lanceolate; flowers bluish violet or white in terminal panicles; fruit capsule.

Medicinal parts: Flowers, Seeds, Seed oil.

Taste: Bitter, Sweet.

Chemical constituents: Seed - Proteins, glucosides, phytin, lecithin, β-carotenoids, cholesterol, campesterol, stigmasterol, sitosterol, 5-dehydro-avenasterol, cyclosterol & 24-methylenecycloartanol.

Seed oil - Proteins, wax, resin, sugar, phosphates, linamarin.

Medicinal properties:

अतसी नीलपुष्पी च पार्वती स्यादुमा क्षुमा।। (भा. प्र.)

"Atasī nīlapuṣpī ca pāṛvatī ṣyādumā ksumā." (Bhā. Pṛa.)

Flowers - Cardiotonic.

Seeds - Acrid, bitter, diuretic, emollient, expectorant, laxative, sweet, thermogenic.

Medicinal uses: Seed - Crushed linseed is used as poultice for relief of Boils & carbuncles, local inflammations, ulcers.

Seed oil - Linseed oil is used for external application.

Ethno- Medicinal uses: Seed – Wounds (Tarafder, 1984); swelling (Deokule & Magdum, 1992; Deokule, 2006); Rheumatism, gout (Mitaliya *et al.*, 2003).

Root - To make black and silky hair (External application) (Jadeja *et al.*, 2006).

LODOICES MALDIVICA (Poir.) Pers. (ARECACEAE)

Regional and Other Names: *English* - Sea Coconut palm; *Gujarati* - Daryanunaiyal; *Hindi* - Darya-ka-nariyal; *Kannada* - Kadalutengu; *Malayalam* - Aklarittenna; *Marathi* - Jahari naral; *Sanskrit* - Arkaragah; *Tamil* - Kadalttengai; *Telugu* - Samudraputenkaya.

Distribution - In Seychelles Islands.

Taxonomic description - A tall palm with smooth annulated trunk bearing a crown of large fan shaped leaves.

Medicinal parts: Husk, Endosperm.

Taste: Sweet, Acrid.

Medicinal properties:

समुद्रनारिकेलस्तु मधुरः कटुको लघुः।
वीर्योश्णः कफवातघ्नः शीतप्रषामनो मतः।। (द्र.वि.)

"Samudṛanārikelaṣtu madhuraḥ katuko laghuḥ
Vīṛyoṣṇaḥ kaphavātaghnaḥ ṣītapṛaṣamano mataḥ. (Dṛa. Vi.)

Kernel - Acrid, carminative, digestive, febrifuge, refrigerant, sweet.

Medicinal uses: Kernel - Cholera, colic, diarrhoea, oedema.

LORANTHUS LONGIFLORUS L. Var. *FALCATUS* (L. f.) Kurz. (LORANTHACEAE)

Syn.: *Dendrophthoe falcata* (L.f.) Etting

Regional and Other Names: *Bengali* – Baramanda; *English* – Mistletoe; *Gujarati* –Vando; *Hindi* – Banda; *Kannada* – Badanike, Banbhulu; *Malayalam* – Iththil; *Marathi* – Iththil; *Sanskrit* – Vruksadani; *Tamil* – Pulluruvi; *Telugu* – Badanika.

Distribution: Throughout India.

Taxonomic description: A semi-parasitic large shrub, generally on Mango trees; leaves opposite, thick. Coriaceous, ovate or linear-oblong, obtuse, midvein usually red; flowers red or yellow or pink white.

Medicinal parts: Leaves, Flowers.

Taste : Bitter.

Chemical constituents: Cytokinins, casein hydrolysate, quercetagetin, quercitrin, kaempferol, qurcetin, myricetin, β-sitosterol, stigmasterol, oleanolic acid.

Medicinal properties:

वृक्षादनी हिमा तिक्ता कषाया मधुरा रसे ।
अश्मरीकफवातास्त्ररक्षोवर्णविषापहा ।। (कै. नि.)

"Vṛikshādanī himā tiḳtā kasāyā madhurā rase
Aṣmarīkaphvātāṣṭrarakshovarṇavisāpahā." (Bhā. Pṛa.)

Carminative, blood purifier, diuretic, expectorant.

Medicinal uses: Asthma, epilepsy, fever, malaria fever, oedema, scorpion sting.

Ethno- Medicinal uses: Stem bark - Antifertility (Mudgal & Pal, 1980); menstrual disorders (Mondal & Mukherjee, 1992; Rai *et al.,* 1992); asthma, wound (Rai *et al.,* 1992); wounds (Kapur & Nanda, 1992); washing cuts and wounds (Singh, 2003).

Stem - Abortifacient (Tarafder, 1985); headache (Goel & Mudgal, 1988); wounds (Chaudhuri *et al.,* 1975; Kapur & Nanda, 1992).

Leaf - Wounds (Goel & Mudgal, 1988); cough, cold (Shukla *et al.,* 1992); intermittent fever (Sivakumar *et al.,* 2003).

Root - Skin diseases (Goel *et. al.,* 1984).

Whole plant- Rheumatism, wounds (Srivastava *et al.,* 2003).

LUFFA CYLINDRICA (L.) M. Roem. (CUCURBITACEAE)

Syn.: *L. aegyptiaca* Mill.

Regional and Other Names: *Bengali* – Dundul; *English* – Sponge gourd; *Gujarati* – Turia; *Hindi* – Khiya tori; *Kannada* – Tuppahire; *Malayalam* – Puttilpiram; *Marathi* – Paroshi; *Sanskrit* – Mahakosataki; *Tamil* – Mulukkupperakkai; *Telugu* – Netibirakaya.

Distribution: Throughout India.

Taxonomic description : A large monoecious climber with stout 5-angled twisted stems; Male flowers in axillary racemes, crowded at the top, female flowers solitary; fruits large, cylindric, smooth, 10-ribbed; seeds black or grey.

Medicinal parts : Fruits, Seeds.

Taste : Astringent.

Chemical constituents: Colosynthine, luffein.

Medicinal Porperties:

महाकोशातकी स्निग्धा रक्तपित्तानिलापहा ।। (भा प्र.)

"Mahākoṣātaki ṣnigdhā raktapiṭtānilāpahā" (Bhā. Pṛa.)

Fruits- Anthlemintic, carminative, depurative, diuretic, emollient, expectorant, laxative.

Medicinal uses: Fruits - Bronchitis, fever, leprosy, syphilis, tumours.

Ethno- Medicinal uses: Fruits - Diarrhoea (Chaudhuri *et. al.,* 1982).

Leaves- Burns (Singh & Singh, 2003).

LYCOPERSICON ESCULENTUM Mill. (SOLANACEAE)

Syn.: *L. lycopersicum* (L.) Kars.

Regional and Other Names: *Bengali* – Tamater; *English* – Tomato; *Hindi* – Tamatar; *Kannada* – Capparabadane; *Malayalam* – Takkali; *Marathi* – Velvangi; *Sanskrit* – Raktamaci; *Tamil* – Takkali; *Telugu* – Simavanga.

Distribution: Cultivated throughout India.

Taxonomic description: An annual herb; leaves unevenly pinnate, pubescent,; flowers yellow in extra axillary cymes; fruits Berries, red on ripening.

Medicinal parts: Fruits.

Taste : Sweet, Acidic.

Chemical constituents: Fruits - Minerals, vitamins, calcium, phosphorus, carotene, thiamine, riboflavin, niacin, crude tomatīne.

Medicinal properties:

रक्तमाची मृदुः स्निग्धा शीतला स्वादु रोचनी ।।

"Raktamācī mṛduḥ ṣnigdhā ṣītalā ṣvādu rōcanī"

Fruits - Aperient, carminative, depurative, digestive, emollient, haematinic, sweet.

Medicinal uses: Fruits - Asthma, bronchitis, constipation, flatulence.

Ethno- Medicinal uses: Plant- Rheumatism, influenza, body pain, frequent urination (Rajan, 1992).

MALAXIS ACUMINATA D. Don. (ORCHIDACEAE)

Syn.: *Microstylis wallichii* Lindl.

Regional and Other Names: *English* – Jeevak; *Hindi* – Jivak; *Kannada* – Jivaka; *Malayalam* – Jivakam; *Sanskrit* – Jivakah; *Tamil* – Jivakam; *Telugu* – Jivakamu.

Distribution: Throughout India.

Taxonomic description : A short stemmed terrestrial herb, with more or less pseudobulb at the base and fibrous roots; leaves simple, sheating, ovate or lanceolate; flowers minute pale Yellow-Green tinged with Purple in terminal racemes.

Medicinal parts : Green swollen stem base covered by brown scales.

Taste : Sweet.

Chemical constituents: 3'-O-Methylbatatasin-III, β-sitosterol, sugars.

Medicinal properties:

जीवको मधुरः शीतो रक्तपित्तानिलान् जयेत् ।
दाहज्वरक्षयान् हन्ति कफशुक्लविवर्धनः ।। (ध. नि.)

"Jīvako madhuraḥ ṣīto raktapiṭtānilāṇ jayeṭ
Dādajvaraksayāṇ haṇti kaphaṣuklavivaṛdhanaḥ." (Dha. Ni.)

Stem base - Aphrodisiac, febrifuge, refrigerant, sweet.

Medicinal uses: Stem base - Burning sensation, fever, seminal weakness, tuberculosis.

MALLOTUS PHILIPPENSIS (Lam.) Muell.-Arg. (EUPHORBIACEAE)

Syn.: *Croton philippense* Lamk.; *Rottlera tinctoria* Roxb.

Regional and Other Names: *Bengali* – Kamila; *English* – Kamala tree; *Gujarati* –Kapilo; *Hindi* – Sindur, Kamala; *Kannada* – Kampillaka; *Malayalam* – Sinduri; *Marathi* – Shendri; *Sanskrit* – Recanakah; *Tamil* – Manjanai; *Telugu* – Sundari.

Distribution: Throughout India.

Taxonomic description : Small, dioecious trees, with ovate to ovate-lanceolate leaves palmately veined and red gland-dotted beneath. Capsules globose.

Medicinal parts : The glandular hairs of the fruit.

Taste : Acrid.

Chemical constituents: Seeds - Rottlerin, isorottlerin, corotoxigenin, coroglaucigenin.

Heartwood - Betulin-3-acetate, lupeol, lupeol acetate, sitosterol, bergenin.

Bark - Acetylaleuritolic acid, α-amyrin, sitosterol, bergenin.

Medicinal properties:

कम्पिल्लः कर्कशश्चन्द्रो रक्ताङ्गो रेचनोऽपि च।। (भा. प्र.)

"Kaṃpiḷlaḥ kaṛkaṣaṣcaṇḍṛo raḳtāṇgo recanoapi ca." (Bhā. Pṛa.)

Glandular hair - Acrid, alexipharmic, depurative, digestive, purgative, styptic, thermogenic, vermifuge.

Medicinal uses: Glandular hair - Constipation, cough, flatulence, haemorrhages, ringworm, scabies, ulcers, wounds.

Ethno- Medicinal uses:

Seed - Anthelmintic (Rajwar, 1983; Negi *et al.,* 1985); boils (Goel *et al.,* 1984); ulcers (Goel *et al.,* 1984; Mondal & Mukherjee, 1992); intestinal worms (Vir Jee *et al.,* 1984); rheumatism (Negi *et al.,* 1985); skin diseases (Sharma *et al.,* 1979); snake bite (Negi *et al.,* 1985).

Fruit - Boils, blisters, constipation, dysentery (Maheshwari & Singh, 1984)

Root - Skin diseases (Malhotra & Moorthy, 1973; Sharma *et al.*, 1979).

Leaves - Skin diseases, abdominal pain (Das et. al., 2006).

Roots bark - Skin diseases, abdominal pain (Das *et. al.*, 2006).

MENTHA ARVENSIS L. (LAMIACEAE)

Regional and Other Names: *Bengali* – Podina; *English* – Mint; Gujarati –Pudina; *Hindi* – Pudina; *Kannada* –; *Malayalam* – Putina; *Marathi* –Pudina; *Sanskrit* – Pudina; *Tamil* – Putina; *Telugu* – Pudina.

Distribution: Western Himalayas, also cultivated throughout India.

Taxonomic description: An erect aromatic herb with suckers; Leaves simple ovate or lanceolate, crenate-serrate; flowers lilac in axillary distant whorls; fruits nutlets, smooth.

Medicinal parts : Leaves.

Taste : Sweet.

Essential oil contains: d-carvone, carene, d-sylvestrene, citronellol, acacetin, apigenin, diosmetin, eriodictyol, hesperitin, luteolin.

Medicinal properties:

व्यंजनो वान्तिहारी च रूचिष्यः शाकशोभनः ।। (नि. र.)

"Vyaṇjano vāṇtihārī ca rucişyaḥ şākaşobhanaḥ." (Ni. Ra.)

Leaves - Acrid, anodyne, anthelmintic, aromatic, carminative, depurative, digestive, diuretic, expectorant, febrifuge, sudroific.

Medicinal uses: Leaves - Amenorrhoea, asthma, bronchitis, colic, cough, cuts, diarrhoea, dysmenorrhoea, dyspepsia, fever, flatulence, helminthiasis, jaundice, skin diseases, vomiting, wound.

Ethno- Medicinal uses: Leaf - Stomachache (Lal & yadav, 1983); malaria (Deka *et al.*, 2006); anthelmintic (Singh *et al.*, 1992); rheumatic pain, indigestion (Islam & Jha, 2003); diarrhoea, indigestion (Kumar *et al.*, 2003).

MENTHA PIPERITA L. (LAMIACEAE)

Syn.: *M. officinalus; M. hircina* Hull.

Regional and Other Names: *English*–Peppermint; *Hindi*–Pepperment.

Distribution: Cultivated in Indian Gardens.

Taxonomic description: An annual or perennial aromatic herb, prostrating with suckers; flowers Bluish-White in verticillaster inflorescence.

Medicinal parts : Whole plant.

Taste : Aromatic, Pungent.

Chemical constituents: Methyl acetate, menthyl acetate, menthol, menthone, hydrocarbons, viridiflorol, menthofuran, isomenthone, neomenthol, neoisomenthol, α-pinene, β-pinene, cineol, carvone.

Medicinal properties: Analgesic, anthelmintic, carminative, diaphoretic, digestive, stomachic.

Medicinal uses: Abdominal pain, cough, dyspepsia, flatulence, headache, hysteria, rheumatism, toothache, vomiting.

Ethno- Medicinal uses: Leaf - Stomach complaint (Dar *et. al.,* 1984); dysentery (Virjee *et. al.,* 1984).

MERREMIA EMARGINATA (Burm. f.) Hall. f. (CONVOLVULACEAE)

Syn.: *M. gangetica* (L.) Cuf.; *Ipomoea reniformis* Choisy.

Regional and Other Names: *Hindi* – Musakari; *Malayalam* – Eliccevi; *Sanskrit* – Akhukarni; *Tamil* – Elikkatukkiari; *Telugu* – Elika jimudu.

Distribution: Throughout India.

Taxonomic description: A creeping perennial herb rooting at the nodes; Leaves simple, long stalked, reniform or ovate-cordate, flowers yellow, axillary on 1-3 flowered, very short peduncles; fruits subglbose capsules with 2-4 glabrous light brown seeds.

Medicinal parts: Whole plant.

Taste: Bitter, Acrid.

Chemical constituents: Seeds contain Caffic acid, ferrulic acid, sinapic acid, p-coumaric acid.

Medicinal properties:

आखुकर्णी त्वाखुकर्णपर्णिका भूदरी भवा ।। (भा. प्र.)

"Ākukarṇī tvākhukarṇaparṇika bhūdarī bhavā." (Bhā. Pṛa.)

Plant - Acrid, anthelmintic, bitter, carminative, digestive, diuretic, refrigerant.

Medicinal uses: Plant - Anaemia, cardiac diseases, fever, leucoderma, strangury.

Ethno- Medicinal uses: Whole plant - Rheumatic pain (Sinha *et al.*, 2006); wounds, boils (Srivastava *et al.*, 1992); fever (Dwivedi, 2003).

MESUA NAGASSARIUM (Burm. f.) Kosterm. (CLUSIACEAE)

Syn. : *Mesua ferrea* Auct. non. L.; *M. coromandelina* Wight.; *M. pedunculata* Wight.; *Calophyllum nagassarium* Burm. f.

Regional and Other Names: *Bengali* – Nageswar; *English* – Mesua; *Hindi* – Nagakesar; *Kannada* – Nagasampige; *Malayalam* – Nanku; *Marathi* – Nagchampaka; *Sanskrit* – Nagakesarah; *Tamil* – Nanku; *Telugu* – Nagakesaramu.

Distribution: Throughout India.

Taxonomic description: A medium sized to large handsome evergreen tree, with white flowers and ovoid fruits.

Medicinal parts: Flowers, Oil.

Taste: Bitter, Astringent.

Chemical constituents: Seed contains Mesual oil, mesuone, mesuagin, mammeigin, mameisin, α & β – amyrin, β-sitosterol, mesuanic acid, mesua ferrones A & B, exanthone, mesuaxanthone A & B, guttiferol, oleic acid, stearic acid, palmitic acid, linoleic acid.

Medicinal Properties:

नागकेसरमल्पोष्णं लघु तिक्तं कफापहम् ।
वस्तिवातामयघ्नं च कण्ठशीर्षरूजापहम् ।। (रा. नि.)

"Nāgakesaramalpoṣṇaṃ laghu tiktaṃ kaphāpahaṃ
Vaṣtivātāmayaghnaṃ ca kaṇthaṣīrsarujāpahaṃ." (Ra. Ni.)

Flowers - Acrid, anodyne, anthelmintic, astringent, bitter, carminative, digestive, febrifuge, sudorific.

Medicinal uses: Flowers - Asthma, cough, dysentery, fever, hiccough, leprosy, leucorhoea, pruritus, scabies, ulcers, vomiting.

Ethno- Medicinal uses: Bark - Anaemia, cough (Rao, 1981).

Flowers - Dysentery (Baruah & Sarma, 1984; Mondal & Mukherjee, 1992); piles (Baruah & Sarma, 1984); vomiting, dysentery, bleeding piles (Jadeja *et al.,* 2006).

Flower bud-Snake bite, dysentery, rheumatism (Nayak *et al.,* 2003).

Leaf - Snake bite (Karnick et. al., 1981); snake bite, dysentery, rheumatism (Nayak *et al.,* 2003); measles (Nath & Maiti, 2003).

Seed - Ulcer (Chaudhuri *et. al.,* 1982).

Seed oil- Snake bite, dysentery, rheumatism (Nayak *et al.,* 2003).

MICHELIA CHAMPACA L. (MAGNOLIACEAE)

Regional and Other Names: *Bengali* – Swarna champa; *English* – Champak; *Gujarati* – Champo; *Hindi* – Campa; *Kannada* – Sampige; *Malayalam* – Campakam; *Marathi* – Sonachampa; *Sanskrit* – Campakah; *Tamil* – Sempakam; *Telugu* – Campangi.

Distribution: Throughout India.

Taxonomic description : A tall handsome evergreen tree, with straight trunk. Flowers solitary axillary enclosed in bud by a greyish-yellow pubescent, spathaceous deciduous bract. Fruit capsule.

Medicinal parts : Whole plant.

Taste : Bitter, Acrid, Astringent.

Chemical constituents: Bark & Flowers contain - Essential oil contains: Mono- & sequiterpenes.

Medicinal properties:

चम्पकः कटुकस्तिक्तः कषायो मधुरो हिमः ।
विषकृमिहरः कृच्छ्रकफवातास्रपित्तहृत् ।। (भा. प्र.)

"Campakaḥ katukaṣtiktaḥ kasāyo madhuro himaḥ
Visakṛmiharaḥ kṛcchṛakaphavātāṣrapiṭtahṛt." (Bhā. Pṛa.)

Root / Root bark - Purgative.

Stem bark - Astringent, diuretic, expectorant, febrifuge, stimulant.

Flowers/ Floral bud/ Fruits - Acrid, anthelmintic, antipyretic, astringent, bitter, carminative, depurative, digestive, diuretic, expectorant, refrigerant, stomachic.

Medicinal uses: Root/ Root bark - Amenorrhoea, constipation, dysmenorrhoea, inflammations.

Stem bark - Bronchitis, cough, debility, fever, stangury.

Flowers/Floral bud/ Fruits - Amenorrheoa, bronchitis, burning sensation, colic, cough, dysmenorrhoea, dyspepsia, fever, flatulence, gout, leprosy, pruritus, skin diseases, ulcers, wounds.

Ethno- Medicinal uses: Bark - Abortifacient (Bhalla et. al., 1982; Tarafder, 1983; Saxena & Dutta, 1975); boils (Tarafder, 1984); antifertility (Billore & Audichya, 1978); skin diseases (Deokule, 2006); amenorrhoea, gastritis, cough (Nayak *et al.,* 2003); remove lice (Nath & Maiti, 2003).

Root - Antifertility (Tarafder, 1983); menstrual complaint (Bhalla *et. al.,* 1982; Saxena & Dutta, 1975).

Fruit- Healing cracks in feet (Islam & Jha, 2003); amenorrhoea, gastritis, cough (Nayak *et al.,* 2003).

Flower- amenorrhoea, gastritis, cough (Nayak *et al.,* 2003).

MIRABILIS JALAPA L. (NYCTAGINACEAE)

Regional and Other Names: *Bengali* – Krishnakoli; *English* – Four O' clock plant; *Hindi*– Gulabasa; *Malayalam* – Antimalari; *Marathi* – Gulbaksh; *Sanskrit* – Trisandhi; *Tamil* – Andhimandarai; *Telugu* – Chandrakantha.

Distribution: A native of tropical America. Throughout India.

Taxonomic description : Erect herbs, with tuberous roots and ovate leaves. Flowers scarlet, showy, in fascicles. Fruits subglobose.

Medicinal parts : Tuber, Root, Leaves.

Taste : Bitter.

Chemical constituents: Leaves - Alkaloid trigonelline, tricosan-12-one, n-hexacosanol, β-sitosterol, tetracosanoic acid; tarteric acid, citric acid, valine, tryptophan, leucine, alanine, glycine.

Medicinal properties:

त्रिसन्धिस्त्रिविधा ज्ञेया रक्ता चान्या सितासिता ।
कफकासहरा रूच्या त्वम्दोषशमनी परा ।। (रा. नि.)

"Trisaṇdhiṣṭrividhā jneyā raḳtā cāṇyā sitāsitā
Kaphakāsaharā rucyā ṭvaṃgdosa ṣamanī parā." (Rā. Ni.)

Aphrodisiac, blood purifier, cooling.

Medicinal uses: Blood purifier, goiter, piles.

Ethno- Medicinal uses: Leaf - Boils (Maheshwari & Singh, 1984; Ramachandran & Nair, 1981; Deokule & Magdum, 1992; Deokule, 2006; Kothari & Londhe, 2003); blister, inflammation, itching (Kothari & Londhe, 2003).

Root - Piles (Saxena *et. al.,* 1931; Kothari & Londhe, 2003); boils (Deokule & Magdum, 1992).

MURRAYA PANICULATA (L.) Jack. (RUTACEAE)

Syn.: *M. exotica* L.

Regional and Other Names: *Bengali* – Mamini; *English* – Chinese boxwood, orange jessamine; *Hindi* – Kamini; *Kannada* – Angarakanagida, Pandry; *Malayalam* – Marmulla; *Marathi* –Pandharikunti; *Tamil* – Kattukaruveppilai; *Telugu* – Nagagolugi.

Distribution: Outer Himalaya from the Jumna eastwards, ascending to 4,500 ft., Assam, Satpura range, Hills of the Peninsula, Ceylone.

Taxonomic description: A small evergreen shrub or tree; leaves pinnately compound; flowers white, fragrant; fruits red berries.

Medicinal parts: Leaves, Flowers, Fruits, Root.

Taste : Bitter, Aromatic.

Chemical constituents: Leaves contain - Phebalocin, Heptamethoxy flavon.

Fruits contain - Paniculatin, coumarin.

Flower contains - Scopoletin, glucose.

Roots contain - Alkaloids: Noracronycine & skimmiacine.

Medicinal properties: Astringent, stimulant.

Medicinal uses: Leaves - Diarrhoea, dropsy, dysentery.

Root bark - Cough, hysteria, rheumatism.

Ethno- Medicinal uses: Leaf - Dysentery, diarrhoea (Sharma *et. al.*, 1979), fever, headache (Rao & Neogi, 1980); inflammation (Saxena, 1986); stomachache (Upadhye *et. al.*, 1986); cuts & wounds (Basak, 2006); dropsy, diarrhoea, dysentery, cuts, cough, rheumatism, hysteria (Srivastava *et al.*, 2003); bodyache, diarrhoea, dropsy (Nayak *et al.*, 2003).

Root - Rheumatism (Kumar *et al.*, 1987).

Root bark- Cough, rheumatism, hysteria (Srivastava *et al.*, 2003).

MUSA PARADISIACA L. (MUSACEAE)

Syn.: *M. sapientum* L.

Regional and Other Names: *Bengali* – Kala; *English* – Banana; *Hindi* – Kela; *Kannada* – Balehannu; *Malayalam* – Kadalivala; *Marathi* –Kele; *Sanskrit* – Kadali; *Tamil* – Kadali; *Telugu* – Ariti.

Distribution: Cultivated throughout India.

Taxonomic description : Tree-like, stoloniferous herbs. Leaves spirally arranged, oblong. Flowers yellow, lower female, upper male in drooping spathaceous spikes. Fruits 3-gonous, oblong.

Medicinal parts: Roots, Leaves, Fruits, Stem.

Taste : Sweet.

Chemical constituents: Serotonin & norepinephrine, dopamine and an unidentified catecholamine.

Medicinal properties:

कदली वरणबुसा रम्भा मोचांशुमत्फला ।। (भा. प्र.)

"Kadalī varaṇabusā raṃbhā mocāṃṣumaṭphalā." (Bhā. Pṛa.)

Root - Anthelmintic, depurative.

Fruits- Anthlemintic, aphrodisiac, astringent, cooling, demulcent, emollient, sweet.

Medicinal uses: Root - Helminthiasis, leprosy, scabies, skin diseases.

Leaves - Blisters, burns, snflammations, scabies.

Fruits - Bronchitis, helminthiasis, pruritus, scabies, strangury.

Flowers - Diabetes, dropsy, dysentery.

Ethno- Medicinal uses: Leaf - Asthma, whooping cough (Jain, 1984); boils (Rai, 1985); Gout (Jadeja *et al.,* 2006).

Flowers - Antifertility (Sharma, 1981); Asthma, whooping cough (Virjee *et. al.,* 1984); Diabetes (Ghosh & Das, 2003).

Root - Diarrhoea (Megoneitso & Audichya, 1978); antifertility (Billore & Audichya, 1978); Joint pain (Janmeda *et. al.,* 2006).

Fruits - Diarrhoea, intestinal worms (Janmeda *et. al.,* 2006); hepatitis (Dutta *et al.,* 2006); diabetes, blood dysentery (Sarma & Baishya, 1992); dysentery (Singh, 2003; Sharma *et al.,* 2003); diarrhoea, burns (Sharma *et al.,* 2003).

Plantain - Diabetes (Ghosh, 2006).

Juice from central trunk - Kidney stone (Rajendra & Rengaswami, 2006).

Pseudostem - Otalgia, haemoptysis (Deokule, 2006); poor lactation (Singh & Singh, 2003); constipation, cold (Sharma *et al.,* 2003).

Petiole- Poor lactation (Singh & Singh, 2003).

MYRICA NAGI Thunb. (MYRICACEAE)

Syn.: *M. rubra* Sieb.; *M. esculenta* Buch-Ham. ex D. Don.; *M. sapinda* Wall.; *M. farquhariana* Wall.

Regional and Other Names: *Bengali* – Kaiphal; *English* – Bay-berry; *Gujarati* – Kariphal; *Hindi* – Kayaphalla; *Malayalam* – Maruta; *Marathi* – Kayaphata; *Sanskrit* – Katphala; *Tamil* –Marudam; *Telugu* – Kaidaryamu.

Distribution: A native of China & Japan. Found in sub tropical Himalayas.

Taxonomic description : A small or moderate-sized evergreen tree; bark is brown and aromatic; flowers red.

Medicinal parts: Bark, Fruit.

Taste: Bitter, Astringent.

Chemical constituents: Bark contains Glycosides, tannin, flavonoids, reducing sugars, resin, proteins, amino acids, calcium, iron, zinc, chloride, phosphorus, myricetin, steroids.

Medicinal properties:

कट्फलस्तुवरस्तिक्तः कटुर्वातकफज्वरान् ।
हन्ति श्वासप्रमेहार्शः कण्डवामयारूचीः ।। (भा. प्र.)

"Kaṭphalaṣtuvarṣtiḳtaḥ katurvatakaphajvarāṇ
Haṇti ṣvāsapṛamehārṣaḥ kaṇdvāmayārucīḥ." (Bhā. Pṛa.)

Anti-inflammatory, astringent, stimulant.

Medicinal uses: Asthma, cough.

Ethno-Medicinal uses: Bark - Diarrhoea, asthma (Negi *et al.*, 1985); cholera (Sharma *et al.*, 1979; Gupta, 1981); dysentery, cough, malaria (Megoneisto & Rao, 1983); menorrhoea (Uniyal, 1968); rheumatism (Gaur *et. al.*, 1980).

MYRISTICA FRAGRANS Houtt. (MYRISTICACEAE)

Syn.: *M. officinalis* L.; *M. moschata* Thunb.; *M. aromatica* Lam.

Regional and Other Names: *Bengali* – Jaiphal; *English* – Nutmeg tree; *Hindi* - Jayphal; *Kannada* – Jajikayi; *Malayalam* – Jati; *Marathi* – Jaiphal; *Sanskrit* – Jati, Jatiphalah; *Tamil* – Jatimaram; *Telugu* – Jajikaya.

Distribution: Cultivated in the hotter parts of India.

Taxonomic description: A moderate sized dioecious aromatic evergreen tree, with creamy yellow flowers & yellow broadly globose or puriform fruits.

Medicinal parts: Seed (nutmeg), aril (mace).

Taste: Bitter, Acrid.

Chemical constituents: Plant - β-pinine, a-terpinene, myristicin, trimyristin, myristic acid, vitamins.

Seeds - Essential oil, saponin.

Medicinal properties:

जातीफलं जातिकोशं मालतीमित्यपि ।। (भा. प्र.)

"Jātīphalaṃ jātikoṣaṃ mālatīphalamịtyapi." (Bhā. Pṛa.)

Nutmeg & Mace - Acrid, anodyne anthelmintic, anti-inflammatory, aphrodisiac, aromatic, astringent, bitter, carminative, constipating, digestive, diuretic, expectorant, febifuge, narcotic, stomachic, sweet, thermogenic.

Medicinal uses: Nutmeg & Mace - Amenorrhoea, asthma, colic, cough, diarrhoea, dysmenorrhoea, dyspepsia, fever, flatulence, general debility. helminthiasis, inflammations, skin diseases, strangury, ulcers.

Ethno- Medicinal uses: Bark - Cold, cough, fever (Singh & Pandey, 1998).

Seeds- Indigestion, stomach pain (Thomas & Britto, 2003).

MYRISTICA MALABARICA Lam. (MYRISTICACEAE)

Syn.: *M. tomentosa* Graham.

Regional and Other Names: *English* – Bombay mace; *Hindi* – Van-Jayphal; *Kannada* – Kanagi; *Malayalam* – Kattujati; *Sanskrit* – Vanyajati; *Tamil* – Puttiri; *Telugu* – Rampatri.

Distribution: Throughout South India.

Taxonomic description: A moderate-sized evergreen tree, with greyish black smooth bark and whorls of branches; flowers unisexual in dichasial cymes; fruits elongate; seeds arillate.

Medicinal parts : Seed, aril.

Taste: Bitter, Acrid.

Chemical constituents: Myristic acid & its triglycerine.

Leaves contain β-sitosterol.

Fruits contain Malabaricones, Lignana, Malabaricanol.

Medicinal properties:

जातीलोशसमा चापि रसगन्धविवर्जिता ।।

"Jātīloṣasamācāpi rasagaṇdhavivaṛjitā"

Aril - Cooling, expectorant, febrifuge.

Medicinal uses: Aril - Bronchitis, burning sesnstion, cough, fever.

Ethno- Medicinal uses: Fruit - Fever and cold of Puerperium woman (Jadeja *et al.*, 2006).

NARDOSTACHYS JATAMANSI DC. (VALERIANACEAE)

Syn.: *N. grandiflora* DC.; *Valeriana walliichii* DC.

Regional and Other Names: *Bengali* – Jatamansi; *English* – Indian nard; *Gujarati* – Jatamasi; *Hindi* – Jatamansi; *Kannada* – Jatamansi; *Malayalam* – Jatamansi; *Sanskrit* – Jatamansi; *Tamil* – Jatamasi; *Telugu* – Jatamamsi.

Distribution: In the Alpine Himalayas, from 3,300-5000 m.

Taxonomic description: A perennial erect herb, with woody, long, stout root-stock covered with reddish brown fibres of the petioles of radical leaves; flowers pink or blue in dense cymes.

Medicinal parts: Rhizome.

Taste : Bitter-Aromatic, Acrid.

Chemical constituents: Rhizome contains - Jatamanson, lupeol, essential oil, alcohol, terpene, jatamansic acid, jatamansin, Alkaloid-Actindin.

Medicinal properties:

मांसी तिक्ता कषाया च मेध्या कान्तिबलप्रदा ।
स्वाद्वी हिमा त्रिदोषास्रदाहवीसर्पकुष्ठनुत् ।। (भा. प्र.)

"Māṃsī tiḳtā kasāyā ca meḍḥyā kāṇtibalapṛadā
Ṣvādṿī himā ṭridosāsṛadāhavīsaṛpakuṣthanuṭ." (Bhā. Pṛa.)

Rhizome - Acrid, anodyne, antiseptic, aphrodisiac, aromatic, bitter, carminative, cooling, digestive, emollient, intellect promoting, laxative, stomachic, sudorific. sweet.

Medicinal uses: Rhizome - Amenorrhoea, asthma, bronchitis, burning sensation, colic, cough, dysmenorrhoea, dyspepsia, epilepsy, erysipelas, flatulence, hysteria, inflammations, leprosy, lumbago, strantgury.

Ethno- Medicinal uses: Rhizome - Blood purifier, bronchitis, dysmenorrhoea, epilepsy, hysteria (Gaur *et. al.,* 1983); epilepsy (Shah, 1982).

Root - Hair tonic, piles (Uniyal, 1968); Epilepsy, hysteria (Singh, 2003; Chhetri, 2005); epilepsy, colic, hysterial cholera (Rai *et al.,* 1992); gastric trouble (Singh, 2003).

Leaves - Promote hair growth (External application) (Jadeja *et al.,* 2006).

NAREGAMIA ALATA Wight & Arn. (MELIACEAE)

Regional and Other Names: *English* – Goanese ipecacuanha; *Hindi* – Tinparni; *Kannada* – Nepanaringa; *Malayalam* – Nilanarakam; *Marathi* – Tinpani; *Sanskrit* – Amlavalli; *Tamil* – Nilanaragam; *Telugu* – Pagapapu.

Distribution: Throughout South India.

Taxonomic description: A small handsome undershrub, with large white flowers & ovoid globose. Capsule fruits.

Medicinal parts : Whole plant.

Taste: Sweet.

Chemical constituents: Root bark Alkaloid naregamin.

Stem, roots β-sitosterol, Heneicosane, Stearic & Palmitic acids.

Medicinal properties:

त्रिपर्णी मधुरा शीता श्वासकास विनाशनी ।
पित्तप्रकोपशमनी विषव्रणहरा परा ।। (रा. नि.)

"Tṛiparnī madhurā ṣītā ṣvāsakāsavināṣanī
Pịttapṛakopaṣamanī visavṛaṇaharā parā." (Ra. Ni.)

Plant - Acrid, alexeteric, aromatic, cooling, depurative, emetic, expectorant, sweet.

Medicinal uses: Plant - Anaemia, asthma, bronchitis, cough, dysentery, dyspepsia, pruritus, scabies.

Ethno- Medicinal uses: Root - Inflammation of navel region (Ramachandran & Nair, 1981); dysentery (Thomas & Britto, 2003).

NEPTUNIA OLERACEA Lour. (MIMOSACEAE)

Regional and Other Names: *Bengali* – Paninajak; *English* – Sensitive water plant; *Hindi* – Lajjalu; *Kannada* – Nidrayam; *Malayalam* – Nirtottavati; *Sanskrit* – Alambusa; *Tamil* – Suntaikkirai; *Telugu* – Nirutalavapu.

Distribution: Throughout India.

Taxonomic description: Free floating slender aquatic herbs with almost each node bearing leaves and penduncles and a large number of fibrous rootlets.

Medicinal parts: Whole plant.

Taste: Sweet, Astringent.

Medicinal properties:

अलम्बुषा खरत्वक् च तथा मेदोगला स्मृता ।। (भा. प्र.)

"Alaṃbusā kharatvak ca tathā medogalā ṣmṛtā." (Bhā. Pṛa.)

Plant - Anodyne, anthelmintic, antidiarrhoeal, astringent, diuretic, refrigerant, sweet.

Medicinal uses: Plant - Burning sensation, diarrhoea, helminthiasis, otalgia, straungury, syphilis.

Ethno- Medicinal uses: Root - Dysentery (Jadhav, 2006).

NICOTIANA TABACUM L. (SOLANACEAE)

Syn.: *N. macrophylla* Lehm.; *N. auriculata* Bert.

Regional and Other Names: *Bengali* – Tamaku; *English* – Tobacco; *Gujarati* – Tabacu; *Hindi* – Tamaku; *Kannada* – Tambaku; *Malayalam* – Pokala; *Marathi* – Tambaku; *Sanskrit* – Tamakhuh; *Tamil* – Pugaiyilai; *Telugu* – Pogaku.

Distribution: Cultivated in the hotter parts of India.

Taxonomic description: Glandular-pubescent herbs, with Pinkish flowers and ovate capsules.

Medicinal parts: Leaves.

Taste: Bitter, Acrid.

Chemical constituents: Leaves Nicotine alkaloid.

Medicinal properties:

तमाखुः क्षारपत्रा च कृमिघ्नी धूम्रपत्रिका ।। (शा. नि.)

"Tamākhuḥ ksārapaṭrā ca kṛmighni dhūmṛapaṭrikā." (Ṣā. Ni.)

Leaves - Abortifacient, acrid, anodyne, anthelmintic, anti-inflmmatory, bitter, carminative, emetic, laxative, narcotic, sedative, styptic, thermogenic.

Medicinal uses: Leaves - Asthma, bronchitis, dyspepsia, flatlulence, haemorrhages, helminthiasis, inflammations, scabies, skin diseases, ulcers.

Ethno- Medicinal uses: Leaf - Eczema, itching (Purohit *et. al.,* 1985); snake bite (Kharkongor & Joseph, 1981); toothache (Megoneisto & Rao, 1983; Malhotra & Moorthy, 1973); wounds (Jain, 1963, 1965); Gout (Jadeja *et al.,* 2006); skin diseases, gastro-intestinal disorders (Mukhopadhyay, 1992); scratching, inflammation of skin (Singh & Singh, 2003); helminthiasis, skin diseases (Nayak *et al.,* 2003).

NIGELLA SATIVA L. (RANUNCULACEAE)

Regional and Other Names: *Bengali* – Kalijira; *English* – Small fennel; *Gujarati* – Kalonjijirum; *Hindi* – Kalajira; *Kannada* – Karijirigae; *Malayalam* – Karincirakam; *Marathi* – Kalajire; *Sanskrit* – Upakuncika; *Tamil* – Karum Ciragam; *Telugu* – Nallajilakarra.

Distribution: In Punjab, Bihar; often cultivated.

Taxonomic description: Erect annual herbs, with white or blue flowers and many seeded capsules.

Medicinal parts : Seeds.

Taste: Bitter, Acrid.

Chemical constituents: Nigellone, nigellicine alkaloid, volatile oil, fatty oil, oleic acid.

Medicinal properties:

पृथ्वीका कटुका पाके रूच्या पित्ताग्निदीपनी ।
श्लेष्माध्मानहराऽजीर्णा जन्तुघ्नी च प्रकीर्त्तिता ।। (ध. नि.)

"Pr̥it̥hvīkā katukā pāke rucyā pit̥tāgnidīpanī
Ṣleṣmādhmānharāajīr̥ṇājan̥tughn̥ī ca pr̥akīr̥ttitā. (Dha. Ni.)

Seeds - Acrid, anodyne, anthelmintic, anti-inflammatory, appetizing, aromatic, bitter, carminative, constipating, digestive, diuretic, expectorant, febrifuge, sudorific, thermogenic.

Medicinal uses: Seeds - Amenorrhoea, cough, diarrhoea, dysentery, dysmenorrhoea, dyspepsia, fever, flatulence, helminthiasis, inflammaions, jaundice, paralysis, skin diseases.

Ethno- Medicinal uses: Seeds - Abortifacient (Tarafder, 1983; Khan *et al.*, 2003); eczema (Saxena & Vyas, 1986).

OLDENLANDIA CORYMBOSA L. (RUBIACEAE)

Syn.: *Hedyotis corymbosa* (L.) Lam.

Regional and Other Names: *Bengali* – Khetpapra; *Gujarati* –Parpat ; *Hindi* – Damanpapar; *Kannada* – Kallasabatrasige; *Malayalam* – Parppatakam; *Marathi* – Khetpapda; *Sanskrit* – Parpatah; *Tamil* – Parpadagam; *Telugu* – Verinellavemu.

Distribution: Throughout India.

Taxonomic description: A small herbs; leaves subsessile, linear-lanceolate, acute, recurved and hairy margins, stipules membranous with few bristles; flowers white, small on solitary long peduncle; fruits globose capsule.

Medicinal parts: Whole plant.

Taste: Bitter.

Chemical constituents: Whole plant - Alkaloids-Biflorine & Biflorone; Sodium, Potassium, Calcium, Chloride; caffeine, fumaric acid, oleanolic acid, ursolic acid, methyl ether.

Medicinal properties:

पर्पटो हन्ति पित्तास्त्रभ्रमतृष्णाकफज्वरान् ।। (भा. प्र.)

Par̥pato han̥ti pit̥tāṣt̥rbr̥hmt̥ruṣṇākaphajvarāṇ (Bhā. Pr̥a.)

Anti-inflammatory, antipyretic, cooling, diuretic, expectorant, styptic.

Medicinal uses: Bronchitis, fever, jaundice, liver disorders, malaria fever, measles.

Ethno- Medicinal uses: Whole plant - Liver complaint (Shah, *et. al.* 1981, 1983; Srivastava *et al.*, 2003); fever (Shah, *et. al.* 1981; Mukherjee, *et. al.* 1986; Kumar & Lal, 2003); jaundice (Singh & Pandey,1980; Shah, 1984; Shah *et. al.*, 1981, 1983; Sharma *et. al.*, 1979; Dwivedi & Pandey, 1992; Sharma & Sharma, 1992; Thomas & Britto, 2003; Srivastava *et al.*, 2003; Kumar & Lal, 2003); liver complaint (Shah, *et. al.* 1983; Thomas & Britto, 2003); malaria (Singh & Pandey, 1980); fever (Sharma & Sharma, 1992; Thomas & Britto, 2003); nervous depressions (Srivastava *et al.*, 2003; Kumar & Lal, 2003); burning sensation (Dwivedi, 2003); toothache, gastric irritation (Kumar & Lal, 2003).

Leaves- Burning sensation of soles and palms (Srivastava *et al.*, 2003); vomiting (Muthukumarasamy *et al.*, 2003).

OPERCULINA TURPETHUM (L.) Silva Manso. (CONVOLVULACEAE)

Syn.: *Merremia turpethum* (L.) G.L. Shah & R.G. Bhat.; *Ipomoea turpenthum* R. Br.

Regional and Other Names: *Bengali* – Dudhkalami; *English* – Indian jalap; *Hindi* – Nisoth; *Kannada* – Sigade; *Malayalam* – Triputa; *Marathi* – Nishottar; *Sanskrit* – Trivrt; *Tamil* – Sivatai; *Telugu* – Tegada.

Distribution: Throughout India.

Taxonomic description: A large perennial twiner, with white flowers & capsule fruits.

Medicinal parts: Roots.

Taste: Acrid/Astringent.

Chemical constituents: Roots contain - Terpethin which is glycoside, Jalapine, Convolvulin, Soluble resin, Volatile oil, Lignin & Salts.

Medicinal properties:

काषायमधुरा रूक्षा विपाके कटुका त्रिवृत् ।
श्लेष्मपित्तप्रशनी रौक्ष्यानिलकोपनी ।। (म. नि.)

"Kāsāyamadhurā ruksā vipāke katukā ṭrivṛt
Ṣleṣmapiṭtapṛaṣamanī raūkṣyāccanilakopanī." (Ma. Ni.)

Roots - Acrid, anthelmintic, antipyretic, bitter, carminative, expectorant, purgative, sweet, thermogenic.

Medicinal uses: Roots - Bronchitis, colic, constipation, dropsy, erysipelas, helminthiasis, inflammation, jaundice, leucoderma, obesity, paralysis, pruritus, tumours.

Ethno- Medicinal uses: Roots - Constipation (Shah & Gopal, 1986); jaundice (Gopal & Shah, 1985).

Leaf- Itching, ringworm (Srivastava *et al.,* 1992)

PEDALIUM MUREX L. (PEDALIACEAE)

Regional and Other Names: *Bengali* – Baraghokru; *Gujarati* – Kadvaghokru; *Hindi* – Bada gokhru; *Kannada* – Dodda neggili; *Malayalam* – Kattunerinnil; *Marathi* – Kalavala; *Sanskrit* – Tiktagoksurah; *Tamil* – Perunerunci; *Telugu* – Peddu palleru.

Distribution: Throughout India.

Taxonomic description: Glandular pubescent herbs, with obovate-oblong, repand-dentate leaves. Flowers pale-yellow. Fruits 4-angled, with a spine at each basal angle.

Medicinal parts: Whole plant.

Taste: Sweet.

Chemical constituents: Leaves - Pedalitin, diosmetin, dinatin, gum.

Medicinal properties:

गोक्षुरः शीतलः स्वादुर्बलकृद्वस्तिषोधनः ।
मधुरो दीपनो वृष्यः पुष्टिदश्चाश्मराहरः ।। (भा. प्र.)

"Goksuraḥ ṣītalaḥ ṣvāduṛbalkṛḍbaṣtiṣodhanaḥ.
Madhuro dīpno vṛṣyaḥ puṣtidaṣcāṣmariharaḥ." (Bhā. Pṛa.)

Plant - Anti-inflammatory, aphrodisiac, carminative, cooling, digestive, diuretic, mucilaginous, sweet.

Medicinal uses: Plant - Amenorrhoea, dysmenorrhoea, dyspepsia, fever, flatulence, inflammations, spermatorrhoea, strangury, ulcers.

Ethno- Medicinal uses: Fruits - Aphrodisiac (Shah *et. al.,* 1981); dysemenorrhoea, leucorrhoea (Saxena & Vyas, 1983); rheumatism (Shekhawat & Anand, 1984; Sharma & Sharma, 1992); urinary complaint (Singh & Pandey, 1980; Kumar *et al.,* 2003); Paralysis (Shubhangi & Patil, 2006); ulcers (Kumar *et al.,* 2003); spermatorrhoea (Nayak *et al.,* 2003).

Leaf - Gonorrhoea (Shekhawat & Anand, 1984; Shah *et. al.,* 1983; Thomas & Britto, 2003); impotency, spermatorrhoea (Shah *et. al.,* 1983); urinary infection, ulcers (Kumar *et al.,* 2003); Diabetes (Bhatt *et al.,* 2003).

Stem- Gonorrhoea (Thomas & Britto, 2003; Nayak *et al.,* 2003); dysuria (Nayak *et al.,* 2003).

Whole Plant- Urinary disorders (Thomas & Britto, 2003); Rheumatism (Mitaliya *et al.,* 2003); spermatorrhoea, puerperal fever (Bhatt *et al.,* 2003); spermatorrhoea, ulcers, fever (Nayak *et al.,* 2003).

Seed- Sexual debility (Bhatt *et al.,* 2003).

PHASEOLUS TRILOBATUS (L.) Schreb. (PAPILIONACEAE)

Syn.: *Vigna trilobata* (L.) Vend.; *Dolichos trilobatus* (L.) Mant.

Regional and Other Names: *Bengali* – Mugani; *English* – Green gram; *Gujarati* – Magavala; *Hindi* – Mooga; *Marathi* –Arkamath; *Sanskrit* – Mudgaparni; *Tamil* – Naripayar; *Telugu* – Pillippersara.

Distribution: Cultivated throughout India.

Taxonomic description: A small perennial diffuse or trailing, prostrating, pubescent, 1-2 feet high herb; leaves trifoliate, each leaflet faintly 3-lobed and coriaceous; flowers in spikes on long peduncle, yellow pod-subcylindric.

Medicinal parts: Whole plant.

Taste: Bitter.

Chemical constituents: Beans - Methionine, tryptophane, tyrosine strepogenin, uridine diphosphate, galacturonic acid.

Seeds - Lysine, valine, leucine, phenylalkanine.

Medicinal properties:

मुद्गपर्णी हिमा कासवातरक्तक्षयापहा ।
पित्तदाहज्वरान् हन्ति चक्षुष्या शुक्रवृद्धिकृत्।। (रा. नि.)

"Muḍagaparṇī himā kāsavātaraḳtaksayāpahā
Pịttadāhajvarāṇ haṇti caksuṣyā ṣuḳravṛḍdh ikṛt." (Rā. Ni.)

Anthelmintic, cooling, demulcent, febrifute, sedative, tonic.

Medicinal uses: Antipyretic, cough, inflammations, Gout, tuberculosis.

Ethno- Medicinal uses: Whole plant - Dysentery (Jadeja *et al.,* 2006).

Fruit - Eye complaints (Deokule, 2006).

Leaf- Tonic, fever, scorpion sting (Bhalla *et al.,* 1992).

PHOENIX DACTYLIFERA L. (ARECACEAE)

Regional and Other Names: *Bengali* – Khejur; *English* – Date palm; *Gujarati* – Khajur; *Hindi* – Khajur; *Kannada* – Kajjuri; *Malayalam* – Ittappana; *Marathi* – Kharjur; *Sanskrit* – Kharjurah; *Tamil* – Periccankay; *Telugu* – Karjurakaya.

Distribution: A native of North America, Egypt & Arabic; now cultivated in Sindh & Punjab.

Taxonomic description: A medium sized palm tree, the trunk covered by persistent petiole bases, the base surrounded by a dense mass of root suckers; leaves pinnately compound; flowers in long spadices, unisexual; fruits oblong berries.

Medicinal parts : Leaves, Flowers, Fruits, Seeds.

Taste: Sweet.

Chemical constituents: Fruits Vitamin- A,B,D.

Pollen grains - Arabinose, galactose, xylose, rhamnose, uronic acid.

Medicinal properties:

खर्जुरीतरूतोयं तु मदपित्तकरं भवेत् ।
वातश्लेष्महरं रूच्यं दीपनं बलशुक्लकृत् ।। (भा. प्र.)

"Khaṛjurī tarutoyaṃ tu madapịttakaraṃ bhaveṭ
Vātaṣleṣmaharaṃ rucyaṃ dīpanaṃ balaṣuḳlakṛt." (Bhā. Pṛa.)

Leaves - Aphrodisiac.

Flowers - Bitter, expectorant, febrifuge, purgative.

Fruit - Aphrodisiac, cooling, diuretic, sweet.

Toddy - Aphrodisiac, appetizing, digestive, intoxicating.

Medicinal uses:

Fruits - Bronchitis, burning sensation, cough, strangury.

Toddy - Bronchitis.

Ethno- Medicinal uses: Root - Toothache (Kumar *et al.,* 2006).

Seed - Pain & Inflammation (Kumar *et al.,* 2006).

Fruit - Rheumatoid arthritis (Kumar *et al.,* 2006).

PHOENIX SYLVESTRIS Roxb. (ARECACEAE)

Regional and Other Names: *Bengali* – Khajur; *English* – Date sugar palm; *Gujarati* – Kajuri; *Hindi* – Khajuri; *Kannada* – Ichalu; *Malayalam* – Itta; *Marathi* – Shindi; *Sanskrit* – Kharjuri; *Tamil* – Icham; *Telugu* – Itha.

Distribution: Throughout India.

Taxonomic description : Usually unbranched palms, with straight or crooked trunk & and large pinnate leaves; leaflets conduplicate, spine-tipped. Spathes woody, separating into boat-shaped valves. Drupes ellipsoid-oblong, orange-yellow.

Medicinal parts: Fruits & Leaves.

Taste : Sweet.

Chemical constituents: Thiamine, riboflavin, nicotinic acid, vitamin-C, calcium, phosphorus, iron, sodium, potassium, copper, cobalt, nickel, magnessium, molybdenum.

Medicinal properties:

खर्जुरी तुवरा ज्ञेयासापक्काम मधुरामता ।
तुवराशीतला वृष्याश्लेष्म शुक्रविवर्धिनी ।। (नि. र.)

"Kharjurī tuvarā jneyā sāpakvāma madhurā matā
Tuvarā ṣītalā vṛṣyā ṣleṣmaṣukṛavivaṛdhinī." (Ni. Ra.)

Fruit - Aphrodisiac, cardiotonic, constipating, cooling, restorative, sweet.

Medicinal uses: Fruit - Abdominal complaints, fever, heart complaints, vomiting.

Root - Toothache.

Ethno- Medicinal uses: Leaf - Diarrhoea, dysentery (Rai, 1985); Gout (Jadeja *et al.*, 2006); Diabetes (Bhatt *et al.*, 2003).

Stem - Gonorrhoea (Tarafder, 1984).

Root - Toothache (Deokule & Magdum, 1992; Janardhanan, 1963); menstrual complaint (Hemadri & Rao, 1983).

PICRORHIZA KURROA Auct. non Royle (SCROPHULARIACEAE)

Syn.: *P. scrophulariiflora* Pennell.

Regional and Other Names: *Bengali* – Kuru; *English* – Picrorhiza, Black-Hellebore; *Gujarati* – Kadu; *Hindi* – Kuru, Kutki; *Kannada* – Katukarohini; *Malayalam* – Katukurohini; *Marathi* –Kutaki; *Sanskrit* – Katvi; *Tamil* – Katugurohini; *Telugu* – Katki.

Distribution: In the Himalayas, from Kashmir to Sikkim at an elevation of 2,700-4,500m.

Taxonomic description: A perennial woody herb with bitter rhizome; flowers white or bluish in dense terminal spicate raceme; fruits ovoid capsules.

Medicinal parts : Dried rhizomes.

Taste: Bitter, Acrid.

Chemical constituents: Rhizome contains A bitter glucoside: Kutkin, Apocyanin, Alkanol, Alkane, Picrorhizin.

Root contains Kutkin, Kurrin, Vanillic acid, Kutkiol, Kutkisterol, Kurrin, Kutkoside.

Medicinal properties:

कटुका तु सरा रूक्षा कफपित्तज्वरापहा ।। (रा. व.)

"Katukā tu sarā ruksa kaphapiṭtajvarāpahā." (Rā. Va.)

Rhizome - Acrid, anthelminthiasis, anti-inflammatory, antiperiodic, bitter, carminative, cooling, depurative, digestive, expectorant, laxative, stomachic.

Medicinal uses: Rhizome - Asthma, brohchitis, burning sensation, cardiac disorders, colic, constipation, cough, diabetes, fever, flatulence, hicchough, inflammations, jaundice, leprosy, leucoderma, skin diseases.

Ethno- Medicinal uses: Root - Abdominal pain (Uniyal, 1968; Sharma *et al.*, 2003); dyspepsia (Singh *et. al.*, 1980; Nautiyal *et al.*, 2003); anaemia (Singh *et. al.*, 1980); cold (Koelz, 1979; Kapur & Nanda, 1992); diarrhoea (Dam & Hajra, 1981; Singh, 2003); dysentery (Gaur *et. al.*, 1983; Nautiyal *et al.*, 2003); jaundice (Shah, 1982; Singh, 2003; Nautiyal *et al.*, 2003); cough, fever (Kapur & Nanda, 1992); stomachache (Singh, 2003; Nautiyal *et al.*, 2003); fever, asthma (Arya & Ved Prakash, 2003).

Rhizome - Asthma, dyspepsia, Cholera (Gaur *et. al.*, 1983); dropsy, improve appitite (Ara & Naqshi, 1992); fever, blood purification (Kala & Manjrekar, 2003).

Flower- Fever, blood purification (Kala & Manjrekar, 2003).

PIPER BETLE L. (PIPERACEAE)

Syn.: *Chavica betle* Miq.

Regional and Other Names: *Bengali* – Pan; *English* – Betel; *Gujarati* –Nagervel ; *Hindi* – Pan; *Kannada* – Villayadele; *Malayalam* – Vettilakkoti; *Marathi* – Pan; *Sanskrit* – Tambulavalli, Tambulah; *Tamil* – Vettilai; *Telugu* – Tamalapaku.

Distribution: Cultivated in the hotter & damper parts of India.

Taxonomic description: Perennial climbers, with cordate leaves and White flowers in Catkin inflorescence.

Medicinal parts: Whole plant.

Taste : Bitter, Acrid, Astringent.

Chemical constituents: Leaves Nicotinic acid, ascorbic acid, carotin, essential amino acids.

Medicinal properties:

ताम्बूलवल्ली ताम्बूली नागिनी नागवल्लरी ।। (भा. प्र.)

"Tāṃbulavaḷlī tāṃbulī nāginī nāgavaḷlarī." (Bhā. Pṛa.)

Plant - Acrid, anthelmintic, aphrodisiac, astringent, bitter, carminative, expectorant, febrifuge, laxative, stomachic, sweet.

Medicinal uses: Plant - Asthma, bronchitis, cough, diarrhoea, dyspepsia, fever, leprosy, rheumatism.

Ethno- Medicinal uses: Leaves - Antiseptic (Rao & Jamir, 1982); eye diseases (Kharkongor & Joseph, 1981); stomach disorders (Nagendra Prasad & Abraham, 1984); wounds (Tarafder, 1984); cuts, injuries (Baruah *et al.*, 2006); Gout (Jadeja *et al.*, 2006); dysmenorrhoea (Sarma *et al.*, 2006); inflammation of eyes (Deokule, 2006); Burns (Singh & Singh, 2003; Thomas & Britto, 2003).

Root - Abortifacient (Tarafder, 1983); anitfertility (Majumdar *et. al.*, 1978; Tarafder, 1983).

Seed- Toothache (Saikh & Subhan C. Nath, 2003).

PIPER CUBEBA L. f. (PIPERACEAE)

Syn.: *Cubeba officinalis* Miq.; *Litsea cubeba* Pers.; *L. citrata* Blume.

Regional and Other Names: *Bengali* – Kabab chini; *English* – Tailed pepper; *Hindi* – Kababcini; *Kannada* – Gandhamenasu; *Malayalam* – Valmulaku; *Marathi* – Himsi mire; *Sanskrit* – Kankolam; *Tamil* – Valmilagu; *Telugu* – Tokamiriyalu.

Distribution: Native of Indonesia, cultivated in Karnataka.

Taxonomic description: A deciduous aromatic climbing shrub or a small tree.

Medicinal parts: Dried unripe berries.

Taste: Bitter, Acrid.

Chemical constituents: Fruits Essential oil contained cubebin, limonene, sabinene, methyltheptenone, citronellal & citrals.

Medicinal properties:

कङ्कोलं कोलकं प्रोक्तं तथा कोशफलं स्मृतम् ।। (भा. प्र.)

"Kaṇkolaṃ kolakaṃ pṛoktaṃ tathā koṣaphalaṃ ṣmṛtaṃ." (Bhā.Pṛa.)

Fruits - Acrid, anodyne, anthelmintic, anti-inflammatory, appetizing, aromatic, bitter, carminative, digestive, diuretic, expectorant, sedative, stimulant, thermogenic, vulnerary.

Medicinal uses: Fruits - Amenorrhoea, asthma, bronchitis, cough, dysmenorrhoea, dyspepsia, flatulence, gonorrhoea. helminthiasis, Inflammations, rheumatism, straungury, ulcers, wounds.

Ethno- Medicinal uses: Fruits - Gonorrhoea, whooping cough (Gupta, 1981).

PIPER LONGUM L. (PIPERACEAE)

Syn.: *Chavica roxburghii* Miq.

Regional and Other Names: *Bengali* – Piplamor; *English* – Indian long pepper; *Gujarati* – Pipli; *Hindi* – Pipli; *Kannada* – Hipli; *Malayalam* – Tippali; *Marathi* – Pimpli; *Sanskrit* – Pippali; *Tamil* – Pippli; *Telugu* – Pippallu.

Distribution: Throughout India.

Taxonomic description: Creeping undershrubs, rooting at nodes; flowers yellow, in elongate spikes; berries red when ripe.

Medicinal parts: Roots, dried spikes.

Taste : Bitter, Acrid.

Chemical constituents: Roots - Piperlongumine, piperlonguminine, sesamin, piperine, methyl-3, 4, 5-trimethoxycinnamate.

Medicinal properties:

पिप्पली ज्वरहा वृष्या स्निग्धोष्णा कटुतिक्तका ।
दीपनी मारूतश्वासकासश्लेष्मक्षयापहा ।। (रा. नि.)

"Pippalī jvarahā vṛṣyā ṣṇigdhoṣṇā katutiktakā
Dīpanī mārutaṣvāsakāṣasleṣmaksayāpahā." (Rā. Ni.)

Root - Anthlemintic, bitter, digestive, diuretic, expectorant, purgative, stomachic, thermogenic.

Dried spikes - Acrid, aphrodisiac, carminative, digestive, emollient, expectorant, febrifuge, laxative, stomachic.

Medicinal uses: Root - Dyspepsia, gout, lumbago.

Dried spikes - Asthma, bronchits, colic, dyspepsia, epilepsy, fevers, flatulence, gonorrhoea. hiccough.

Ethno- Medicinal uses: Root - Child birth (Tarafder, 1984); cold, cogh (Jain & De. 1966; Mondal & Mukherjee, 1992); indigestion (Hajra & Baishya, 1981); snake bite (Mukherjee & Roy, 1987); Fever (Jadhav, 2006); muscular pain, asthma, dysentry, leprosy (Mukhopadhyay, 1992).

Fruits - Cold (Maheshwari *et. al.,* 1980, 1981; Singh, 2003); Paralysis, Rheumatism (Mukherjee & Roy, 1987); fever (Chhetri, 2005); Cough (Chhetri, 2005; Maheshwari *et. al.,* 1980, 1981; Singh, A. K., 2003); severe headache (Satapathy, 1992).

Seed- Asthmatic complaints, gas troubles (Sivakumar *et al.,* 2003).

Whole plant- Urinary trouble (Thomas & Britto, 2003).

PIPER NIGRUM L. (PIPERACEAE)

Syn.: *P. trioicum* Roxb.

Regional and Other Names: *Bengali* – Golmoirch; *English* – Black pepper; *Gujarati* – Kalamari; *Hindi* – Kalimirc; *Kannada* – Miri; *Malayalam* – Kurumulaku; *Marathi* – Kalimire; *Sanskrit* – Ṁaricam; *Tamil* – Marisam; *Telugu* – Miriyalu.

Distribution: Throughout India.

Taxonomic description: Climbing shrubs, rooting at nodes; flowers pale yellow in spikes.

Medicinal parts: Fruits.

Taste: Acrid.

Chemical constituents: Fruits α-cis-bergamotene & β-cis-berg from essential oil, Pipercide.

Medicinal properties:

मरिचं वेल्लजं कृष्णभूषणम् धर्मपत्तनम् ।। (भा. प्र.)

"Maricaṃ veḷlajaṃ kṛṣṇamūsaṇaṃ ghaṛmapaṭtanaṃ." (Bhā. Pṛa.)

Fruits - Acrid, alexeteric, alterant, anthelmintic, aphrodisiac, bitter, carminative, digestive, diuretic, rubefacient, stimulant.

Medicinal uses: Fruits - Arthritis, asthma, cough, dysentery, dyspepsia, fever, flatulence, hiccough.

Ethno- Medicinal uses: Fruits/Seed - Antifertility (Tiwari *et. al.,* 1982); cold, fever, sore throat, stomachic (Nagendra Prasad & Abraham, 1984) carminative stimulant, stomachic (Mukherjee & Roy, 1987); constipition, flatulence, gout (Jadeja *et al.,* 2006); malaria (Deka *et al.,* 2006); Skin diseases (Mokat & Deokule, 2006); Cough (Nagendra Prasad & Abraham, 1984; Sarma *et al.,* 2006; Gupta, 2006); To make smooth and silky hair (External application) (Jadeja *et al.,* 2006); cold, fever (Gupta, 2006); back pain (Gopalakrishnan & Krishna Prasad,1992); purgative (Srivastava *et al.,* 2003).

PIPER SYLVATICUM Roxb.(PIPERACEAE)

Regional and Other Names: *English* – Small pepper; *Hindi* – Chhoti piper.

Distribution: Upper and lower Assam, Bengal, Burma.

Taxonomic description: A week stemed twiner, many feet long; leaves are heart shaped, simple and like leaves of *Ficus religosa*; fruits in dried catkin.

Medicinal parts: Roots, Fruits, Seeds.

Taste : Acrid.ss

Chemical constituents: Seed contains - Alkamides, sylvetin, piperic acid, flavon, sesamine, lignon, piperine.

Root contains - Piper longamine.

Whole plant - Sylvon.

Medicinal properties: Aphrodisiac, appitiser, aromatic, carminative, digestive, stomachic, tonic.

Medicinal uses: Asthma, cold, cough, diarrhoea, dyspepsia, headache, indigestion, piles, rheumatims. tuberculosis.

Ethno- Medicinal uses: Snake bite (Mukherjee & Roy, 1987).

PISTACIA CHINENSIS Rich. f. (ANACARDIACEAE)

Syn.: *P. integerrima* Brandis.

Regional and Other Names: *Bengali* – Kakra; *English* – Kakra; *Gujarati* – Kakra; *Hindi* – Karkatakasrngi; *Malayalam* – Karkkatakasrngi; *Marathi* –Kakra; *Sanskrit* - Karkatasrngi; *Tamil* – Kakkatasrngi; *Telugu* – Kakarasrnga.

Distribution: Himalayas, Garhwal, Kumoan, Bengal, Assam.

Taxonomic description: A moderate sized deciduous tree upto 18m. high with dark grey or blackish bark; flowers small, reddish in lateral panicles; fruits globose drupes, grey when ripe.

Medicinal parts: Galls.

Taste: Bitter, Acrid, Astringent.

Chemical constituents: Galls contain Triterpenic acid, β-sitosterol, essential oil.

Medicinal properties:

शृङ्.गी कर्कटशृङ्.गी च स्यात्कुलीरविषाणिका ।
अजशृङ्.गी च वक्रा च कर्कटाख्या च कीर्त्तिता ।। (भा. प्र.)

"Sṛṇgī kaṛkataṣṛngī ca ṣyaṭkulīravısaṇika
Ajaṣṛṇgī ca vakṛa ca kaṛkataḳhya ca kīṛttita." (Bhā. Pṛa.)

Galls - Acrid, anti-inflammatory, aromatic, astringent, bitter, constipating, depurative, digestive, expectorant, febrifuge, thermogenic.

Medicinal uses: Galls - Asthma, bronchitis, cough, diarrhoea, dysentery, fever, hiccough, leprosy, psoriasis, skin diseases, ulcers.

Ethno- Medicinal uses: Kernel - Scorpion sting, snake bite, dysentery (Negi *et. al.*, 1985).

Fruit- Cough, cold (Singh, 2003).

PISUM SATIVUM L. (PAPILIONACEAE)

Syn.: *P. arvense* L.

Regional and Other Names: *Bengali* – Matar; *English* – Garden pea; *Gujarati* –Patana; *Hindi* – Mathar; *Kannada* – Vatano; *Malayalam* – Pattanippayar; *Marathi* – Watani; *Sanskrit* – Kalayah; *Tamil* – Pattani; *Telugu* – Battani.

Distribution: West Asia and North India.

Taxonomic description: A sub-erect or climbing annual. Leaflets ovate to oblong. Flowers usually white or Vari-coloured. On long peduncles. Pods broad seeds round, white.

Medicinal parts: Seeds.

Taste : Sweet.

Medicinal properties:

कलायो मधुरः स्वादुः पाके रूक्षश्च शीतलः ।। (भा. प्र.)

"Kalāyo madhuraḥ ṣvāduḥ pake ruksaṣca ṣītalaḥ." (Bhā. Pṛa.)

Seeds - Acrid, cooling, depurative, emollient, laxative, sweet.

Medicinal uses: Seeds - Bronchitis, burning sensation, cough, cuts, leprosy, measles, skin diseases, wounds.

Ethno- Medicinal uses: Seeds - Antifertility (Majumdar *et. al.,* 1978); diabetes (Lal & Yadav, 1983); wound, burns, measles (Bhalla *et al.,* 1992); Poor lactation (Singh & Singh, 2003).

Root- Fever (Manandhav, 2003).

PLANTAGO OVATA Forssk. (PLANTAGINACEAE)

Regional and Other Names: *Bengali* – Eshopgol; *English* – Spongel seeds; *Hindi* – Isabgol; *Kannada* – Issabagolu; *Malayalam* – Ispaghal; *Sanskrit* – Snigdhajirakah; *Tamil* – Isphogol; *Telugu* – Isapgaluvittulu.

Distribution: Cultivated in Punjab, Gujarat & Haryana.

Taxonomic description: Subcaulscent herbs, with linear leaves in rosette. Flowers in dense condensed spikes born on scapes; corolla-lobes rounded. Capsules ellipsoid; seed boat-shaped.

Medicinal parts: Seeds.

Taste : Sweet.

Chemical constituents: Seed contain Holoside planteose.

Husk of seeds contain Colloidal muscilage (Polysaccharides).

Seed oil contain Linoleic acid.

Medicinal properties:

ईषद्गोलं स्निग्धबीजं श्लक्ष्णजीरश्च कीर्त्तित : ।। (शा. नि.)

"Īsaḍgolaṃ ṣnigdhabījaṃ ṣlakṣṇajīraṣca kīṛttitaḥ." (Ṣā. Ni.)

Seeds - Sweet, antidysenteric, anti-inflammatory aphrodisiac, astringent, diuretic, emollient, expectorant, laxative, mucilaginous, refrigerant.

Medicinal uses: Seeds - Burning sensation, constipaition, cough, diarrhoea, dysentery, erysipelas, gonorrhoea, gout, strangury.

Ethno- Medicinal uses: Seed - Constipation, gout (Jadeja *et al.,* 2006); diarrhoea, dysentery (Kataria & Gauchan, 2006); urinary infection, indigestion (Kumar *et al.,* 2003).

Leaves - Gout (Jadeja *et al.,* 2006).

PLUCHEA LANCEOLATA Oliver & Hiern. (ASTERACEAE)

Regional and Other Names: *English* – Rasna; *Gujarati* –Rashana; *Hindi* – Baisari; *Marathi* –Rasna; *Sanskrit* –Rasna.

Distribution: Punjab, Gangetic Plan as far as Cawnpore, Sind.

Taxonomic description: A shrub, stem and branches are terete, viscous hairy, about 30-60 cm. high; leaves sessile, coriaceous, dirty green, lanceolate acute at both ends, apiculate; flowers are small in capitulum of purple colour at the end of thin branchlets.

Medicinal parts : Whole plant, Leaves & Roots.

Taste : Bitter.

Chemical constituents: Leaves contain Quercetin, isorhamtene, resin, volatile oil, calcium oxalate.

Medicinal properties:

रास्नाऽऽमपाचनी तिक्ता गुरूष्णा कफवातजित् ।
शोथश्वाससमीरामवातशूलोदरापहा ।
कासज्वर विषातिवातिकामयसिध्महृत् ।। (भा. प्र.)

"Rāsnāaampācinī tiktā guruṣṇā kaphavātajiṭ
Ṣothṣwāsasamīrāmvātaṣūlodarāpahā
Kāsjvar visātivātikamāysighmahṛṭ." (Bhā. Pṛa.)

Analgesic, anti-inflammatory, antipyretic, laxative, thermogenic.

Medicinal uses: Abdominal pain, arthritis, bronchitis. cough, dyspepsia, rheumatism.

Ethno- Medicinal uses: Root - Fever during pregnancy (Jadeja *et al.,* 2006).

Leaves- Rheumatism, arthritis, gout, sciatica (Mitaliya *et al.,* 2003).

PLUMERIA RUBRA L. (APOCYNACEAE)

Syn.: *P. acuminata* Ait.; *P. acutifolia* Poir.

Regional and Other Names: *Bengali* – Gorurchampa; *English* – Pogodo tree; *Hindi* – Cameli; *Kannada* – Kadusampige; *Malayalam* – Kunkumakkalli; *Marathi* – Sonchampa; *Sanskrit* – Svetacampaka; *Tamil* – Kallimandarai; *Telugu* – Vadaganneru.

Distribution: Throughout India.

Taxonomic description: An evergreen or partly deciduous trees; flowers cream coloured with Yellow centre.

Medicinal parts : Root, Bark, Leaves, Latex.

Taste : Bitter, Acrid, Astringent.

Chemical constituents: Bark contains Fulvopluimerin plumieride, amyrin, Lupeol, bitter glucoside, essential oil, plumeric acid.

Medicinal properties:

श्वेतस्तु चम्पकः प्रोक्तः सरस्तिक्तः कटुः स्मृतः ।
तुवरोष्णः कुष्ठकण्डूव्रणशूलकफापहः ।। (नि. र.)

"Ṣvetaṣtu ca campakaḥ proktaḥ saraṣtiktaḥ katuḥ ṣmṛtaḥ.
Tuvarōṣṇaḥ kaṣthakaṇdūvṛaṇaṣūlakaphapaḥ." (Ni. Ra.)

Root bark - Acrid, astringent, bitter, carminative, laxative, thermogenic.

Medicinal uses: Root bark - Leprosy, pruritus, ulcers.

Ethno- Medicinal uses : Flowers - Antifertility (Tiwari *et. al.,* 1982).

Leaf - Lactation (Gupta, 1981).

Bark - Malaria fever (Tarafder, 1986).

Root - Abortifacient (Tarafder, 1953); bone fractures (Prasad *et al.,* 2003).

Fruits - Abortifacient (Tarafder, 1953).

Milky juice/Latex - Rheumatism (Deokule, 2006; Mitaliya *et al.,* 2003; Nayak *et al.,* 2003); skin diseases (Sattapathy & Brahmam, 2003); gout (Mitaliya *et al.,* 2003); ulcers, leprosy (Nayak *et al.,* 2003); bodyache (Prasad *et al.,* 2003); toothache (Tigga *et al.,* 2003).

PREMNA CORYMBOSA Rottl. (VERBENACEAE)

Syn.: *P. integrifolia* L.; *P. obtusifolia* R. Br.; *P. serratifolia* L.

Regional and Other Names: *Bengali* – Gambari; *Gujarati* –Arni; *Hindi* – Ageta; *Kannada* – Takkila; *Malayalam* – Munna; *Marathi* – Aran; *Sanskrit* – Agnimanthah; *Tamil* – Munnai; *Telugu* – Padmaka.

Distribution: Throughout India.

Taxonomic description: Shrubs; 1-2 m. high; flowers yellowish in panicled cymes; calyx enlarged in fruit.

Medicinal parts: Root, Leaves.

Taste : Bitter, Acrid, Sweet, Astringent.

Chemical constituents: Premnine & ganikarine alkaloids.

Medicinal properties:

अग्निमन्था जया सा स्यात् श्रीपर्णी गणिकारिका ।
जया जयन्ती तर्कारी नादेयी वैजयन्तिका ।। (भा. प्र.)

"Agnimaṇthā jayā sā ṣyāt s̩rīparnī gaṇikārikā
Jayā jayaṇtī ta̩rkārī nā deyī vaijayaṇtikā." (Bhā. P̩ra.)

Roots - Acrid, alexeteric, alterant, anodyne, anti-inflammatory, astringent, bitter, carminative, depurative, digestive, expectorant, febrifuge, laxative, stomachic, sweet, thermogenic.

Leaves - Carminative, stomachic.

Medicinal uses: Roots - Asthma, bronchitis, cardiac disorders, colic, constipation, cough, diabetes, dysepesia, fever, flatulence, inflammations, leprosy, skin diseases.

Leaves - Colic, cough, dyspepsia, fever, flatulence, toumours.

Ethno- Medicinal uses : Leaf- Stomach problem (Nayak *et al.,* 2003).

Root- Cardiac trouble, cold fever (Nayak *et al.,* 2003).

Whole plant- Rheumatism, neuralgia (Nayak *et al.,* 2003).

PRUNUS AMYGDALUS Batsch. (ROSACEAE)

Syn.: *P. communis* Arcang.; *P. dulcis* (Mill.) D.A. Webb.; *Amygdalus communis* L.

Regional and Other Names: *Bengali* – Badam; *English* – Almond tree; *Gujarati* –Badam; *Hindi* – Badam; *Kannada* – Badami; *Malayalam* – Badam; *Marathi* – Badam; *Sanskrit* – Vatamah; *Tamil* – Vatamakottai; *Telugu* – Badamvittulu.

Distribution: Cultivated in Kashmir & Punjab.

Taxonomic description: A middle sized trees; leaves oblong, lanceolate, petiole glandular, stipules fimbriate; flowers copious, pink, sessile; fruits drupe, velvety, pericarp dry.

Medicinal parts : Kernel, Oil.

Taste : Sweet.

Chemical constituents: Kernel & Almond oil contains Prunasin, decosterin, sitosterol, HCN glucosides, fatty acids, proteins.

Medicinal properties:

वातादो वातवैरी स्यात् नेत्रोपमफलस्तक्तथा ।। (भा. प्र.)

"Vātādo vātavaīrī ṣyāṭ neṭropamaphalaṣtathā." (Bhā. Pṛa.)

Kernel - Aphrodisiac, emollient, demulcent, diuretic, laxative, sweet, thermogenic.

Oil - Cooling, laxative, rejuvenating, sedative, sweet, vulnerary.

Medicinal uses: Kernel - Amenorrhoea, ascites, burning sensation, colic, cough, inflammations, otalgia, peptic ulcers, pruritus, skin diseases, strangury.

Oil - Burning sensation, colic, cough, gleet, otalgia, ulcers, wounds.

Ethno- Medicinal uses: Fruits - Diabetes (Tiwari *et. al.,* 1979).

PRUNUS CERASOIDES D. Don (ROSACEAE)

Syn.: *R. puddum* Roxb.

Regional and Other Names: *Bengali* – Padmak; *English* – Himalayan wild cherry; *Gujarati* – Padmak; *Hindi* – Patmakh; *Kannada* – Padmaka; *Malayalam* – Patumukam; *Marathi* – Padmaka; *Sanskrit* – Padmakah; *Tamil* – Patumugam; *Telugu* – Padmakla.

Distribution: In the Himalayas, at an altitude of 900 to 2300 m.

Taxonomic description: A medium sized or large tree, with Pink flowers and drupe fruits.

Medicinal parts: Heartwood.

Taste : Bitter, Acrid, Astringent.

Chemical constituents: Stem contains - Flavones glucoside: Puddumin-A; Flavonoid Glucosides; β-sitosterol, prunetin, n-pentacosane, triacontane, n-octacosanol, ursolic acid, oleic acid, palmitic acid, stearic acid, kaempferitin, naringenin.

Medicinal properties:

पद्मकं पद्मगंधि स्यात्तथा पद्माह्वयं स्मृतम् ।। (भा प्र.)

"Paḍmakaṃ paḍmagaṇdhi ṣyāttathā paḍmāḥvayaṃ ṣmṛtaṃ."
(Bhā. Pṛa.)

Heartwood - Acrid, anodyne, astringent, bitter, constipating, demulcent, digestive, diuretic, refrigerant, vulnerary.

Medicinal uses: Heartwood - Asthma, burning sensation, dysmenorrhoa, fevers, hiccough, leprosy, pruritus, sprains, ulcers, vomiting, wounds.

Ethno- Medicinal uses: Bark - Bone fractures (Uniyal, 1968); fever, diarrhoea (Megoneitso & Rao, 1983); burns, cuts, wounds (Shah & Joshi, 1971); pain, swelling, bone fractures (Dash *et al.*, 2003).

PRUNUS DOMESTICA L. (ROSACEAE)

Syn.: *P. communis* Huds.

Regional and Other Names: *Bengali* – Alubakhra; *English* – Common plum; *Hindi* – Alubukhara; *Kannada* – Albokhala; *Malayalam* – Plums; *Marathi* – Nashpati; *Sanskrit* – Arukam; *Tamil* – Aluppukkarappalam; *Telugu* – Alpagodapandu.

Distribution: Cultivated at high altitudes in Nilgiris & Himachal Pradesh.

Taxonomic description: An unarmed small tree with glabrous branches; flowers white to cream-coloured; fruits drupes.

Medicinal parts : Fruits.

Taste : Sweet.

Chemical constituents: Fruit contains d-galactose, d-mannose, L-arabinose, L-rhamnose, glucuronic acid, iron, calcium, magnessium, phosphates, vitamin-C.

Medicinal properties:

आरूकं वीरसेनं च चीना चीनारूकं तथा ।
विधाज्जातिविशेषण तच्चतुर्विधमारूकम् ।। (कै. नि.)

"Ārukaṃ vīrasenaṃ ca cīnā cīnārukaṃ tathā
Vidyājjātiviṣesena taccatuṛvidhamārukaṃ." (Kaī. Ni.)

Fruits - Appetizing, digestive, laxative, refrigerent, sour, sweet.

Medicinal uses: Fruits - Colic, dyspepsia, flatulence, nausea.

Ethno- Medicinal uses: Body pain (Singh, 2003).

Fruit- Leucorrhoea, irregular menstruation (Rajan, 1992).

PRUNUS PERSICA Benth. & Hook. f. (ROSACEAE)

Syn.: *Amygdalus persica* L.

Regional and Other Names: *Bengali* – Nashpati; *English* – Peach, Nectarine; *Hindi* – Aru, Shaftalu; *Kannada* – Berikai; *Malayalam* – Sabarjil; *Marathi* –Berikai; *Sanskrit* – Aruka; *Tamil* – Nashpati; *Telugu* – Berikai.

Distribution: Native of China, Cultivated in Himalayas; grows in tropical and semitropical regions and in temperate climates usually under grass.

Taxonomic description: A large deciduous shrub or small trees, with Pink flowers in racemes, fruits downy, succulent.

Medicinal parts: Flowers, Fruits, Leaves, Bark.

Taste: Sweet-Acrid.

Chemical constituents: Leaves HCN, hentriacontane, hentrianontanol, β-sitosterol, ursolic acid.

Flowers Kaempferol-3-rhamnoside, quercetin.

Medicinal properties:

नात्युष्णं गुरू संपक्वं स्वादुप्रायं मुखप्रियम् ।
बृंहणं जीर्यति क्षिप्रं नातिदोषलमारूकम् ।। (नि. र.)

"Nāṭyuṣṇaṃ guru saṃpakvaṃ ṣvādupṛāyaṃ mukhapṛiyaṃ
Bṛṃhaṇaṃ jīṛyati ksipṛaṃ nātidosalamārukaṃ." (Ni. Ra.)

Plant - Diuretic, expectorant, sedative.

Medicinal uses: Plant - Bronchitis, cough.

Ethno- Medicinal uses: Seed oil - Eczema, headache (Shah, 1982); eczema (Shah & Joshi, 1971); stomach disorders (Nautiyal *et al.,* 2003).

Leaf - Scabies (Megoneito & Rao, 1983).

PTEROCARPUS SANTALINUS L. f. (PAPILIONACEAE)

Regional and Other Names: *Bengali* – Lal chandan; *English* – Red sanders; *Gujarati* –Ratanjili; *Hindi*–Raktacandan; *Kannada* – Raktacandana; *Malayalam* – Raktacandanam; *Marathi* – Tambada chandan; *Sanskrit* – Raktacandanah; *Tamil* – Sivappuccandanam; *Telugu* – Raktagandhamu.

Distribution: Andhra Pradesh, Tamil Nadu & Karnataka.

Taxonomic description: A tall deciduous trees; bark cleft into rectangular plates; leaves thick; flowers axillary; petals long-clawed; pod winged.

Medicinal parts: Heartwood, Fruits.

Taste: Bitter, Sweet.

Chemical constituents: Heart wood Pterocarpol, pterocarptriol, isopterocarpolone, pterocarpodiolone, santalin B.

Medicinal properties:

रक्तचन्दनमाख्यातं रक्ताङ्.गं क्षुद्रचन्दनम् ।
तिलपर्णं रक्तसारं तत् प्रबालफलं स्मृतम् ।। (भा. प्र.)

"Raktacaṇdanamāḳḥyātaṃ raktārigaṃ ksudracaṇdanam
Tilapaṛṇaṃ raktasāraṃ taṭ p̣rabālaphalaṃ ṣmaṛtaṃ." (Bhā. P̣ra.)

Heart wood - Acrid, alexeteric, anthelmintic, anti-inflammatory, aphrodisiac, bitter, constipating, cooling, depurative, diaphoretic, febrifuge, sweet.

Fruits - Astringent.

Medicinal uses: Heart wood - Burning sensation, diarrhoea, dysentery, fever, leprosy, skin diseases, ulcers, vomiting.

Fruits - Dysentery.

PUERARIA TUBEROSA DC. (PAPILIONACEAE)

Regional and Other Names: *Bengali* – Shimiabatraji; *English* – Indian kudzu; *Gujarati* – Karwinai; *Hindi* – Vidarikand; *Kannada* – Dari; *Malayalam* – Mutukku; *Marathi* – Badra; *Sanskrit* – Vidari; *Tamil* – Dari; *Telugu* – Vadari kandha.

Distribution: Throughout India.

Taxonomic description: A large spreading tuberous herbaceous twiner with very large tuberous roots; flowers blue or purplish blue in leafless racemes; fruits membranous, flat jointed pods clothed with silky brown hairs.

Medicinal parts: Tuberous roots.

Taste : Sweet.

Chemical constituents: Hydroxytuberosone, anhydroxytuberosin, 3-O-methylandydrotuberosin, puerarostan, puerarone, daidzein, stigmasterol, puetuberosanol.

Medicinal properties:

विदारी स्वादुकन्दा च सा तु क्रोष्ट्री सिता स्मृता ।। (भा. प्र.)

"Vidārī ṣvādukaṇdā ca sā tu kṛoṣṭṛī sitā ṣmṛtā." (Bhā. Pṛa.)

Roots - Aphrodisiac, diuretic, emetic, emollient, expectorant, febrifuge, laxative, refrigerant, sweet.

Medicinal uses: Root - Arthritis, burning sensation, constipation, cough, dyspepsia, fevers, leprosy, spermatorrhoea, strangury, tuberculosis.

Ethno- Medicinal uses: Tuberous root - Asthma (Saxena, 1986); fever (Gupta, 1981; Kumar & Lal, 2003); bodyache (Gupta, 1981; Jain *et al.,* 2003); dyspepsia (Sattapathy & Brahmam, 2003); fever, swelling of joints (Kumar & Lal, 2003); renal complaint (Islam & Jha, 2003); Diarrhoea, abdominal pain (Joshi *et. al.,* 1980); cholera (Maheshwari *et. al.,* 1986); fever (Singh & Pandey, 1980; Bhargava, 1959; Rajwar, 1980; Manandhav, 2003); rheumatism (Singh & Pandey, 1980); swelling (Srivastava & Varma, 1981; Bhargava, 1959; Rajwar, 1983); body pain (Nadanakunjidam, 2003); sexual debility (Bhatt *et al.,* 2003).

Whole plant- Boils, ulcers, swelling (Sarma & Baishya, 1992).

Flower- Diabetes (Bhatt *et al.,* 2003).

PUNICA GRANATUM L. (PUNICACEAE)

Regional and Other Names: *Bengali* – Dalim; *English* – Pomegranate; *Hindi* – Anar, Dhalim; *Kannada* – Dalimbe; *Malayalam* – Talimatalam; *Marathi* – Dalimba; *Sanskrit* – Dadimah; *Tamil* – Madalam; *Telugu* – Dadima.

Distribution: Cultivated throughout India.

Taxonomic description: A large deciduous shrub or small tree, with spiny or thorny branches and dark Grey bark.

Medicinal parts: Roots, Bark, Flowers, Fruits, Seeds.

Taste: Sweet, Astringent.

Chemical constituents: Bark - Alkaloid-Pelletierine.

Root - Alkaloids, pseudo-pelletierine, pelletierine, isopelletierine, methyl-pelletierine.

Flowers - Sitosterol, tannins-punicalagin & punicalin.

Fruits - Mannose, galactose, rhamnose, arabinose, glucose, galactouronic acid.

Medicinal properties:

दाड़िमः करको दन्तबीजो लोहितपुष्पकः ।। (भा. प्र.)

"Dādimaḥ karako daṇtabījo lohitapuṣpakaḥ." (Bhā. Pṛa.)

Root & Stem bark - Anthelmintic, astringent, cooling.

Flowers - Styptic.

Fruits - Aphrodisiac, astringent, cooling, diuretic. laxative, sour, sweet.

Seed - Diuretic, stomachic.

Medicinal uses: Root & Stem bark-Good for tapeworm and for strengthening the gums.

Flowers - Hydrocelc, ulcers, vomiting.

Fruits - Anaemia, bronchitis, otalgia.

Seed - Vomiting, scabies.

Ethno- Medicinal uses: Leaf - Miscarriages (Tarafder, 1984); eye complaint (Bhall *et. al.,* 1982); dysentery (Das *et al.,* 2006).

Fruit - Diarrhoea (Dar *et. al.,* 1984; Shah *et. al.,* 1981); stomachache (Rao & Jamir, 1982); dysentery (Sarma *et al.,* 2006; Kapur & Nanda, 1992); Diarrhoea, dysentery (Jadeja *et al.,* 2006); diabetes (Ghosh, 2006).

Seed - Pimples (Shah & Joshi, 1971); jaundice (Das & Sharma, 2003).

Flowers - Stomachache, dysentery (Ganesan *et. al.,* 2006).

Root - Dysentery (Sarma *et al.,* 2006); Anthelmintic (Basak, 2006).

Floral bud - Children's cough (Deokule, 2006).

Fruit wall- Diarrhoea (Kapur & Nanda, 1992; Deokule & Magdum, 1992; Beigh *et al.,* 2003; Islam & Jha, 2003); dysentery (Arinathan *et al.,* 2003; Deokule & Magdum, 1992; Islam & Jha, 2003); impotency (Shukla *et al.,* 2003).

Stem- Toothache (Ganai & Nawchoo, 2003).

PYRUS MALUS L. (ROSACEAE)

Syn.: *Malus sylvestris* Hort. non Mill.

Regional and Other Names: *Bengali* – Apel, sev; *English* – Apple; *Hindi* – Seb, Sev; *Kannada* – Sebu, Sevu; *Malayalam* –; *Marathi* – Safar chand.

Distribution: Indigenous in Europe & W. Asia; Wild in N.-W. Himalaya, also cultivated.

Taxonomic description : A medium sized trees; leaves oval or elliptic to broad ovate. Flowers Pink; fruit on a short pedicel. Fruits edible.

Medicinal parts : Fruit, Bark, Root.

Taste : Sweet, Astringent.

Chemical constituents: Leaves & Buds contain - Glycoside, sorbitol, sucrose, glucose.

Fruit cuticle contains - Glucoside, diglucoside, galactoside, rhamnoside, arabinoside, P-coumaric acid, phlorizin.

Fruit contains - Malic acid, licythin; Salts-potassium, calcium oxalate.

Medicinal properties:

सेवं समीरपित्तघ्नं बृंहणं कफकृद् गुरू ।
रसे पाके च मधुरं शिशिरं रूचिशुक्रकृत् ।। (भा. प्र.)

"Sevaṃ samirpiṭtaghnaṃ bṛihṇaṃ kaphakṛuḍ guru
Rase pāke ca madhuraṃ ṣiṣiraṃ ruciṣukṛakṛuṭ." (Bhā. Pṛa.)

Appitiser, cardia tonic.

Medicinal uses: Asthma, diarrhoea, dyspepsia, hemorrhagic diseases.

Ethno- Medicinal uses: Fruits - To make strong and black hair (External

application) (Jadeja *et al.,* 2006).

QUISQUALIS INDICA L. (COMBRETACEAE)

Syn.: *Q. densiflora* Wall. ex. Miq.

Regional and Other Names: *Bengali* – Brahmolata; *English* – Rangoon Creeper; *Gujarati* – Barmasini bel; *Hindi* – Rangunachi veli; *Marathi* –Lal chameli; *Tamil* – Irangun-malli; *Telugu* – Rangonimalli.

Distribution: Indigenous in Africa & Indo-Malaysin region, cultivated throughout India.

Taxonomic description: A large, scandent, shrubby and woody vine, with compact terminal spike inflorescence and capsule fruits.

Medicinal parts : Leaves, Seeds.

Taste: Bitter.

Chemical constituents: Leaves - Trigonelline, L-proline, L-asparagine, quisqualic acid.

Seed oil - Linolenic, oleic, palmitic, stearic, arachidic acids, sterol, fatty acids.

Medicinal properties: Seeds - Anthelmintic, antidiarrhoeal, febrifuge.

Leaves - Carminative.

Medicinal uses: Seeds - Diarrhoea, fever, helminthiasis, rickets, ringworm.

Leaves - Colic, constipation, helminthiasis.

Ethno- Medicinal uses: Leaves- Tonsilitis (Jadhav, 2006); anthelmintic (Deokule, 2006).

RANDIA DUMETORUM Poir. (RUBIACEAE)

Syn.: *Xeromorphis spinosa* Thunb. Keay.; *Catunaregum spinosa* (Thunb.) Tiru.

Regional and Other Names: *Bengali* –; *English* – Emetic nut; *Gujarati* – Mindhal; *Hindi* – Mainphal; *Kannada* – Kara; *Malayalam* – Kara; *Marathi* –Ghela; *Sanskrit* – Madana; *Tamil* – Marikkallankay; *Telugu* – Manga mainphal.

Distribution: Sub-Himalayan tract, Konkan & Peninsular India.

Taxonomic description: - A deciduous thorny shrub or small tree; Leaves elliptic to obovate, hairy on the veins beneath; flowers white, turning yellowish, solitary or fascicled in the axils; seeds embedded in pulp.

Medicinal parts: Fruits.

Taste: Bitter.

Chemical constituents: 6 saponins-dumetoronins A, B, C, D, E & F-isolated, all of them contained oleanolic acid as glycone.

Medicinal properties:

मदनो मधुरस्तिक्तो वीर्योष्णो लेखनो लघुः ।
वान्तिकृद्विद्धिहरः प्रतिश्यायव्रणान्तकः ।
राक्षः कुष्ठकफानाहशोथगुल्मव्रणापहः ।। (भा. प्र.)

"Madano madhuraṣtiḳto vīṛyeṣṇo lekhano laghuḥ
Vāṇtikṛdvidradhiharaḥ pṛatiṣyāyavṛaṇāṇtakaḥ
Ruksaḥ kuṣthakaphānāhasothaguḷmavṛaṇāpahaḥ." (Bhā. Pṛa.)

Anodyne, anthlemintic, anti-inflammatory, carminative, expectorant, emetic, febrifuge, pungent, sudorific.

Medicinal uses: Amenorrhoea, cold, cough, dysmenorrhoea, fever, flatulence, inflammations, piles, rheumatism, swelling, ulcers.

Ethno- Medicinal uses: Fruit - Abortifacient (Tarafder, 1983); pimples, boils (Purohit *et. al.*, 1985); dysentery, cough, bronchitis(Bhatt *et al.*, 2003); dandruff (Ravikumar & Vijaya Sankar, 2003).

Root- Malaria, fever (Sharma & Singh, 1988).

Stem bark - Dysentery (Upadhye *et. al.*, 1986).

Stem- Rheumatism (Samvatsar & Diwanji, 2003).

RAPHANUS SATIVUS L. (BRASSICACEAE)

Syn.: *R. caudatus* L.

Regional and Other Names: *Bengali* – Mula; *English* – Radish; *Gujarati* –Mura; *Hindi* – Muli; *Kannada* – Mulangi; *Malayalam* – Mullanki; *Marathi* – Mula; *Sanskrit* – Mulika; *Tamil* – Mullanki; *Telugu* – Mullangi.

Distribution: Throughout India, cultivated.

Taxonomic description: Annual herbs, with fusiform roots and white or lilac flowers.

Medicinal parts: Roots, Leaves, Seeds.

Taste: Acrid.

Chemical constituents: Seeds- Glycoside, enzyme, methyl mercaptan, sulforaphene, essential oil.

Medicinal properties:

मूलकं तीक्ष्णमुष्ण च कटुष्णं ग्राहि दीपनम् ।
दुर्नामगुल्म हृद्रोग वातघ्नम् रूचिदं गुरू ।। (रा. नि.)

"Mulakaṃ tīkṣṇamṣṇaṇa ca katuṣṇaṃ gṛāhi dīpanaṃ
Duṛnāmaguḷma hṛdṛoga vātaghnaṃ rucidaṃ guru." (Rā. Ni.)

Roots- Acrid, anodyne, anti-inflammatory, appetizing, bitter, depurative, digestive, laxative, stomachic, thermogenic.

Leaves- Antibacterial, diuretic, laxative.

Seeds - Carminative, diuretic, expectorant, laxative.

Medicinal uses: Root - Colic, diarrhoea, dyspepsia, flatulence, inflammations, leprosy, nausea, skin diseases.

Seeds - Amenorrhoea, cough, dyspepsia, flatulence, paralysis, strangury,

Ethno- Medicinal uses: Leaf - Acidity (Shah, 1984); diuretic, laxative (Kothari & Rao, 2003); general weakness (Kumar *et al.,* 2003).

Seed - Ringworm (Purohit *et. al.,* 1985); skin diseases (Saxena & Vyas, 1986).

Root - Acidity (Kumar & Chauhan, 2005); Jaundice, kidney stone (Ballabh & Chaurasia, 2006); general weakness (Kumar *et al.,* 2003).

Whole plant- Jaundice (Kothari & Rao, 2003).

RHINACANTHUS NASUTA (L.) Kurz. (ACANTHACEAE)

Syn.: *R. communis* Nees.; *Justicia nasuta* L.

Regional and Other Names: *Hindi* – Juyipani; *Kannada* – Nagamulli; *Malayalam* – Pulukkolli; *Marathi* –Gajakarni; *Sanskrit* – Yuthikaparni; *Tamil* – Nagamalli; *Telugu* – Nagamulli.

Distribution: Throughout India.

Taxonomic description: An annual or binneal undershrubs, with White flowers & 4-seeded capsule fruits.

Medicinal parts: Whole plant.

Taste: Bitter, Acrid.

Chemical constituents: Root & Bark contains Rhinocanthin.

Medicinal properties:

गजकर्णी स्वादुपाका तिक्ता चोष्णा कफापहा ।
शीतज्वरं च वातं च नाशयेदिति कीर्तिता ।। (नि. र.)

"Gajakarṇī ṣvādupākā tiktā cosṇā kaphāpahā
Ṣītajvaraṃ ca vātaṃ ca nāṣayediti kīrtitā." (Ni. Ra.)

Plant- Acrid, anthelmintic, antiseptic, aphrodisiac, bitter, depurative, thermogenic.

Medicinal uses: Plant - Eczema, helminthiasis, inflammations. leprosy, obesity, ringworm, scurvy,

Ethno- Medicinal uses: Root - Eczema, Ringworm (Janardhanan, 1963).

ROSA DAMASCENA Mill. (ROSACEAE)

Regional and Other Names: *English* – Persian rose; *Hindi* – Gulaaba; *Malayalam* – Penimirpushpam; *Sanskrit* – Satapatri; *Tamil* – Erosa; *Telugu* – Gulabi.

Distribution: Cultivated throughout India.

Taxonomic description: An erect woody perennial shrub.

Medicinal parts: Flowers.

Taste: Bitter.

Chemical constituents: Flowers - Cyanidin 3, 5-diglucoside; essential oil contain citronell, nerol, geraniol, phenylethanol; fatty oil; organic acids.

Medicinal properties:

शतपत्री हिमा तिक्ता कषाया कुष्ठनाशनी ।
मुखस्फोटहरा रूच्या सुरभिः पित्तदाहनुत् ।। (रा. नि.)

"Ṣatapaṭrī himā tiktā kasāyā kuṣthanāṣanī
Mukhaṣphotaharā rucyā surabhiḥ piṭtadāhanuṭt." (Rā. Ni.)

Appitiser, aromatic, artringent, cardiac tonic, digestive.

Medicinal uses: Burning sensation, Skin diseases.

Ethno- Medicinal uses: Flowers - Dandruff (External application) (Jadeja *et al.,* 2006).

SANSEVIERIA ROXBURGHIANA Schult. f. (AGAVACEAE)

Syn.: *S. zeylanica* Roxb.

Regional and Other Names: *Bengali* – Murba; *English* – Indian bow-string hemp; *Hindi* – Murva, Marul; *Kannada* – Manjinanaru; *Malayalam* – Cadenaku; *Marathi* –Nagfan; *Sanskrit* –Maruva ; *Tamil* – Marul; *Telugu* – Sagal.

Distribution: Throughout India, cultivated in Gardens.

Taxonomic description : A perennial herb with underground rhizome; radical tough leaves with light green intruppted bands.

Medicinal parts: Rhizome.

Taste: Slightly sweet.

Chemical constituents: Rhizome - Salycilic acid.

Medicinal properties:

मुर्वा स्वादुः स्वादुपाका गुरूष्णा तिक्ता सरा ।
जयेत् त्रिदोषकुष्ठास्त्रमेदोमेहवमिज्वरान् ।। (कै. नि.)

"Muṛvā ṣvāduḥ ṣvādupākā guruṣṇā tiktā sarā
jayeṭ ṭridoshkuṣthāṣṭṛmedomehavmijvarāṇ." (Ni. Ra.)

Expectorant, laxative, pungent.

Medicinal uses: Arthirits, boils, fever, tuberculosis.

Ethno- Medicinal uses: Rhizome - Snakebite (Pal & Jain, 1989).

Leaf - Earache (Ramachandran & Nair, 1981; Ganesan & Kesavan, 2003); Snake bite (Rao *et. al.*, 2006).

Root - Cough (Puri, 1983); Snake bite (Rao *et. al.*, 2006).

SACCHARUM OFFICINARUM L. (POACEAE)

Regional and Other Names: *Bengali* –Ganna; *English* –Sugarcane; *Gujarati* –Sheradi; *Hindi* – Ganna, Ikh; *Kannada* –Basarimara; *Malayalam* - Karimba; *Marathi* –Aos; *Sanskrit* –Asipatra; *Tamil* – Karimpu; *Telugu* – Charki.

Distribution: Cultivated throughout India.

Taxonomic description Tall, perennial, rhizomatous plants, with juicy culms and leaves wide and laminate right to the base. Spikelets awnless; glumes glabrous

Medicinal parts: Whole plant.

Taste: Sweet.

Chemical constituents: Stem- Flavonoids, sucrose, glucose, fructose, fibres, nitrogenous substances, fats, waxes, gums, pectins, free acids, combined acids, saccharetin.

Cane juice- Glycans as saccharans A, B, C, D, E & F, neocarlinoside, neoisoschaftoside, orientin, ferulic acid, caffeic acid, sugars, carbohydrates, hemicellulose, pentosans, starch, pectins, proteins, peptose, carboxylic acids, inorganic salts, silica, amino acids, vitamins as Thiamine, riboflavin, niacin, biotin, gums, phenols, calcium oxalate, vitamin-D.

Medicinal properties:

मुंजद्वयं तु मधुरं तुवरं शिशिरं तथा ।
दाह्तृष्णा विसर्पास्त्र मूत्रकृच्छ क्षिरोगजित् ।।
दोषत्रयह्रं वृष्यं मेखलासूपयुज्यते । (भा. प्र.)

"Munjadvayam tu madhuram tuvaram sisiram tatha
Dahatrsna visarpastr mutrakrcchksirogjit
Dosatrayaharam vrsyam mekhalasupayujyate" (Bha. Pra.)

Stem- Apetizre, aphrodisiac, cooling, diuretic, emollient, expectorant, laxative, stomachic, sweet.

Root- Cooling, demulcent, diuretic, stimulent.

Medicinal uses: Stem- Anaemia, asthma, cardiac debility, diarrhoea, dysuria, erysipelas, fatigue, flatulence, gastric disorders, gonorrhoea, hiccough, jaundice, leprosy, seminal weakness, tuberculosis.

Ethno- Medicinal uses: Cane juice- Gall bladder (Rao & Jamir, 1982); constipation (Maheshwari & Singh, 1984); jaundice (Deokule, 2006; Dutta *et al.,* 2006); leprosy, intestinal trouble (Kumar & Yadav, 2006).

SHOREA ROBUSTA Gaertn. f. (DIPTEROCARPACEAE)

Regional and Other Names: *Bengali* – Shal; *English* – Sal tree; *Gujarati* – Ral; *Hindi* – Sal; *Kannada* – Kabba; *Malayalam* – Maramaram; *Marathi* –Ral; *Sanskrit* –Agnivallabha; *Tamil* – Shalam; *Telugu* – Gugal.

Distribution: In North-East & Central India.

Taxonomic description: A large deciduous trees; flowers cream or Pale yellow, in racemes.

Medicinal parts: Bark, leaves, resin & fruits.

Taste: Acrid.

Chemical constituents: Seed - Fatty oil.

Wood - Oleoresin.

Medicinal properties:

> शालं फलं रूक्षं शीतं मधुरं स्तम्भनं गुरू ।
> कषायं लेखनं स्तन्यवाताध्मानविबन्धकृत् ।
> पित्तदाहतृषाकासक्षतक्षयविषास्त्रनुत् ।। (भा. प्र.)

> "Ṣālaṃ phalaṃ rukshaṃ ṣītaṃ madhuraṃ ṣtaṃbhaṃ guru
> Kasāyaṃ lekhnaṃ ṣtaṇyavātāghmānvibaṇdhkṛuṭ
> Pịṭṭadāhṭrusākāsakshatkshāyviṣaṣtrnuṭ." (Bhā. Pra.)

Bark & Leaves - Acrid, alexeteric, anodyne, anthelmintic, astringent, cooling, diuretic.

Resin - Acrid, anodyne, aphrodisiac, astringent, carminative, cooling, detergent, diuretic, expectorant, stomachic.

Fruits - Aphrodisiac, astringent, cooling, sweet.

Medicinal uses: Bark, Leaves, Seed - Anaemia, asthma, bleeding piles, cough, diabetes, diarrhoea, dysentery, ear diseases, fracture, gonorrhoea, leprosy, sprain, wounds.

Fruit - Burning sensation, seminal weakness, tubercular ulcers.

Resin - Burns, diarrhoea, dysentery, fever, gonorrhoea, pruritus, ulcers, wounds.

Ethno- Medicinal uses: Bark - Diarrhoea (Kharkongor & Joseph, 1981; Nayak *et al.*, 2003); dysentery (Jain & De, 1966; Kharkongor & Joseph, 1981); Wounds (Bhalla *et. al.*, 1982; Saxena & Dutta, 1975; Nayak *et al.*, 2003); ulcers, seminal weakness (Nayak *et al.*, 2003).

Fruit - Diarrhoea (Jain, 1965; Nayak *et al.*, 2003); Dysentery (Gupta, 1981; Roy & Chaturvedi, 1986); loose motion (Jain, 1963; Negi *et. al.*, 1985; Sharma & Singh, 1988); ulcers, wound, seminal weakness (Nayak *et al.*, 2003).

Resin - Stomachache, chest pain (Saxena *et al.*, 1981; Islam & Jha, 2003); diarrhoea (Gupta, 1981; Upadhyay & Chauhan, 2003); gonorrhoea (Negi *et al.*, 1985; Kumar & Lal, 2003); dysentery (Roy & Chaturvedi, 1986; Negi *et al.*, 1985; Sharma *et al.*, 1979; Maheshwari *et al.*, 1980; Singh, 2003; Kumar & Lal, 2003); Skin diseases (Gaur *et al.*, 1980); toothache (Aditya *et al.*, 2006); indigestion (Kumar & Lal, 2003); ulcers, diarrhoea, wounds, seminal weakness (Nayak *et al.*, 2003); chest pain (Upadhyay & Chauhan, 2003).

Tender leaf - Diabetes (Ghosh, 2006).

Root- Contraception (Narain & Singh, 2006a).

Seed- Colic pain (Singh *et al.*, 1992).

SMILAX CHINA L. (LILIACEAE)

Regional and Other Names: *English* – China root; *Hindi* – Chopchini; *Kannada* –Cinipavu; *Malayalam* –Pavu; *Sanskrit* –Madhusnuhi; *Tamil*– Parankicekkai; *Telugu* – Parangicekka .

Distribution: In China & Japan.

Taxonomic description: A large woody extensive armed, tendril climber; leaves simple, stipulate; stipules are modified into tendrils.

Medicinal parts: Rhizome.

Taste : Bitter.

Chemical constituents: Root tuber contains Fat, sugar, gum, starch, saponin, glucosides, tannins, resin.

Medicinal properties:

वातव्याधीनपास्मारमुन्मादं तनुवेदनाम् ।
व्यपोहति विशेषेण फिरङ्.गामयनाशिनी ।। (भा. प्र.)

"Vātavyādhīnapāṣmāramuṇmādaṃ tanuvedanāṃ
Vyapohati viṣesena phiraṇgāmayanāṣinī." (Bhā. Pra.)

Rhizome - Acrid, anodyne, anti-inflammatory, anti-leprotic, aphrodisiac, carminative, depurative, digestive, laxative, rejuvenator, stimulant, stomachic, sudorific, thermogenic, tonic.

Medicinal uses: Rhizome - Dyspepsia, epilepsy, fever, flatulence, goiter, gout, kidney diseases, leoprosy, nervous diseases, paralysis, psoriasis, rheumatism, skin diseases, syphilis, tuberculosis, ulcers.

SOLANUM MELONGENA L. (SOLANACEAE)

Regional and Other Names: *Bengali* – Begoon; *English* – Brinjal, egg-plant; *Gujarati* – Ringana; *Hindi* – Baingan; *Kannada* – Badanekayi; *Malayalam* – Vazhuthana; *Marathi* – Vangi; *Sanskrit* – Vartaki; *Tamil* – Kathirikai; *Telugu* – Vankayachettu.

Distribution: Cultivated throughout India.

Taxonomic description: A herbaceous prickly perennial herb or undershrubs; flowers purple, solitary axillary; berries large green or purple, globular or obovate oblong.

Medicinal parts: Root, Leaves, Fruits, Seeds.

Taste: Acrid-Sweet.

Chemical constituents: Fruit - Arginine, aspartic acid, solanine, histidine, leucine, methionine, pipecolic acid, phenylalanine, theonine, tryptophan, valin, choline, nicotinic acid, riboflavin, vitamin A & C, fructose, glucose, sucrose, anthocyanin, lycoxanthin, caffic acid & chlorogenic acid.

Medicinal properties:

वार्त्ताकी कटुका रूच्या मधुरा पित्तनाशनी ।
बलपुष्टिकरी हृद्या गुरूर्वातेषु निन्दिता ।। (रा. नि.)

"Vāṛtākī katukā rucyā madhurā pittnāṣanī
Balapuṣtikarī hṛdyā guruṛvātesu niṇditā." (Rā. Ni.)

Root -Analgesic, cardiotonic, laxative.

Unripe fruit - Acrid, aphrodisiac, bitter, cardiotonic, sweet.

Leaves- Antiherpetic, narcotic.

Medicinal uses: Fruits - Liver diseases, rheumatism.

Leaves - Asthma, bronchitis, cholera, disuria, fever.

Roots - Asthma, cardiac debility, inflammation.

Ethno- Medicinal uses: Fruit stalk - Fistula, Piles (Tarafder, 1987).

Mature fruit- Stomach pain (Rajan *et al.,* 2003).

Leaf- Burns (Thomas & Britto, 2003).

SOYMIDA FEBRIFUGA A. Juss. (MELIACEAE)

Syn.: *Swietenia febrifuga* Roxb.

Regional and Other Names: *Bengali* – Rohan; *English* – Indian redwood tree; *Gujarati* –Rohani; *Hindi* – Rohan, Rohera; *Kannada* – Suani; *Marathi* – Rubin; *Sanskrit* – Mansarohini; *Tamil* – Shem̩; *Telugu* – Sumi.

Distribution: Common in the forests of Central India, Bihar and other hilly ares of Konkan and Khandesh on rocky soil.

Taxonomic description: A tall glabrous deciduous trees; flowers Greenish-White, in terminal or axillary panicles.

Medicinal parts: Bark.

Taste : Bitter.

Chemical constituents: Bark contains Bitter resinous substance, tannic acid, galic acid.

Medicinal properties:

स्यान्मांसरोहिणी वृष्यासरादोषत्रयापहा ।
रसे पाके तु कटुका तुवराशीतला च सा ।
शीता कषाया रूच्या च क्रिमिघ्नी कण्ठशोधिनी ।। (भा. प्र.)

"Ṣyāṇmānsarohiṇī vṛṣyā sarā dosaṭrayāpahā
Rase pāke tu katukā tuvarāṣītalā ca sā
Ṣītā kasāyā rucyā ca kṛimighnī kaṇthaṣodhiṇī." (Bhā. Pṛa.)

Aphrodisiac, astringent, bitter, cooling, febrifuge, nutritive, wound healing.

Medicinal uses: Chronic fever, diarrhoea, dysentery, malaria fever, skin diseases, throat diseases, wounds.

Ethno- Medicinal uses: Root - Abortifacient (Bhatt & Sabnis, 1987).

Bark - Cold (Sudhakar & Rolla, 1985); diarrhoea (Sudhakar & Rolla, 1985; Malhotra & Moorthy, 1973; Singh & Pandey 1980; Joshi *et. al.,* 1980; Sharma & Sharma, 1992); dysentery (Singh & Pandey, 1980; Sharma & Sharma, 1992); fever (Sudhakar & Rolla, 1985; Mudgal & Pal, 1980; Mitaliya & Bhatt, 2003); Sprain (Pandey & Rout, 2006); Rheumatism (Samvatsar & Diwanji, 2003); stomach pain, menstrual trouble (Prasad *et al.,* 2003); skin diseases (Mitaliya & Bhatt, 2003).

Gum - Blood pressure (Shah *et al.*, 1981).

Flowers - Dyspepsia (Jadeja *et al.*, 2006).

SPINACEA OLERACEA L. (CHENOPODIACEAE)

Regional and Other Names: *Bengali* – Palang; *English* – Spinach; *Hindi* – Palak; *Kannada* – Spinaksoppu; *Malayalam* – Basala cheera; *Marathi* – Palak; *Tamil* – Vasayleykeerai; *Telugu* – Palakoora.

Distribution: Cultivated in field during winter season throughout India.

Taxonomic description: A small erect annual herb. Leaves large, radical, cauline leaves smaller, becoming lanceolate in the inflorescence; staminate flowers in spikes or panicles; the pistillate clustered.

Medicinal parts: Whole plant, Leaves & Seeds.

Taste: Acrid-Sweet.

Chemical constituents: Vitamin-B-complex, ascorbic acid, carotene, vitamin K & A, thiamine, riboflavin, oxalate, nicotinic acid, folic acid, amino acids, histamines, acetylcholine, α-sitosterol, stigmasterol, cholesterol, flavin, petuletin, quercetin, rutin, saponin, catechol, lipid, iodine, lecithin.

Medicinal properties:

पलक्या वातला शीता श्लेष्मला भेदिनी गुरूः ।
विष्टम्भिनी मदश्वास्स पित्तरक्तकफापहा ।। (भा. पु.)

"Palakyā vātalā ṣītā ṣleṣmlā bhedinī guruḥ
Viṣtṃbhinī madṣvāspịttraktakaphāpahā" (Bhā. Pra.)

Anti-inflammatory, astringent, cooling, digestive, diuretic, emollient, expectorant, laxative, rejuvenator.

Medicinal uses: Asthma, calculii, constipation, gout, inflammation of lungs, intestinal troubles, jaundice, liver pain, respiratory troubles, tumours.

Ethno- Medicinal uses: Plant - Fever (Deokule, 2006).

STRYCHNOS NUX-VOMICA L. (STRYCHNACEAE)

Syn.: *Strychnos colubrina* Wight.

Regional and Other Names: *Bengali* – Kuchila; *English* – Nux vomica; *Gujarati* –Kuchala; *Hindi* – Kuchalaa; *Kannada* – Hemmusthti; *Malayalam* – Kariram; *Marathi* – Jharkatachura; *Sanskrit* – Karaskara; *Tamil* – Etti; *Telugu* – Mushti.

Distribution: Throughout India.

Taxonomic description: A middle sized deciduous trees offen with short spines; leaves lustrous; flowers greenish, in compound pubescent cymes; berries orange-red.

Medicinal parts : Root, Leaves, Seeds, Bark, Wood.

Taste: Bitter.

Chemical constituents: Fruits contain - Glucoside loganin.

Leaves & Roots contain - Brucine, Strychnine, Vomicine, methoxystrychnine.

Root - C-mavacurine.

Seeds - Isostrychnine.

Plant - Vanillic, P-hydroxybenzoic, 2-hydroxy-4-methoxybenzoic, sinapic, syringic acids; kaempferol, quercetin, 3'-O-methylquercetin.

Medicinal properties:

कुपीलु शीतलं तिक्तं वालंच मदकृल्लघुः ।
परं व्यवहारं ग्राहि कफपित्तस्त्रनाशनम् ।। (द्र. वि.)

"Kupīlu ṣītalaṃ tiktaṃ vālaṇca madakṛllaghuḥ.
Paraṃ vyathahāraṃ g̣rāhi kaphapiṭtaṣṭranāṣanaṃ." (Dra. Vi.)

Aphrodisiac, blood purifier, digestive, stimulant, stomachic, tonic.

Medicinal uses: Asthma, cardiac disorders, constipation, cough, dyspepsia, facial paralysis, lumbago, nervous disorders, rheumatism.

Ethno- Medicinal uses: Seed - Fever (Nagendra & Abraham, 1984); piles, paralysis, snake bite (Sen *et. al.,* 1983); skin diseases, eczema (Saxena & Dutta, 1975); rheumatism (Sen *et. al.,* 1983; Ganesan *et. al.,* 2006); Gastric trouble, dyspepsia (Pandey & Rout, 2006); cholera, anaemea, malaria fever, paralysis, asthma ulcers, seminal weakness (Nayak *et al.,* 2003); worm trouble (Thomas & Britto, 2003); diabetes, gonorrhoea, scorpion sting (Mitaliya & Bhatt, 2003).

Root - Syphilis, fever (Sen *et. al.,* 1983).

Bark - Stomachache (Trebedi *et. al.,* 1982); cholera, anaemea, malaria fever, paralysis, asthma ulcers, seminal weakness (Nayak *et al.,* 2003); dandruff (Prasad *et al.,* 2003); scorpion sting (Subramani & Goraya, 2003).

Leaf - Wound (Malhotra & Moorthy, 1973); paralysis, rheumatism (Sen *et. al.,* 1983); cholera, anaemea, malaria fever, paralysis, asthma ulcers, seminal weakness (Nayak *et al.,* 2003); dandruff (Prasad *et al.,* 2003).

Fruit - Dog bite (Naran & Singh, 2006).

SWERTIA CHIRAYITA (Roxb. ex Flem.) Kar. (GENTIANACEAE)

Syn.: *Swertia chirata* Buch.-Ham.; *S. tongluensis* Burkill.; *Gentiana chirayata* Roxb.; *S. chirata* (Wall.) Clarke.; *Ophelia chirata* Griseb.

Regional and Other Names: *Bengali* – Chirta; *English* – Chiretta; *Gujarati* –Chirayata ; *Hindi* – Chiraayata; *Kannada* – Nelabevu; *Malayalam* – Nilaveppa; *Marathi* – Chirayita; *Sanskrit* – Kirata; *Tamil* – Nila-vembu; *Telugu* – Nila-vembu.

Distribution: In Temperate Himalayas.

Taxonomic description: An erect annual herbs upto 1.5 m. tall, with opposite sessile leaves; flowers greenish with Purple tingue.

Medicinal parts - Whole plant.

Taste - Bitter.

Chemical constituents: Ophelic acid, chiratin, swertinin, swertianin, swerchirin, decussatin, isobellidifolin, friedelin, β-sitosterol.

Medicinal properties:

किरातः सारको रूक्षः शीतलस्तिक्तको लघुः ।
सन्निपातज्वरश्वास कफपित्तास्त्रदाहनुत् ।
कासशोथतृशाकुष्ठहरज्वर व्रणक्रिमिप्रणूत् ।। (भा. प्र.)

"Kirātaḥ sārako rukshaḥ ṣītalaṣtiktko laghuḥ
Saṇnipātajvaraṣvāsa kaphapiṭtāṣṛadāhanuṭ
Kāsaṣothaṭrsākuṣthajvar vṛaṇakṛimipṛaṇūṭ." (Bhā. Pṛa.)

Anthlemintic, appitiser, diuretic, febrifuge, laxative, stomachic.

Medicinal uses: Anaemia, asthma, cough, heart diseases, indigestion, jaundice, leprosy, leucoderma, malaria fever, menorrhagia, sabies, ulcers, urinary diseases.

Ethno- Medicinal uses: Whole plant - Skin diseases, fever (Shah & Joshi, 1971); Blood purifier (Shah & Joshi, 1971; Chhetri, 2005); chronic fever, bronchial asthma, debility, dyspepsia (Kumar & Lal, 2003); fever, stomachache (Sharma *et al.,* 2003).

Root - Fever (Gupta, 1981); leoprosy, leucoderma, scabies, skin diseases (Purohit *et. al.,* 1985).

Seeds - Gout (Jadeja *et al.,* 2006).

Fruit- Cold, fever (Kapur & Nanda, 1992).

TABERNAEMONTANA DIVARICATA (L.) R. Br. ex Roem. & Schult. (APOCYNACEAE)

Syn.: *E. coronaria* (Jacq.) Stapf.; *Ervatamia divaricata* (L.) Burkill.; *T. coronaria* (Jacq.) Willd.

Regional and Other Names: *Bengali* – Tagar; *English* – East India rosebay; *Gujarati* –Tager ; *Hindi* – Chandni, Tagara; *Kannada* – Kottuhale; *Malayalam* – Takaram, Nantiyavattam; *Marathi* –Tagar; *Sanskrit* – Tagar; *Tamil* – Nanthiarvattam, Kuruduppalai; *Telugu* – Nandivardhanamu, gandhitagarapu.

Distribution: Throughout India.

Taxonomic description: Glabrous shrubs or small trees, with oblong or obovate-lanceolate, acuminate leaves; flowers white, with about 5 cm. long follicles.

Medicinal parts: Root, Root-bark, Leaves, Stem-bark, Flowers, Wood, Milky juice.

Taste: Bitter.

Chemical constituents: Seed contains Citric, oleic, palmitic acid.

Leaves, Stem/Roots contain Dregamine, epiervatamine, tabernaemontaine, vobasine, voaconjine, voacamine, flavonoid, flavonol.

Flowers contain Janetine, hecubine, kampferol.

Stem bark contains α-Amyrin, lupeol, β-sitosterol, coronaridine, apparicine, ervaticine, ervatinine.

Latex contains Enzymes, amino acids, proteins, galactose.

Medicinal properties:

तगरं शीतलं तिक्तं दृष्टिदोषविनाशनम् ।
विशार्त्तिशमनं पथ्यं भूतोन्मादभयापहम् ।। (रा. नि.)

"Tagaraṃ ṣītalaṃ tiktaṃ dṛṣtidosa vināsanaṃ
Visāṛttiṣamanaṃ paṭḥyaṃ bhutoṇmādabhayāpahaṃ." (Rā. Ni.)

Root - Acrid, bitter, thermogenic, anodyne, astringent, vermifuge.

Flowers - Cooling, fragrant.

Latex - Cooling, fragrant.

Medicinal uses: Root - Paralysis, strangury.

Flowers - Burning sensation.

Latex - Wounds.

Ethno- Medicinal uses: Leaf - Boils (Kumar *et. al.,* 1987); fever, headache (Kharkongor & Joseph, 1981); swelling (Nath & Maiti, 2003).

Floral bud - Eye complaint (Shah *et. al.,* 1981; Ramachandran & Nair, 1981).

Latex - Eye complaint (Kumar *et. al.,* 1987).

Root - Jaundice (Pereira, 2006); toothache (Basak, 2006; Aditya *et al.,* 2006); scorpion sting (Shukla *et al.,* 2003).

Flower - Eye diseases (Sarma *et al.,* 2006).

TAGETUS ERECTA (L.) Willd. (ASTERACEAE)

Regional and Other Names: *Bengali* – Gendu; *English* – Marigold; *Gujarati* – Guljharo; *Hindi* – Zenddu; *Kannada* – Seemeshamantige; *Malayalam* – Chendumalli; *Marathi* – Zendu; *Sanskrit* – Jhandu; *Tamil* – Rojiachaphul; *Telugu* – Banti chettu.

Distribution: Native of France & Mexico; Cultivated throughout India.

Taxonomic description: A hairy erect annual herb, with pinnate leaves and yellow campanulate heads.

Medicinal parts: Leaves, Flowers.

Taste : Bitter.

Chemical constituents: Salicylic acid, calendulin, essential oil.

Medicinal properties:

झण्डुः कटुकषाया स्यातिक्ता शीता च वीर्यतः ।
कफपित्तप्रशमनं रक्तसांग्राहिकं परम् ।। (द्र. वि.)

"Jhaṇduḥ katukasaya ṣyatiḳta ṣīta ca. vīṛyataḥ
Kaphapiṭtapṛasmanaṃ raktsangṛahikaṃ paraṃ." (Dṛavyagunā)

Anti-inflammatory, antidote, antipyretic, astringent, diuretic.

Medicinal uses: Bleeding piles, earache, fever, inflammation, piles, menorrhagia, ulcers.

Ethno- Medicinal uses: Flowers - Earache (Rai, 1985); urinary complaint, cuts, wounds (Tarafder, 1987); piles (Mokat & Deokule, 2006; Deokule, 2006).

Leaves - To make silky hair (External application) (Jadeja *et al.,* 2006); earache (Shukla *et al.,* 1992; Kumar *et al.,* 2003); wound, cuts, tonsilitis (Dash *et al.,* 2003); check bleeding, boils, carbuncles (Islam & Hasin, 2003); allergy caused by insects (Singh & Singh, 2003).

TERAMNUS LABIALIS (L. f.) Spr. (PAPILIONACEAE)

Regional and Other Names: *Bengali* – Mashani; *English* – Wild udad; *Gujarati* – Valiyovela; *Hindi* – Masparni; *Sanskrit* – Ardramasha.

Distribution: Throughout India.

Taxonomic description: A climbing wide spreading hairy herb; leaves trifoliate, leaflets are of unequal size; flowers pink or bluish white..

Medicinal parts : Leaves, Fruits, Seeds.

Taste: Bitter.

Chemical constituents: Galactomannan, carbohydrates, sugars, amino acids, fatty acids, carotene, saponins, sapogenin, diosgenin, gitogenin, neogitogenin; Alkaloids, Saponeritin, neogigenin, tigogecnin, vicenin, vitexin, luteolin, yamogenin, furastanolglycosides, kaempfrol, quercetin.

Medicinal properties:

माषपर्णी सूर्यपर्णी काम्बोजी हयपुच्छिका ।
माण्डुलोमशपर्णी च कृष्णवृन्ता महासहा ।। (भा. प्र.)

"Māsparṇī sūryaparṇī kāṃbojī haypucchikā
māṇdulomasparṇī ca kṛiṣṇavṛiṇtā māhāsahā." (Bhā. Pṛa.)

Seeds - Aphrodisiac, astringent, carminative, demulcent, diuretic, tonic.

Medicinal uses: Seeds - Anaemia, colic, cough, diabetes, diarrhoea, dropsy, dysentery, rheumatism, rickets.

Ethno- Medicinal uses: Pod - Nervous disorders (Sudhakar & Rolla, 1985).

Plant- Rheumatism (Samvatsar & Diwanji, 2003).

TERMINALIA CRENULATA Roth.(COMBRETACEAE)

Regional and Other Names: *Bengali* –Asani; *English* –Black murdah; *Gujarati* –Hadri; *Hindi* – Asaina; *Kannada* – Asana; *Malayalam* – Karimarutu; *Marathi* – Madal; *Sanskrit* – Chagakarnah; *Tamil* – Karumarudu; *Telugu* – Nallamaddi.

Distribution: Throughout India.

Taxonomic description : A medium sized to large tree, with simple leathery leaves and winged fruits.

Medicinal parts : Bark.

Taste: Bitter.

Chemical constituents: Bark - B-sitosterol, arjunic acid, betulinic acid, ellagic acid, tannin.

Medicinal properties:

मद्ययोनि: कफहर: कषायो व्रणरोपण: ।
स्वेदापहो मलहर: क्रमिघ्नो हृयजकर्णक: ।। (म. नि.)

"Madyayoniḥ kaphaharaḥ kasāyo vṛaṇarōpaṇaḥ
Ṣvedāpaho malaharaḥ kṛimighno ḥyajakarṇakaḥ" (Ma. ni.)

Bark- Anthelmintic, astringent, bitter, cardiotonic, constipating, cooling, diuretic, expectorant, styptic, vulnerary.

Medicinal uses: Bark - Bronchitis, burning sensation, cough, diarrhoea, dysentery, gonorrhoea, haemorrhages, leucorrhoea, ulcers.

Ethno- Medicinal uses:

Bark - Diarrhoea, vomiting (Joshi *et al.,* 1980); Diuretic (Shah *et al.,* 1983); Diabetes (Bhatt *et al.,* 2003).

Stem/ Root- Diabetes (Bhatt *et al.,* 2003).

THESPESIA POPULNEA (L.) Soland. ex Correa. (MALVACEAE)

Syn.: *Hibiscus populnea* L.

Regional and Other Names: *Bengali* – Palaspipal; *English* –Portia tree; *Gujarati* – Paraspiplo; *Hindi* –Paraspipal; *Kannada* –Arasi; *Malayalam* – Puvarasu; *Marathi* –Paraspiper; *Sanskrit* – Haripucchah; *Tamil* – Puvarasamkalli; *Telugu* – Gangaravi.

Distribution: Throughout India.

Taxonomic description: Small evergreen trees, with yellow flowers and brown capsule fruits.

Medicinal parts: Bark, stem, leaves, root, fruit.

Taste: Bitter, Astringent.

Chemical constituents: Leaves contain Lupeol, lupenone, B-sitosterol.

Stem contains Calycopterin, sequiterpenoid quinones.

Fruits contains Thespesin, gossypol, populinin, populneol, herbacetin, populnetin, gossypectin, epoxyleic acid, isoquercitrin, rutin, B-sitosterol, thespesone.

Medicinal properties:

परीशो दुज्जरः स्निग्धः क्रिमिशुक्रकफप्रदः।
फलेम्लो मधुरो मूले कषायः स्वादुमज्जकः।। (द्र. वि.)

"Parīṣo durjjaraḥ ṣnigdhaḥ kṛimiṣukṛakaphapṛadaḥ
Phalemḷo madhurō mule kasāyaḥ ṣvādumajjakaḥ" (Dṛavyaguṇa)

Bark - Alterative, antidiabetic, antidysenteric, astringent, cooling, diuretic.

Leaves - Anti-inflammatory, antipyretic, astringent, cephalalgic.

Root - Anti-inflammatory, antiscorbutic, antiseptic, sweet.

Fruit - anticancer, antifertility, antimalaria, antitumour, antiviral.

Medicinal uses: Bark - Cough, diabetes, dysentery, dyspepsia, gonorrhoea, headache, itching, influenza, indigestion, psoriasis, typhoid, ulcers.

Leaves - Cough, eczema, fever, headache, inflammations, influenza, psoriasis, scabies.

Root - Inflammations, psoriasis, scabies.

Fruit - Cancer, eczema, malaria, migrain, scabies, psoriasis, ringworm, tumours.

Ethno- Medicinal uses: Leaves-Scabies (Nagendra Prasad & Abraham, 1984); skin diseases, scabies (Deokule, 2006); sore (Nadanakunjidam, 2003).

Fruits - Skin diseases ((Shah *et al.,* 1981; Shah, 1984); skin diseases, scabies (Deokule, 2006); wound, boils (Bhatt *et al.,* 2003).

Bark- Wound, boils (Bhatt *et al.,* 2003); scabies (Sivakumar *et al.,* 2003).

THEVETIA PERUVIANA (Pers.) Schum. (APOCYNACEAE)

Syn.: *T. nerifolia* Juss. ex Steud.; *Cascabela thevetia* (L.) Lipp.

Regional and Other Names: *Bengali* – Koklaphul; *English* – Yellow oleander; *Gujarati* –Pilokaner; *Hindi* – Pili kaner; *Kannada* – Kadukasi; *Malayalam* – Manja areli; *Marathi* – Pilwalakanher; *Sanskrit* – Pitapuspa; *Tamil* – Tiruvachippu; *Telugu* – Pachagannera.

Distribution: Throughout India.

Taxonomic description: A large evergreen shrub or small trees, with linear leaves, yellow flowers and subglobose fruits.

Medicinal parts: Root, Leaves, Bark, Kernel, Seeds, Latex.

Taste: Bitter.

Chemical constituents: Seeds contain - Theveside, viridoside, thevefolin, thevetin, thevetoxin, peruvoside, ruvoside.

Flowers & Fruits contain - Epiperuviol acetate, α - & β – amyrin, kaempferol, quercetin, glycoside- thevetin & other thevetoxin.

Medicinal properties:

पाटजिकातिशीता स्यात् श्लेश्मवातशिरोऽतिनुत् ।। (कै. नि.)

"Pātjikātiṣītā ṣyāṭ ṣleṣhmavātaṣiroatinuṭ." (Kaī. Ni.)

Antipyretic, cardiotonic, diuretic, febrifuge.

Medicinal uses: Bark - Dropsy, oedema, rheumatism.

Ethno- Medicinal uses: Seed - Skin diseases (Maheshwari *et al.,* 1986); Rheumatism (Samvatsar & Diwanji, 2003).

Latex - Psoriasis (Ganesan *et al.,* 2006).

Plant- Bronchitis, skin diseases, piles, worms, wounds (Mukhopadhyay, 1992).

TRAPA BISPINOSA (Roxb.) Makino. (TRAPACEAE)

Syn.: *T. quadrispinosa* Wall.; *T. natans* L. var. *bispinosa* (Roxb.) Makino.

Regional and Other Names: *Bengali* – Pani-phal; *English* – Water chestnut; *Hindi* – Singaadha; *Kannada* – Singhara; *Malayalam* – Karimpolam; *Marathi* – Singarha; *Sanskrit* – Srngataka; *Tamil* – Singhara; *Telugu* – Kubyakama.

Distribution: Throughout India.

Taxonomic description: An aquatic floating herbs; leaves of two kinds; submerged opposite pectinate; floating clustered, rhomboid, red and villous beneath; petioles inflated purple, solitary; fruits 2-horned.

Medicinal parts: Seeds.

Taste : Sweet/Astringent.

Chemical constituents: Fruit contains - Citric acid, tannin, amylose, amylopectin, carbohydrates, β-amylase, phosphorylase enzymes, protein, fat, nicotinic acid, riboflavin, thiamine, vitamine A & C, mangenese.

Medicinal properties:

शृंड.गाटकं हिमं स्वादु गुरू वृष्यं कशायकम् ।
ग्राहि शुक्रानिलश्लेश्मप्रदं दाहास्त्रपित्तनुत् ।। (भा. प्र.)

"Ṣṛgātakaṃ himaṃ svādu guru vṛṣyaṃ kasāyakaṃ
Gṛāhi ṣukṛānilaṣleṣmarpṛadaṃ dāhāṣṛapiṭtanuṭ." (Bhā. Pṛa.)

Anti-inflammatory, astringent, refrigerant, stomachic, tonic.

Medicinal uses: Fruits - Diarrhoea, leucorrhoea, seminal weakness.

Ethno- Medicinal uses: Seed - Gonorrhoea (Singh & Pandey, 1998; Kumar *et al.,* 2003); bronchitis, cough, dropsy (Jain & Tarafder, 1970); stomachic (Srivastava *et al.,* 2003); Backache, lumbago (Mitaliya *et al.,* 2003).

Fruit rind-·Backache, lumbago (Mitaliya *et al.*, 2003).

Fruit- Chronic, fevers, lumbago, pain, biliousness, bronchitis (Gogoi & Das, 2003); sexual debility (Bhatt *et al.*, 2003).

TRICHOSANTHES DIOICA Roxb. (CUCURBITACEAE)

Regional and Other Names: *Bengali* – Potol; *English* – Pointed gourd, sespadula; *Gujarati* – Potala; *Hindi* – Parwal; *Kannada* – Kaadupadavala; *Malayalam* – Patolam; *Marathi* – Parwar; *Sanskrit* – Patola; *Tamil* – Kombupudalai; *Telugu* – Kommupotla.

Distribution: Throughout India.

Taxonomic description: A dioecious climber with a perennial rootstock; leaves cordate-ovate, acute, sinuate dentate; flowers white; fruits smooth, spherical, oblong, green streaked, obtuse at both ends.

Medicinal parts: Whole plant.

Taste: Bitter.

Chemical constituents: Root contains - Amorphous saponin, hentriacontane, essential oil, fixed oil.

Medicinal properties:

पटोली बालकृत्स्वादुः पथ्या दीपन पाचनी ।
रूच्या पुष्टिकरी ज्ञेया वातपित्त ज्वरापहा ।। (नि. र.)

"Patolī balakṛtṣvāduḥ paṭhyā dīpana pācanī
Rucyā puṣtikarī jneyā vātapiṭta jvarāpahā." (Ni. Ra.)

Fruits - Antipyretic, expectorant, laxative.

Leaves - Aphrodisiac, appetizer, digestive, febrifuge, stomachic.

Root - Purgative.

Seeds - Anthelmintic, antipyretic, stomachic.

Medicinal uses: Fruits - Fever, jaundice, leprosy, pruritus.

Seeds - Fever, helminthiasis.

Leaves - Blood purifier.

Ethno- Medicinal uses: Fruits - Boils (Tarafder, 1984); spermatorrhoea (Bhalla *et. al.,* 1982); Diabetes (Ghosh & Das, 2003); cancer like conditions (Srivastava *et al.,* 2003).

TRIGONELLA FOENUM-GRACEUM L. (PAPILIONACEAE)

Syn.: *Trifolium foenum-graceum; Foenum-graceum* officinale.

Regional and Other Names: *Bengali* – Methi; *English* – Fenugreek; *Gujarati* – Methi; *Hindi* – Methee; *Kannada* – Menthe; *Malayalam* – Venthiam; *Marathi* – Methi; *Sanskrit* – Methika; *Tamil* – Vendayam; *Telugu* – Mentulu.

Distribution: Cultivated throughout India.

Taxonomic description: An aromatic, erect, annual herbs with 3-foliate leaves and pale yellow flowers in axils of young leaves; pods 8-10 cm. long, with long beak.

Medicinal parts: Seeds.

Taste: Bitter.

Chemical constituents: *Seed contains* - Quercetin, luteolin, trigonelline, choline, nicotinic acid, fixed oil, essential oil, mucilage, bitter extractive, colouring matter, 2 steroidal saponins.

Medicinal properties:

मेथिका कटुरूष्या च रक्तपित्त प्रकोपनी ।
अरोचकहरा दीप्तिकरा वातघ्न दीपनी ।। (रा. नि.)

"Methikā katuruṣyā ca raktapiṭta p̣rakopinī
Arocakaharā dīptikarā vātaghnadīpanī." (Ra. Ni.)

Seeds - Anti-inflammatory, anaphrodisiac, aromatic, astringent, bitter, carminative, diuretic, emollient, stomachic, thermogenic, tonic.

Medicinal uses: Seeds - Bronchitis, cough, dropsy, epilepsy, fever, gout, paralysis, vomiting.

Ethno- Medicinal uses: Seeds - Carminative, gas trouble (Shah *et. al.,* 1984); piles (Saxena & Vyas, 1986); dyspepsia, dysentery (Jadeja *et al.,* 2006); diarrhoea, dysentery (Kataria & Gauchan, 2006); diabetes (Ghosh, 2006; Manandhav, 2003); rheumatism (Shah *et. al.,* 1984; Saxena & Vyas, 1986;

Kumar *et al.*, 2006; Mitaliya *et al.*, 2003); swelling (Deokule, 2006); arthritis, gout (Mitaliya *et al.*, 2003); indigestion (Manandhav, 2003).

Whole plant- Chronic, rheumatism, oral contraceptive, spondylitis (Kumar *et al.*, 2003).

TYLOPHORA INDICA (Burm. f.) Merr. (ASCLEPIADACEAE)

Syn.: *T. asthmatica* (Linn. F.) Wight. & Arn.

Regional and Other Names: *Bengali* – Antomul; *English* – Indian ipecacuanha; *Hindi* – Antmula; *Kannada* – Adumutadhagida; *Malayalam* – Vallipaala; *Marathi* – Khodikiraasna; *Sanskrit* – Antamula; *Tamil* – Nachchuruppam; *Telugu* – Verripaala.

Distribution: Throughout India.

Taxonomic description: A twining perennial shrubs; stems smooth; leaves opposite, 5-10 cm. long, thick, slightly hairy beneath; flowers in racemose cymes, greenish yellow, purple near base; follicles 5-10 cm. long.

Medicinal parts: Leaves, Root.

Taste: Bitter.

Chemical constituents: Leaves contain - Triterpene, α-amyrin, flavonoids, alkaloids: tylophorine, tylophoridine; wax, resin, tannin, glucose, calcium salts, potassium, chloride, essential oil.

Medicinal properties:

लताक्षीरी तु मधुरा विपाके कटुका स्मृता ।

"Latāksirī tu madhurā vipāke katukā ṣmrtā"

Acrid, anti-inflammatory, aromatic, blood purifier, carminative, diaphoretic, emetic, expectorant, stimulant, stomachic, sweet.

Medicinal uses: Roots & Leaves - Asthma, bronchitis, diarrhoea, dysentery, dyspepsis, flatulence, rheumatism, ulcers, whooping cough, wounds.

Ethno- Medicinal uses: Leaf - Asthma (Sudhakar & Rolla, 1985; Ganesan *et. al.*, 2006; Deokule, 2006; Rosakutty *et al.*, 2003; Bhatt *et al.*, 2003; Nayak *et al.*, 2003); backache (Jain, 1997); whooping cough, bronchitis (Nayak *et al.*, 2003; Bhatt *et al.*, 2003).

Whole plant - Wound (Chaudhuri *et. al.,* 1977); emetic & expectorant (Basak, 2006).

Stem- Backache (Jain, 1997).

Root- whooping cough, bronchitis, asthma (Nayak *et al.,* 2003).

URARIA PICTA Desv. (PAPILIONACEAE)

Syn.: *Hedysarum pictum* Jacq.

Regional and Other Names: *Bengali* – Sankarjata; *Gujarati* – Pitwan; *Hindi* – Pithwan; *Marathi* –Pitvan; *Sanskrit* – Pristhiparni; *Tamil* – Sittirappaladai.

Distribution: Throughout India.

Taxonomic description: An erect, little-branched perennial undershurbs; upper leaflets white-clouded; flowers purple; pods white or greyish, polished.

Medicinal parts: Whole plant.

Taste: Bitter, Sweet.

Chemical constituents: 5-hydroxy-7, 4-dimithoxy flavonol & 5 other flavonoids.

Medicinal properties:

पृश्निपर्णी त्रिदोषघ्नीवृष्योष्णा मधुरा सरा ।
हन्तिदाहज्वरश्वास रक्तातिसारतृड.वमीः ।। (भा. प्र.)

"Pṛṣniparṇī ṭridosaghnī vṛṣyoṣṇā madhurā sarā
Haṇtidāhajvaraṣvāsa raktātisāratudvamīḥ." (Bhā. Pra.)

Antibiotic, anti-inflammatory, alterative, carminative, stomachic, tonic.

Medicinal uses: Bleeding piles, burning sensation, cough, diarrhoea, intermittent fever, rheumatism, ulcer.

Ethno- Medicinal uses: Root - Bodyache, snake bite, vomiting, abdominal pain (Joshi *et. al.,* 1980); snake bite (Jain *et. al.,* 1973; Jain & Tarafder, 1963; Bhalla *et al.,* 1992); fever (Saxena, 1986; Bhalla *et al.,* 1992; Kumar & Lal, 2003); Bleeding piles (Bhalla *et al.,* 1992); cough, gonorrhoea (Kumar & Lal, 2003).

VETIVERIA ZIZANIOIDES (L.) Nash. (POACEAE)

Syn.: *Andropogon muricatus* Retz.

Regional and Other Names: *Bengali* – Khas-Khas; *English* – Vetiver, Kahs-Khas grass; *Gujarati* – Valo; *Hindi* – Khas-Khas; *Kannada* – Vattiveeru; *Malayalam* – Ramaccham; *Marathi* – Vala; *Sanskrit* – Usira; *Tamil* – Vettiver; *Telugu* – Kuruveeru.

Distribution: Throughout India.

Taxonomic description: A densely tufted, erect perennial aromatic grasses; sessile spikelets awnless; yellow scabrous when mature.

Medicinal parts: Roots.

Taste: Bitter, Sweet.

Chemical constituents: Root contains - Essential oil, resin, acidic substance, iron, calcium, salts, citronellal, geraniol, terpene, Lignin.

Medicinal properties:

उशीरं पाचनं शीतं स्तंभनं लघु तिक्तकम् ।
मधुरं ज्वरह्द्वान्तिमदजित् कफपित्तनुत् ।। (भा. प्र.)

"Uṣīraṃ pācanaṃ ṣītaṃ ṣtaṃbhanaṃ laghu tiktakaṃ
Madhuraṃ jvrāhrd vantimadajiṭ kaphapiṭtanuṭ." (Bhā. Pṛa.)

Roots - Acrid, anthelmintic, aromatic, bitter, carminative, digestive, diuretic, expectorant, febrifuge, refrigerant, stimulant, stomachic, styptic, sweet.

Medicinal uses: Roots - Anaemia, asthma, burning sensation, colic, dyspepsia, fever, hiccough, leprosy, menorrhagia, skin diseases, ulcers, vomiting.

Ethno- Medicinal uses: Root - Headache (Chaudhuri & Pal, 1978; Molla & Pal. 1992; Dwivedi, 2003); toothache (Chaudhuri & Pal, 1978; Molla & Pal. 1992); malaria fever (Singh & Mahehwari, 1983; Sharma *et. al.,* 1979; Kumar *et al.,* 2003); Rheumatism (Kumar & Chauhan, 2005; Samvatsar & Diwanji, 2003); burning sensation, ulcers, diseases of blood (Mukhopadhyay, 1992); sore throat, cough, cold (Molla & Pal. 1992);. dysuria (Sattapathy & Brahmam, 2003); eye infection (Kumar *et al.,* 2003); abdominal pain for childern (Thomas & Britto, 2003).

Seed - Dandruff (External application) (Jadeja *et al.,* 2006).

Root oil- Abdominal pain, gas problem, vomiting (Srivastava & Singh, 2006).

VIOLA ODORATA L. (VIOLACEAE)

Syn.: *Viola suavis* Bixb.; *V. imberbis* Leighton.; *V. alba* Besser.

Regional and Other Names: *Bengali* – Banosa; *English* – Sweet viola; *Gujarati* – Banaphsa; *Hindi* – Banafshah, vanfsa; *Kannada* – Violethoo; *Malayalam* – Vayi; *Marathi* – Bagabanosa; *Sanskrit* – Banapsika; *Tamil* – Vialettu.

Distribution: Kashmir; Planted in many hill stations.

Taxonomic description: A small, pubescent perennial herb with perennial stock; leaves cordate, pubescent, arising from root stock; flowers zygomorphic and purple in colour, spurred.

Medicinal parts: Whole plant, Flowers.

Taste : Sweet.

Chemical constituents: Flower contains - Volatile oil, cyanin, glycoside, sugar.

Leaves contain - Essential oil, alkaloid, colouring matter, friedelin, β-sitosterol.

Medicinal properties:

बनफ्सा कटुतिक्तोष्णा शीतज्वरनिवारणी ।
कासश्वासहरा त्वच्या सरा वातकफापहा ।। (द्र. वि.)

"Banfsā katutiktoṣṇā ṣītjwarniwārṇī
Kāsaṣvāsharā tvachyā sarā vātakaphāpahā." (Dṛa. Vi.)

Anti-inflammatory, blood purifier, carminative, cooling, diaphoretic, expectorant, febrifuge, laxative.

Medicinal uses: Catarrh, constipation, cough.

Ethno- Medicinal uses: Flowers - Headache (Dar *et. al.,* 1984; Kapur & Nanda, 1992); purgative, throat infection (Virjee *et. al.,* 1984; Beigh *et al.,* 2003); fever, cough, throatache (Ara & Naqshi, 1992); cold (Ara & Naqshi, 1992; Kapur & Nanda, 1992).

Leaf - Throatache (Dar *et. al.,* 1984; Beigh *et al.,* 2003); toothache (Kapur & Nanda, 1992).

Whole plant- Cough, cold, intermittent fever (Singh, 2003).

VITIS VINIFERA Dunal. (VITACEAE)

Regional and Other Names: *Bengali* – Angurphal; *English* – Grape vine; *Gujarati* –Darakh; *Hindi* – Angura, dakh; *Kannada* – Draksha; *Malayalam* – Muntiringa; *Marathi* – Draksha; *Sanskrit* – Draksa; *Tamil* – Munthiryvally; *Telugu* – Draksha.

Distribution: Cultivated throughout India.

Taxonomic description : A large, deciduous, climber with long bifid tendrils.

Medicinal parts: Fruits, Leaves.

Taste: Sweet-Astringent.

Chemical constituents: Fruits contain - Gum, tannin, grape-sugar, citric, racemic, mali acids; chlorides of potassium & sodium, sulphate of potash, tartarate of lime, mangnesia, alulm, iron.

Medicinal properties:

द्राक्षातिमधुराम्ला च शीता पित्तार्तिदाहजित् ।
मूत्रदोषहरा रूच्या वृष्या सन्तर्पर्णा परा ।। (रा. नि.)

"Drāksāti mahurāmlā ca ṣītā piṭtāṛti dāhajiṭ
Muṭradosaharā rucyā vṛṣyā saṇtaṛpaṛṇa parā." (Rā. Ni.)

Fruits - Appitiser, cardiotonic, depurative, digestive, diuretic, emollient, expectorant, febrifuge, laxative, nervine tonic, nutritive, refrigerant, stomachic, sweet, tonic.

Medicinal uses: Fruits - Anaemia, asthma, blood pressure, bronchitis, burning sensation, cough, fever, flatulence, general debility, jaundice, kidney diseases, leprosy, liver diseases, skin diseases, vertigo.

Ethno- Medicinal uses: Leaf - Boils, toothache (Dar *et. al.,* 1984).

Fruits - Epilepsy (Tiwari *et. al.,* 1979).

WRIGHTIA TINCTORIA (Roxb.) R. Br. (APOCYNACEAE)

Syn.: *W. rothii* G. Don.; *Nerium tinctorium* Roxb.

Regional and Other Names: *Bengali* – Kurchi; *English* – Sweet indrajao; *Gujarati* –Indarjou; *Hindi* – Indrajau, Kutaj; *Kannada* – Kodamurki; *Malayalam* – Kotakappalla; *Marathi* – Kala kuda; *Sanskrit* – Indrayava; *Tamil* – Veypale; *Telugu* – Reppalu.

Distribution: Throughout India.

Taxonomic description: A small tree with glabrous young parts; leaves elliptic-oblong; flowers in lax, terminal corymbose, dichotomous cymes. Fruits follicles. Seeds with a tuft of hairs at the base.

Medicinal parts: Root, Leaves, Bark, Seed.

Taste: Bitter.

Chemical constituents: Seed contains - Fixed oil.

Bark - β-sitosterol, β-amyrin, lupeol benzoate.

Medicinal properties:

इन्द्रयवा कटुस्तिक्ता शीता कफवातरक्तपित्तहरा ।
दाहातिसारशमनी नानाज्वरदोषशूलमूलघ्नी ।। (रा. नि.)

"Indrayavā katuṣtiktā ṣītā kaphavātaraktapittaharā
Dāhātisāraṣamanī nānānjvaradosaṣūlamūlaghnī." (Rā. Ni.)

Bark & Seeds - Acrid, anthelmintic, antipyretic, aphrodisiac, astringent, bitter, carminative, digestive, stomachic, thermogenic.

Leaves - Acrid, anodyne, thermogenic.

Medicinal uses: Bark & Seeds - Burning sensation, colic, diarhroea, dropsy, dysentery, fever, flatulence, helminthiasis, leprosy, psoriasis.

Leaves - Hypertension.

Ethno- Medicinal uses: Leaf - Throat pain, toothache, asthma (Shah *et. al.,* 1983); Psoriasis, eczema (Ganesan *et. al.,* 2006); jaundice (Kothari & Londhe, 2003); eczema (Ganesan & Kesavan, 2003).

Bark - Bronchitis, abdominal pain (Joshi *et. al.,* 1980); piles (Malhotra & Moorthy, 1973); liver disorders (Kothari & Rao, 2003); skin diseases, tonic

(Kothari & Londhe, 2003; Srivastava *et al.,* 2003); constipation (Singh, 2003); flatulence, worms, colic (Bhatt *et al.,* 2003).

Latex - Wounds (Shah *et. al.,* 1983; Joshi *et. al.,* 1980; Goel & Mudgal, 1988).

Leaves - Toothache, skin diseases (Sasidharan & Augustine, 2006); swelling (Rajendra & Rengaswami, 2006); asthma, toothache (Kothari & Rao, 2003).

Seed- Liver disorders (Kothari & Rao, 2003); stomach disorders (Kothari & Londhe, 2003); promote sexual desire (Srivastava *et al.,* 2003); flatulence, worm, colic (Bhatt *et al.,* 2003).

ZANTHOXYLUM ARMATUM DC. (RUTACEAE)

Syn.: *Z. alatum* Roth.

Regional and Other Names: *Bengali* –Tambul; *English* –Toothache tree; *Hindi* –Tumru; *Kannada* –Tumburudu; *Malayalam* –Tumpunal; *Sanskrit* –Tumburuh; *Tamil* – Tumpunalu; *Telugu* – Gandhalu

Distribution: In the Himalayas upto 2,100m and in Andhra Pradesh upto 1,350m.

Taxonomic description: A shrub or small tree, armed with stout prickles. Leafless 2-6 pairs, gland-dotted, petoiles narrowly winged. Flowers yellow, in loose panicles. Fruit drupe, pale red.

Medicinal parts: Bark, Fruits.

Taste: Bitter, Acrid.

Chemical constituents: Stem bark - Dictamnine.

Fruits - Essential oil (Wartara oil), a source of linalool.

Medicinal properties:

तुम्बुरूः कटुतीक्ष्णोष्णः कफवातशूलजित् ।
अपतन्त्रोदराध्मान कृमिघ्नो वह्निदीपनः ।। (ध. नि.)

"Tumburuḥ katutīksnoṣṇāḥ kaphavātaṣūlajịt
Apatantrodarādhmāna krmighno vahnidīpanaḥ " (Dha. ni.)

Bark and Fruit - Acrid, anthelmintic, antiseptic, aromatic, bitter, carminative, constipating, depurative, digestive, febrifuge, liver tonic, stimulant, stomachic, sudorific, tonic.

Medicinal uses: Bark anf Fruit - Asthma, cardiac debility, colic, cough, diabetes, diarrhoea, dyspepsia, fever, general debility, gout, helminthiasis, leprosy, leucoderma, paralysis, skin diseases, strangury, tumours.

Ethno- Medicinal uses: Seed - Toothache (Shah & Joshi, 1971; Chhetri, 2005); Piles, cough (Malhotra & Balodi, 1984); anthelmintic (Uniyal, 1968); itching, eczema, leucoderma (Purohit *et al.,* 1985); indigestion, stomachache (Singh *et al.,* 1985).

Fruits - Cough (Malhotra & Balodi, 1984; Arya & Ved Prakash, 2003); Toothache (Singh *et al.,* 1980); cold (Arya & Ved Prakash, 2003).

Bark - Fever, stomachache (Chhetri, 2005); Cholera, fever (Singh *et al.,* 1985); small pox (Kumar *et al.,* 1980).

Root - Snake bite (Jain *et al.,* 1973).

Twigs- Mouth, gum, teeth diseases (Singh, 2003).

ZEA MAYS L. (POACEAE)

Regional and Other Names: *Bengali* –Bhutta; *English* –Corn; *Hindi* –Makka; *Kannada* –Musukojola; *Malayalam* –Colam; *Sanskrit* –Makayah; *Tamil* – Makkaccolam; *Telugu* –Mokkajonnalu.

Distribution: Cultivated throughout India.

Taxonomic description: Monoecious annuals. Male spikelets usually in terminal racemes, white. Female inflorescence consists many spikelets seated on a spongy axis.

Medicinal parts: Grains.

Taste : Sweet, Astringent.

Chemical constituents: Grain - Starch fructose, fucose, sucrose, raffinose, vitamin B, C, E, K; carotene, maysin, sorbitol, zeanin.

Medicinal properties:

मकायस्तु महाकायो करिजः काण्डजः स्मृतः ।
शिखालुः संपुटान्तस्थो यवनाळसमो गुणैः ।। (भा. प्र.)

"Makāyastu mahākāyo karijaḥ kānajaḥ smṛtaḥ
Ṣikhāluḥ saṃputāṇtastho yavanālasamo gunaiḥ " (Bha. Pra.)

Grain - Appetiser, astringent, diuretic, nutritious, sweet.

Medicinal uses: Grain - Anorexia, general debility, haemorrhoids, stangury.

Ethno- Medicinal uses: Grain - Stomachcahe (Lal & Yadav, 1983); piles (Kumar & Yadav, 2006); tuberculosis (Srivastava & Singh, 2006).

Inflorescence - Kidney trouble (Vir jee *et al.,* 1984); whooping cough (Ved Prakash & Mehrotra, 1988).

Styles - Diseases of kidney and bladder (Kumar & Yadav, 2006).

Male flower- Asthma (Srivastava & Singh, 2006).

GLOSSARY OF MEDICAL TERMS

Abortifacient	an agent that induces abortion
Acrid	biting, pungent
Adenitis	inflammation of a gland or group of glands (or glandlike structures)
Agalactia	absence or failure of secretion of milk
Alexipharmic	antidote to poison
Alexiteric	protective to infectious diseases
Alopecia	loss of hair: a malady in which the hair falls from one or more circumscribed round or oval areas, leaving the skin smooth and white
Alterative	causing a favourable change in the disordered functions of the body or metabolism
Amenorrhoea	failure of menstruation
Amentia	an arrest of the development of the mind from birth to early age
Anaemia	lack of enough blood causing paleness
Analgesic	an anodyne
Anaphrodisiac	having the power to lessen or inhibit sexual feeling
Anodyne	a medicine that allays pain
Anorexia	a condition of having lost the appetite for food
Anthelmintic	destroying or expelling worms
Antibacterial	active against bacteria
Antidote	an agent which neutralises or opposes the action of a poison
Anti-inflammatory	acting against inflammation
Anti-leprotic	any agent which prevents or cures leprosy

Antilithic	an agent which prevents the formation of calculi
Anti-periodic	preventing the regular recurrence of a disease
Antipyretic	counteracting fever
Antiscorbutic	acting against scurvy
Anti-septic	a chemical sterilising substance to kill or control pathogenic microbes
Antispasmodic	opposing Spasms
Anuria	failure of the kidneys to produce urine
Aperient	A laxative
Aphrodisiac	drug which stimulates sexual desire
Areata	ocurring in circumscribed areas or patches
Arthritis	inflammation of joints
Ascities	an abnormal accumulation of a fluid in the peritoneal cavity
Astringent	a drug which contracts the organic tissues & canals of the body, & therby checking or deminishing bleeding of excessive discharges
Azoospermia	the comlete absence of sperm from the seminal fluid
Baldness	absence of hair from areas where it normally grows
Beriberi	a deficiency disease caused by imbalance of carbohydrate and vitamin B
Biliousness	a symptom complex comprising nausea
Boil	tender inflamed area of the skin containing pus
Bronchitis	inflammation of the bronchi
Bronchodilator	an agent that causes widening of the air passages by relaxing bronchial smooth muscle
Bubo	an inflammatory swelling of a lymph gland
Calculi	a hard pebble-like mass formed within the body, particularly in the gall bladder or anywhere in the urinary tract
Cancer	the abnormal and uncontrolled division of cells that then invade and destroy the surrounding tissues
Carbuncle	an infection of the skin and subcutaneous tissue by Staphylococcus aureus

Carminative	drug curing flatulence
Catarrh	inflammation of a mucous membrane
Cathartic	having the power of cleansing the bowels- purgative
Cephalagia	headache
Cephalic	a remedy for disorders of the head
Cholera	a severe infectious epidemic disease due to Vibrio cholerae
Chronic bronchitis	the patient coughs up excessive mucus secreted by enlarged bronchial mucous glands
Conjunctivitis	inflammation of conjunctiva
Colic	a severe spasmodic griping pain
Consumption	pulmonary tuberculosis
Contraceptive	drug which prevents unwanted pregnancy
Convulsion	a violent involuntry contraction of the skeletal musculature
Cystitis	inflammation of a bladder, especially the urinary bladder
Dandruff	dead scarf-skin seperating in small scales and entangled in the hair
Deafness	partial or total loss of hearing in one or both ears
Demulcent	soothing
Depurative	an agent that purifies the blood
Diabetes	here it refers to diabetes mellitus: a disorder of carbohydrate metabolism in which sugars in the body are not oxidized to produce energy due to lack of the pancreatic hormone-insulin. The accumulation of sugar leads to its appearance in the blood
Diaphoretic	a drug which induces perspiration
Diarrhoea	frequent bowel evacuation or the passage of abnormally soft or liquid faeces
Diptheria	a specific infectious disease caused by virulent strains of a bacillus
Diuretic	promoting the discharge of urine
Dropsy	an excessive accumulation of a clear or watery fluid in any of the tissues or cavities of the body

Dysentery	an infection of the intestinal tract causing severe diarrhoea with blood and mucus
Dysmenorrhoea	painful menstruation
Dysopia	defective vision
Dyspepsia	indigestion
Dysuria	difficulty or pain while passing urine
Earache	pain in the ear
Eczema	a noncontagious inflammatory disease of the skin with much itching and burning
Elephantiasis	gross lymphatic oedema of the limbs leading to hypertrophy
Emetic	causing vomiting
Emollient	softening
Epilepsy	an affection of the nervous system resulting from excessive or disordered discharge of cerebral neurons
Eruptions	the outbreak of a rash
Erysipelsa	an inflammatory disease generally on the face marked by a bright redness of the skin
Expectorant	aiding the secretion of the mucous membrane of the air passages & the removal of fluid by spitting
Fatigue	mental or physical tiredness, following prolonged or intense activity
Febrifuge	that which drives off fever
Fever	a rise in body temperature above the normal
Fistula	an open channel from the anus or rectum to the skin near the anus
Flatulence	distention of stomach
Foetid	bad-smelling, fetid
Gleet	chronic discharge of thin mucus from the vagina
Goitre	enlargement of the thyroid gland
Gonorrhoea	an inflammatory disease of the urinogenital passagaes characterised by pain and discharge

Gout	a disease of purine metabolism characterised by attacks of arthritis with an associated raised level of serum uric acid
Haematemesis	vomitting of blood
Haematinic	any substance which is required for the production of RBCs & its constituents
Haemoptysis	spitting of blood
Haemorrhage	the escape of blood from a ruptured blood vessel, externally or internally
Haemorrhagic diseases	associated with or resulting from blood loss
Haemostatic	styptic
Hallucination	a false perception of something that is not really there
Headache	pain felt deep within the skull
Helminthiasis	morbid state due to infestation with worms
Helminthic	Anthelmintic, vermifugal
Hemicrania	headache confined to one side
Hepatomegaly	enlargement of the liver
Hiccough	abrupt involuntary lowering of the diaphragm and closure of the sound-producing folds at the upper end of the trachea, producing a characteristic sound as the breath is drawn in
Hydrocele	a circumscribed collection of fluid in the tunica vaginalis testis
Hydrophobia	exaggerated fear of water as in rabies
Hypertension	high arterial blood pressure
Hysteria	a neurotic disorder with varying symptoms
Impotency	inability to perform the sexual act due to failure of the reflex mechanism
Inflammation	the body's response to injury, which may be acute or chronic
Insecticidal	any agent which kills or destroys insects
Insomnia	-the condition a being unable to sleep/

Intermittient fever	a fever that rises, subsides, then returns again
Itcing	discomfort or irritation of the skin, prompting the sufferer to scratch or rub the affected area
Jaundice	a yellowing of the skin or whites of the eyes, indicating excess bilirubin(a bile pigment) in the blood
Laxative	a drug used to stimulate or increase the frequency of bowel evacuation, or to encourage the passage of a softer or bulkier stool
Leprosy	a chronic disease, caused by the bacterium Mycobacterium leprae, that affects the skin, mucous membranes, and nerves
Leucoderma	loss of pigments in areas of the skin, resulting in the appearance of white patches or bands
Leucoma	white opacity occurring in the cornea
Leucorrhoea	whitish or yellowish discharge of mucus from the vaginal opening
Lumbago	pain in lower back
Mammillitis	inflammation of the nipple
Menorrhagia	excessive or prolonged menstruation
Migrain	condition resulting from spasm and subsequent overdilatation of certain arteries in the brain, which causes a recurrent throbbing headache that characteristically affects one side of the head
Miscarriages	the expulsion or removal of an embryo or fetus from the uterus at a stage of pregnancy when it is incapable of independent survival
Mumps	an acute infectious disease caused by a virus
Nasitis	-inflammation of the nose
Nightblindness	the inability to see in dim light or at night
Obesity	an excessive accumulation of fat in the body
Oedema	excessive accumulation of fluid in the body tissues
Oleaginous	oily
Ophthalmia	a term usually applied to conjunctivitis
Ophthalmopathy	any disease of the eye

Otalgia	pain in the ear
Otorrhoea	any discharge from the ear, commonly a purulent discharge in chronic middle ear infection
Paralysis	a muscle weakness that varies in its extent, its severity, and the degree of spasticity or flaccidity according to the nature of the underlying disease and its distribution in the brain, spinal cord, peripheral nerves, or muscles
Pectoral diseases	effective in diseases of the chest
Peptic ulcer	a breach in the lining (mucosa) of the digestive tract produced by digestion of the mucosa by pepsin and acid
Piles	enlargement of the normal spongy blood-filled cushions in the wall of the anus, usually a consequence of prolonged constipation or ocassionally, diarrhoea
Pneumonia	a general disease in which the essential lesion is an inflammation of the spongy tissue of the lung with consolidation of the alveolar exudate
Pneumonosis	any lung disorder
Polyuria	the production of large volumes of urine, which is dilute and of a pale colour
Procreant	the drug which begets
Prophylactic	pertaining to the prevention of the development of a disease
Prurigo	an eruption of the skin causing severe itching
Pruritus	itching
Pyorrhoea	disease of the tissues that support and attach the teeth-the gums, periodontal membrane, and alveolar bone
Refrigerant	cooling
Remittent fever	a remittent fever is one in which body temperature flactuates but does not return to normal
Renal calculi	calculi relating to kidney
Resolvent	causing resolution of a tumour or swelling
Retention of urine	inability to pass urine, which is retained in the bladder
Revulsive	causing revulsion in drawing away of blood from a pathological area to another area

Rheumatalgia	rheumatic pain
Rheumatism	any disorder in which aches and pains affect the musclas and joints
Rheumatoid arthritis	it is the second most common form of arthritis. It typically involves the joints of the fingers, wrists, feet and ankles with later involvement of the hips, keens, shoulders and neck
Rhinitis	inflammation of the nasal mucous membrane
Ringworm	fungus infection of the skin, the scalp, or the nails
Rubefacient	reddening of the skin
Scabies	sarcoptic infestation of the human skin particularly a contagious skin disease caused by invasion of the epidermis
Sciatica	pain felt down the back and outer side of the thigh, leg, and foot
Scrofula-	tuberculous cervical adenitis with or without ulceration
Scurvy	a deficiency disease due to lack of vitamin C
Sinusitis	inflammation of one or more of the mucous- membrane-lined air spaces in the facial bones that communicate with the nose
Slipdisc	a colloquial term for a prolapsed intervertebral disc
Small Pox	an acute infectious virus disease causing high fever and a rash that scars the skin
Somatalgia	pain in the body
Soporific	inducing sleep
Sore throat	pain at the back of the mouth, commonly due to bacterial or viral infection of the tonsils
Spasmolytic	a drug that relieves spasm of smooth muscle
Splenopathy	any disease of the spleen
Spermatorrhoea	the involuntary discharge of semen without orgasm
Stomachache	pain in the stomach
Stomachic	a medicine that increases the functional activity of the stomach

Stomatitis	generalised inflammation of the oral mucosa
Strangury	severe pain in the urethra referred from the base of the bladder and associated with an intense desire to pass urine
Styptic	having the power to arrest bleeding
Sudorific	an agent which induces sweating
Sun stroke	raised body temperature (pyrexia), absence of sweating, and eventual loss of consciousness due to failure or exhaustion of the temperature-regulating mechanism of the body
Syphilis	contagious venereal disease
Tetanus	an infective disease due to toxin of Clostridium tetani
Tuberculosis	an infectious disease caused by the bacillus Mycobacterium tuberculosis and characterized by the formation of nodular lesions in the tissues
Tumour	any abnormal swelling in or on a part of the body
Typhoid	an infection of the digestive system by the bacterium Salmonella typhi, causing general weakness, high fever, a rash of red spots on the chest and abdomen
Ulcers	a break in the skin extending to all its layers, or a break in the mucous membrane lining the alimentary tract, that fails to heal and is often accompained by inflammation
Urethrorrhoea	abnormal discharges from the urethra
Urticaria	an itchy rash resulting from the release of histamine by mast cells
Uteralgia	pain in the uterus
Veneral diseases	any disease transmitted by sexual intercourse
Verminosis	infestation with vermin
Vertigo	dizziness
Vesical calculi	stone in the urinary bladder
Vomiting	the reflex action of ejecting the contents of the stomach through the mouth
Vulnerary	an agent that promotes healing of wounds

Warts	a circumscribed cutaneous excrescence
Whooping cough	an acute infectious disease, primarily of infants, caused by the bacterium Bordetella pertusis, which affects the respiratory tract
Wounds	a break in the structure of an organ or tissue caused by an external agent

BIBLIOGRAPHY

Abraham, Z. 1981. Ethnobotany of the Todas, the Kotas and the lrulas of the Nilgiris, 308 – 320. In S. K. Jain (Ed.) *Glimpses of Indian Ethnobotany.*

Aditya, P., A. Kumar & D. K. Yadav. 2006. Herbal remedies for Dental care system in Gaya district, Bihar. *J. Econ. Taxon. Bot.* 30(Suppl.): 167-170.

Agarwal, V. S. & Arya, M. 2005. *Alternanthera sessilis* DC. (Amaranthaceae): A new source for the treatment of rickets and marasmus. *Ethnobotany.* 17:200-201.

Ahluwalia, K.S. 1968. Medicinal plants of Kerala-VI. *Nagarjun* 11: 392-382.

Ahmad, A. 1995. Drugs of plant origin as used by certain tribes of eastern (Purvanchal) U. P. (Part -IV). *Int J Mendel* 12 (1-4): 12 – 14.

Ahmad, A. 1996. Drugs of plant origin as used by certain tribes of eastern (Purvanchal) U. P. (Part -V). *Indian J Appl Pure Biol:* 11: 41-52.

Aminduddin, Girach, R. D. & Khan, 1993 Treatment of Malaria through herbal drugs from Orissa. *Fitoterapia* 64: 545 – 548.

Amit Tomar & H. Singh. 2006. Exotic medicinal plants from Baghpat district, Uttar Pradesh *J. NTFPs* 13(4): 273-280.

Apparanantham, T. & V. Chelladurai, 1986. Glimpses on folk medicines of Dharmapuri forest division, Tamil Nadu, *Anc. Sci. Life.* 5: 182 – 185.

Ara, Shoukat & A. R. Naqshi 1992. Ethnobotanical studies in Gurais valley- Kashmir. *J. Econ. Taxon. Bot. Addl. Ser.* 10: 185-191.

Arinathan, V., V. R. Mohan & A. John De Britto 2003. Ethnomedicinal survey among Palliyar tribals of Srivilliputhur Grizzled giant squirrel wildlife sanctuary, Tamil Nadu. 707-710. In: Singh *et al.* (ed.). Ethnobotany and Medicinal Plants of India and Nepal. Vol-II. Scientific Publishers (India), Jodhpur.

Arinathan, V., A. Amuthavalli & M. Malaiarasi. 2006. Studies of medicinal plants in Thoothukudi, Tamilnadu. *J. Econ. Taxon. Bot.* 30(Suppl.): 353-357.

Arinathan, V., J. Joseph Visuvasam & R.G. Muthu. 2006. Survey of medicinal plants in Kulathur, Tamilnadu. *J. Econ. Taxon. Bot.* 30(Suppl.): 370-374.

Arya, K. R. & Ved Prakash. 2003. Ethnomedicinal study of a remote tribal area of Almora district: A survey report- Part-I. 247-252 In: Maheshwari, J.K. (ed.). *Ethnobotany and Medicinal Plants of Indian Subcontinent.* Scientific Publishers (India), Jodhpur.

Audichya, K. C., K. V. Billore, T. H. Joseph & D. D. Chaturvedi, 1983. Role of indigenous folk remedies for certain acute illnesses in primary health care. *Nagarjun.* 26: 199 – 201.

Bajpai, A. Ojha, J.K. & Sant H.R. 1995. Medicobotany of the Varanasi district, U.P. India. *Int. J. Pharmacog.* 33: 172-176.

Balaji Rao, N.S. Rajasekhar, D., Chengal Raju, D. & Nagaraju, N. 1996. Ethno-medicinal notes on some plants of Tirumala hills for dental disorders. *Ethnobotany* 8: 88-91.

Ballabh, Basant & O.P. Chaurasia 2006. Ethnobotanical studies on Boto tribe in Ladakh. *Ethnobotany* 18: 87-95.

Balodi, B. & Singh, D.K. 1997. Medico-ethnobotany of Ladakh. *Ann For* 5: 189-197.

Banerjee, A.K. & Banerjee, I. 1986. A Survey of the medicinal plants in Shevaroy hills. *J. Econ. Taxon. Bot.* 8: 271-290.

Barua, K. N., I. C. Barua & Mrigen Das. 2003. Ethnobotany of Rajbanshis of Assam. 609-614. In: Maheshwari, J.K. (ed.). Ethnobotany and Medicinal Plants of Indian Subcontinent. Scientific Publishers (India), Jodhpur.

Baruah, P. & G.C. Sarma. 1984. Studies on the medicinal uses of plants by the Boro tribals of Assam II. *J. Econ. Taxon. Bot.* 5: 599 – 604.

Baruah, Parukutty & G.C. Sarma, 1987. Studies on the medicinal uses of plants by the Northeast tribes – III. *J. Econ. Taxon. Bot.* 11: 71– 76.

Baruah, M. K., P. D. Choudhury & G. C. Sarma. 2006. Ethnomedicinal plants used by Khasi tribe of Cachar district, Assam. *J. Econ. Taxon. Bot.* 30(Suppl.): 110-114.

Basak, S. K. 1997. Medicinal plants of Bankura (W.B.) and their uses. *J. Nat Bot Soc.* 51: 61 – 68.

Basak, S. K. 2006. Medicinal plants of Bankura (West Bengal) and their uses. *J. Econ. Taxon. Bot.* 30(Suppl.): 217-224.

Basu, R. 2003. Ethnomedicinal information of yellow flowered 'Palas' and 'Silk cotton' in Bankura District of West Bengal. 580-581. In: Singh *et al.* (ed.). *Ethnobotany and Medicinal Plants of India and Nepal*. Vol-II. Scientific Publishers (India), Jodhpur.

Bedi, S. J. 1978. Ethnobotany of the Ratan Mahal Hills, Gujarat, India, *Econ. Bot.* 32: 278 – 284.

Behura, S. & N. C. Rout. 2003. Diversity of Zingiberaceae plant from Orissa. 546-550. In: Singh *et al.* (ed.). Ethnobotany and Medicinal Plants of India and Nepal. Vol-II. Sci. Publ. (India), Jodhpur.

Beigh, S. Y., Irshad A. Nawchoo & Muhammad Iqbal. 2003. Plants in traditional medicine of Kashmir Himalaya. 99-104. In: Singh *et al.* (ed.). Ethnobotany and Medicinal Plants of India and Nepal. Vol-I. Scientific Publishers (India), Jodhpur.

Bennet, S.S.R. 1985. Ethnobotanical studies in West Sikkim. *J. Econ. Taxon. Bot.* 7: 317 – 321.

Bhalla, N.P., T.R. Sahu, G.P. Mishra & R.N. Dakwale. 1982. Traditional Plant medicines of Sagar Distt. Madhya Pradesh, India. *J. Econ. Taxon. Bot.* 3: 23 – 32.

Bhalla, S., J. R. Patel & N. P. Bhalla. 1992. Ethnomedicinal herbal Legumes of Bundelkhand region, M. P. *J. Econ. Taxon. Bot. Addl. Ser.* 10: 105-109.

Bhatt, R.P. & S.D. Sabnis, 1987. Contribution to the Ethnobotany of Khedbrahma region of north Gujarat. *J. Econ. Taxon. Bot.* 9: 139 – 145.

Bhatt, D. C., N. K. Patel, K. D. Mitaliya & H. M. Ant. 2003. Herbal magic by contact therapy among tribals and rurals of Gujarat. 205-207. In: Singh *et al.* (ed.). Ethnobotany and Medicinal Plants of India and Nepal. Vol-I. Scientific Publishers (India), Jodhpur.

Bhatt, D. C., N. K. Patel, K.D. Mitaliya & H. M. Ant. 2003. Herbal magic by contact therapy among tribals and rurals of Gujrat. 205-207. In: Singh *et al.* (ed.). Ethnobotany and Medicinal Plants of India and Nepal. Vol-I. Scientific Publishers (India), Jodhpur.

Bhatt, D. C., K. D. Mitaliya & A. V. Babaria. 2003. Observations on some ethnobotanical plants of Malnath Hillocks of Gogha Tehsil, district Bhavnagar, Gujarat State. 217-220. In: Singh *et al.* (ed.). Ethnobotany and Medicinal Plants of India and Nepal. Vol-I. Scientific Publishers (India), Jodhpur.

Bhatt, D. C., S. K. Mehta, M. A. Nurani & U. S. Baxi. 2003. Studies on some ethnobotanical plants of Barda Hills from Saurashtra. 221-227. In: Singh *et al.* (ed.). Ethnobotany and Medicinal Plants of India and Nepal. Vol-I. Scientific Publishers (India), Jodhpur.

Bhatt, D. C., B. A. Jadeja, N. K. Odedra & U. S. Baxi. 2003. Enumeration of wild plants used as anti-diabetic in Barda hills of Gujarat. 897-903. In: Singh *et al.* (ed.). Ethnobotany and Medicinal Plants of India and Nepal. Vol-II. Scientific Publishers (India), Jodhpur.

Bhatt, D. C., A. M. Patel, P. P. Parekh & R. P. Parmar. 2003. Plants used for sexual debility in Central Gujarat. 943-946. In: Singh *et al.* (ed.). Ethnobotany and Medicinal Plants of India and Nepal. Vol-II. Scientific Publishers (India), Jodhpur.

Bhattacharjee, S., K.C. Tiwari, R. Majuumdar & A.K. Mishra. 1980. Folklore medicine from district Kamrup (Assam). *Bull. Medico – ethnobot. Res.*1: 447 – 460.

Bhuyan, L. R. 2003. Some plants used as medicine by the Nishi tribe of Arunachal Pradesh: A preliminary study. 447-450. In: Singh *et al.* (ed.). Ethnobotany and Medicinal Plants of India and Nepal. Vol-I. Scientific Publishers (India), Jodhpur.

Billore, K.V. & K.C. Audichya. 1978. Some oral contraceptives; family planning tribal way, *J. Res. Indian Med. Yoga & Homeo.*13: 104.

Billore, K.V., Joseph, T.G. & Dave, S.K. 1998. Interesting folk remedies by the 'Lok, Vaidyas' of Rajasthan for 'Swas Roga'. *Ethnobotany.* 10: 42 – 45.

Bora, P. J. 2003. A study on Ethnomedicinal uses of plants among the Bodo tribe of Sonitpur district, Assam. 604-608. In: Maheshwari, J.K. (ed.). Ethnobotany and Medicinal Plants of Indian Subcontinent. Scientific Publishers (India), Jodhpur.

Borthakur, S.K. 1976. Less known medicinal uses of plants among the tribals of Mikir Hills. *Bull. Bot. Surv. India.*18: 166 -171.

Borthakur, S.K. 1993. Native Phytotherapy for child and women diseases from Assam. *Ethnobotany* 75: 87-89.

Borthakur, S.K. & Goswami, N. 1995. Herbal remedies from Dimoria of kamrup district Assam in Northeastern India. *Fitoterapia* 66: 333-340.

Borthakur, S.K. 1996. Postnatal care of women in traditional system in Assam. *Ethnobotany*. 8: 51-55.

Borthakur, S.K. Nath, K. & Gogoi, P. 1996. Herbal remedies of the Nepalese of Assam, *fitoerapia*.67: 231 – 237.

Caius, J.F. 1998. The Medicinal and Poisonous Plants of India, Scientific Publishers, Jodhpur.

Chaghtai, S.A. & Javed Ahmad. 1978. An ethnobotanical study of Baghrendah (*Jatropha curcas* L.) *J. Res. Indian Med. Yoga & Homeo.*13: 134 – 136.

Chandra, K., Pandey, B.N. Sudha, G.N. & Pandey, P. 1989. Medicinal plants wealth of the Rajgir Bihar. *Bull. Med. Ethnobot. Res.* 1: 124-161.

Chandra, K. 1995. An Ethnobotanical study on some medicinal plants of District Palamau (Bihar). *Sachitra Ayurved.*48: 311 – 314.

Chatterjee, S. & A. Bhatterjee. 2006. Some Ethnomedicinal plants of North 24 Paragana, West Bengal. *J. Econ. Taxon. Bot.* 30(Suppl.): 281-282.

Chaudhuri, Rai H.N., D.C. Pal & Tarafder. 1975. Less known uses of plants from the tribal areas of Orissa. *Bull. Bot. Surv India.*17: 132 – 136.

Chaudhuri, Rai H.N. & D.C. Pal. 1976. Preliminary observations on Ethnobotany of Midnapur district West Bengal. *India. Mus. Bull.*11: 51 – 53.

Chaudhuri, Rai H.N., H.A. Molla, D.C. Pal & B. Roy. 1982. Plants used in traditional medicine by some tribals of Jalpaiguri district, West Bengal. *Bull. Bot. Surv. India.* 24: 87 – 90.

Chaudhuri, Rai, H.N., D.C. Pal, N.C. Saha & B. Roy. 1985. Some wild edible plants in Calcutta markets. *Man & Life.*11: 45 – 58.

Chauhan, V. & Chauhan, N.S. 1988. Ethno-botany of Trans-Giri area of Sirmour district of Himachal Pradesh, *Bull Med Ethnobot Res.* 9: 106-122.

Chelvan, P.T. 1998. Traditional Phytotherapy among the migrant Tamilian settlers in South Gujarat. *Biojournal* 10: 9 – 14.

Chetty, K.M. & Rao, K.N. 1989. Ethnobotany of Sarakulla & adjacent areas of Chittor district, A.P. *Vegetos* 2: 51-58.

Chetty, K.M., Chetty, M.L. Sudhakar, A. & Ramesh, C. 1998. Ethno-medico botany of some aquatic angiosperm in Chittoor district of A.P., India. *Fitoterapia* 69: 7-12.

Chhetri, D.R. 2005. Ethnomedicinal plants of the Khangchendzonga National Park, *Sikkim, India. Ethnobotany.*17: 96 – 103.

Chopra, R.N. Nayar, S.L. & Chopra, I.C. 1956. Glossary of Indian medicinal plants. CSIR.

Chopra, R.N. Badhwar, R.L. & Ghosh, S. 1965. Poisonous plants of India. Vol. I & II. ICAR, New Delhi.

Dar, G.H., Vir jee, P. Kachroo & G.M. Buth. 1984. Ethnobotany of Kashmir – I. Sind Valley. *J. Econ. Taxon. Bot.*5: 668 – 675.

Das, S.N., K.P. Janardhanan & S.C. Roy. 1983. Some observations on the ethnobotany of the tribes of Totopara and adjoining areas in Jalpaiguri district, West Bengal. *J. Econ. Taxon. Bot.*4: 453 – 474.

Das, S.R. 1995. Some beneficial weeds of cultivation from Nadia district, West Bengal. *Bull. Med. Ethnobot. Res.*16: 74 – 81.

Das, A.K. & G.D. Sharma. 2003. Ethnomedicinal uses of plants by Manipuri and Barman communities of Cachar district, Assam. 421-429. In: Singh *et al.* (ed.). Ethnobotany and Medicinal Plants of India and Nepal. Vol-I. Scientific Publishers (India), Jodhpur.

Das, A.K., B.K. Dutta & G.D. Sharma. 2006. Study of Medicinal plants used by the different tribes/communities of Cachar district Assam. *J. Econ. Taxon. Bot.* 30 (Suppl.): 294-309.

Das, S., T. E. Sheeja & A. B. Mandal. 2006. Ethnomedicinal uses of certain plants from Bay Islands. *IJTK* 5(2):207-211.

Dash, S. S., A. Maiti & S. K. Rai. 2003. Traditional uses of plants among the urban population of Gangtok- Sikkim. 317-324. In: Singh *et al.* (ed.). Ethnobotany and Medicinal Plants of India and Nepal. Vol-I. Scientific Publishers (India), Jodhpur.

Datta, M.L. & Nath, S.C. 1998. Ethno-medicobotany of the deories of Assam, India. *Fltoterapia* 69: 147-154.

Deka, D., G. C. Sarma, N. Devi & N. Pathak. 2006. Indigenous herbal medicines used against Malaria in Goalpara and Morigaon district of Assam. *J. Econ. Taxon. Bot.* 30(Suppl.): 177-183.

Deokule, S. S. & D. K. Magdum. 1992. Enumeration of Medicinal plants from Baramati area, district Pune, Maharashtra State. *J. Econ. Taxon. Bot. Addl. Ser.* 10: 289-299.

Deokule, S. S. 2006. Ethno-medicinal plants of Baramati region of Pune district, Maharashtra. *J. Econ. Taxon. Bot.* 30(Suppl.): 59-69.

Deshmukh, V. R. & S. P. Rothe. 2003. Ethnomedicinal study from Melghat tribal region of Amravati district, Maharashtra. 582-584. In: Singh *et al.* (ed.). Ethnobotany and Medicinal Plants of India and Nepal. Vol-II. Scientific Publishers (India), Jodhpur.

Dhar, U. & Siddique, M.A.A. 1993. Ethnobotanical studies and biological diversity of Suru Valley (Zanskar), *Glimpses Plant Res.* 10: 31-39.

Dobriyal, R.M., Singh, G.S., Rao, K.S. & Saxena, K.G. 1997. Medicinal plant resources in Chhakinal watershed in the North-Western Himalaya, *J Herb Spices Med plant* 5: 15-27.

Duthie, J.F. 1994 (Reprint). Flora of the Upper Gangetic plain. Bishen singh Mahendra Pal Singh, Dehradun.

Dutta Choudhury, M. & S. Shil. 2006. Some traditional antihepatitis plants used by the People of Manipur. *J. Econ. Taxon. Bot.* 30(Suppl.): 289-293.

Dwarakan, P. & A.A. Ansari. 1992. Ethnobotanical notes of Valikadupatti and surroundings of Kollimalais Salem DT., Tamil Nadu. *J. Econ. Taxon. Bot. Addl. Ser.* 10: 495-499.

Dwivedi, S. N. & Archana Pandey. 1992. Ethnobotanical studies on wild and indigenous species of Vindhyan Plateau. *J. Econ. Taxon. Bot. Addl. Ser.* 10: 143-150.

Dwivedi, S. N. 2003. Ethnobotanical studies and conservational strategies of wild and natural resources of Rewa district of M.P. 233-244. In: Singh *et al.* (ed.). Ethnobotany and Medicinal Plants of India and Nepal. Vol-I. Scientific Publishers (India), Jodhpur.

Dwivedi, S. N., Dwivedi, S. and Patel, P.C. 2005. Herbal remedies used by the rural people in the treatment of joint diseases. *Ethnobotany*. 17: 193-196.

E. Vargese S.V.D. 1996. Applied ethnobotany-A case study among the Kharias of central India. *Deep publications*. New Delhi.

Ganai, K. A. & Irshad A. Nawchoo. 2003. Traditional treatment of toothache by the Gujjar and Bakerwal tribes of Kashmir in India. 105-107. In: Singh *et al.* (ed.). Ethnobotany and Medicinal Plants of India and Nepal. Vol-I. Scientific Publishers (India), Jodhpur.

Ganesan, S. & L. Kesavan. 2003. Ethnomedicinal plants used by the ethnic group valaiyans of vellimalai hills (Reserved forest) Tamil Nadu. 754-760. In: Singh *et al.* (ed.). Ethnobotany and Medicinal Plants of India and Nepal. Vol-II. Scientific Publishers (India), Jodhpur.

Ganesan S., Venkateshan G. & Banumathy N. 2006. Medicinal plants used by ethnic group Thottianaickans of Semmalai hills (reserved forest), Tiruchirappalli district, Tamil Nadu. *IJTK*. 5(2): 245-252.

Gantait, S., Kundu, S. K. & Giri, G.S. 2006. Some important medicinal plants of North-East India. *J. Econ. Taxon. Bot.* 30(Suppl.): 283-288.

Gaur, R.D., M.P. Sharma & J.K. Semwal. 1980. Ethnotoxic plants of Garhwal hills in India. *East. Anthrop.* 33: 159 – 163.

Ghosh, S. & Sensarma, P. 1997. Ethnomedicine to modern medicine: an observational study in some villages of West Bengal. *Ethnobotany*. 9: 80-84.

Ghosh, R. B. & Debabrata Das 2003. A preliminary census and systematic survey of antidiabetic plants of Midnapore district, West Bengal. 535-538. In: Maheshwari, J.K. (ed.). Ethnobotany and Medicinal Plants of Indian Subcontinent. Scientific Publishers (India), Jodhpur.

Ghosh, A. 2006. Medicinal plants used for treatment of Diabetes by the tribals of Bankura, Purulia and Medinipur of West Bengal. *J. Econ. Taxon. Bot.* 30(Suppl.): 233-238.

Girach, R. D., S. Singh, M. Brahmam & M.K. Misra. 2003. Traditional treatment of skin diseases in Bhadrak district, Orissa. 499-504. In: Maheshwari, J.K. (ed.). Ethnobotany and Medicinal Plants of Indian Subcontinent. Scientific Publishers (India), Jodhpur.

Goel, A.K., A.K. Sahoo & V. Mudgal. 1984. A contribution to the ethnobotany of Santal Pargana, Bihar. *Bot. Surv. India*.

Goel, A.K. & V. Mudgal. 1988. A survey of medicinal plants used by the tribals of Santal Pargana (Bihar). *J. Econ. Taxon. Bot.* 12: 329 – 335.

Gogoi, P. & C.L. Boissya. 1984. Informations about a few herbal medicines used by the people of Assam (India) against Jaundice, *Himal. Res. Dev.* 2: 41 – 44.

Gogoi, R., D. Bokolial & D. Hazarika. 2003. Preliminary observation on the medicinal plants of Chandrapur area of Kamrup District, Assam. 410-415. In: Singh *et al.* (ed.).

Ethnobotany and Medicinal Plants of India and Nepal. Vol-I. Scientific Publishers (India), Jodhpur.

Gogoi, R. & M. K. Das. 2003. Observations on some weeds of Medicinal importance in the Brahmaputra Valley of Assam. 434-441. In: Singh *et al.* (ed.). Ethnobotany and Medicinal Plants of India and Nepal. Vol-I. Scientific Publishers (India), Jodhpur.

Gogte, V.V.M. Vaidya. 2000. Ayurvedic pharmacology and Therapeutic uses of medicinal plants (Dravyaguna Vignyan). Bhartiya Vidya Bhawan, Mumbai.

Gopakumar, K., Vijayalakshmi, B., Shantha, T.R. & Yoganarasimhan, S.N. 1991. Plants used in Ayurveda from Chikmangalur district, Karnataka – II. *J. Econ. Taxon. Bot.*15: 379 – 389.

Gopal, G.V. & G.L. Shah. 1985. Some folk medicinal plants used for jaundice in Gujarat, India. *J. Res. Edu. Indian Med.* 4: 45 – 49.

Gopal, G. V. & K. S. Jagadish Chandra. 2003. Ethnobotany of soligas of Biligirirangana Hills, Karnataka. 640-647. In: Singh *et al.* (ed.). Ethnobotany and Medicinal Plants of India and Nepal. Vol-II. Scientific Publishers (India), Jodhpur.

Gopalakrishnan, K. & V. A. Krishna Prasad. 1992. Some folklore medicine of the tribals (Irulars) of Attappady region (Kerala State). *J. Econ. Taxon. Bot. Addl. Ser.* 10: 385-380.

Gupta, S.P. 1981. Native medicinal uses of plants by the Asurs of Netarhat plateau (Bihar), 218 – 231. In S.K. Jain (Ed.) *Glimpses of Indian Ethnobotany.*

Gupta, Rajendra. 1981. Plants in folk medicine of the Himalayas. 83 – 90. In S.K. Jain (Ed.) *Glimpses of Indian Ethnobotany.*

Gupta, V.C., Hussain, S.J. & Imam, S. 1997. Medico – ethonbotanical survey at Paderu forests of Araku Valley, Andhra Pradesh, *Fitoterapia.*68: 45 – 48.

Gupta, A.K., Mishra, S.K. & Khan, A.A. 1999. Ethnobotanical notes on some herbs from Chhatisgarh region of Madhya Pradesh. *Adv Plant Sci.*12: 163 – 166.

Gupta, A.K. & Tandon, N. 2004(Edited). Reviews on Indian Medicinal Plants. *Vol.* I, II, III & IV. *Indian Council of Medical Research. New Delhi.*

Gupta, A.K. 2005 (Edited). Quality standards of Indian Medicinal Plants. *Vol.* I, II & III . *Indian Council of Medical Research. New Delhi.*

Gupta, V. 2006. Traditional medicinal plants of the Bangnis of East Kameng district, Arunachal Pradesh. *J. Econ. Taxon. Bot.* 30(Suppl.): 310-319.

Handa, S.S. & Kapoor, V.K. 1999. Pharmacognosy. Vallabh Prakashan, Delhi.

Harja, P.K. & A.K. Baishya. 1981. Ethnobotanical notes on the Miris (Mishings) of Assam Plants, 161 – 169. In S.K. Jain (Ed.): *Glimpses of Inidian Ethnobotany.*

Hemadri, K., Raj, P.V., Rao, S.S. & Sarma, C.R.R. 1980. Folklore clamis from A.P.-I. *J. Sci. Res. Plant Med.* 1: 37-49.

Hemadri, K. & S.S. Rao. 1983. Leucorrhoea and menorrhagia : Tribal medicine. *Anc. Sci. Life.* 3: 40 – 41.

Hemadri, K. & S.S. Rao. 1984. Jaundice: Tribal medicine. *Anc. Sci. Life.* 3: 209– 212.

Hemadri, K. & Rao, S.S. 1989. Folk-lore claims of Koraput and Phulbani district of Orissa state. *Indian Med.* 1(4): 11-13.

Hemadri, K. & Rao, S.S. B. 1990. Folklore claims of Koraput and Phulbani district of Orissa state. *Indian Med.* 2(1): 4-6.

Hemadri, K. 1992. Tribals of Andhra Pradesh: their knowledge in nutritional and medicinal herbs. *Indian Med.* 4(1): 1– 6.

Hembrom, P.P. & Goel, A.K. 2005. Horopathy: Ethnomedicine of Mundas. *Ethnobotany* 17: 89 – 95.

Islam, M. A. & R. K. Jha. 2003. Ethnopharmacology of tribals of Ranchi district in Jharkhand. 300-310. In: Singh *et al.* (ed.). Ethnobotany and Medicinal Plants of India and Nepal. Vol-I. Scientific Publishers (India), Jodhpur.

Islam, M. A. & F. Hasin. 2003. Ethnobotany of certain Asteraceous plants of Assam and its neighbouring areas. 442-446. In: Singh *et al.* (ed.). Ethnobotany and Medicinal Plants of India and Nepal. Vol-I. Scientific Publishers (India), Jodhpur.

Jadeja, B. A., N. K. Odedra & S. I. Choudhary. 2006a. Ethnomedicinal plants used by the tribals of Gujarat to cure digestive disorders. *J. Econ. Taxon. Bot.* 30(Suppl.): 115-123.

Jadeja, B. A., N. K. Odedra, H. N. Mori & D.C. Bhati. 2006b. Medicinal plants of Gujarat used in Gout. *J. Econ. Taxon. Bot.* 30(Suppl.): 225-232.

Jadeja, B. A., N. K. Odedra & Gajera, M.R. 2006c. Plants used in traditional phytotherapy for hair care in Gujarat. *J. Econ. Taxon. Bot.* 30(Suppl.):258 - 268.

Jadhav, D. 2006. Ethnomedicinal plants used by Bhil tribe of Bibdod, Madhya pradesh. *IJTK.* 5(2): 263 – 267.

Jadhav, D. 2006. Plant sources used for the treatment of types of fevers by Bhil tribe of Ratlam district, Madhya pradesh. *J. Econ. Taxon. Bot.* 30(4): 909– 911.

Jadhav, D. 2006. Ethnomedicinal plants used for curing skin afflictions by Bhil tribe of Ratlam district, Madhya pradesh. *J. Econ. Taxon. Bot.* 30 (Suppl.). 124-127.

Jadhav, D. 2006. Ethno-medicinal survey of Maalgamdi in Ujjain district, Madhya pradesh, India. *Ethnobotany* 18(1 & 2): 157 – 159.

Jadhav, D. 2007. Ethno-medicinal plants used in the treatment of Diarrhoea and Dysentery by Bhil tribe of Ratlam district (M.P.). *Indian forester*. August: 1097- 1100.

Jain, S.K. 1963 a. Studies in Indian ethnobotany – Less known uses of 50 common plants from tribal areas of Madhya Pradesh. *Bull. Bot. Surv. India.* 5: 223 – 226.

Jain, S.K. 1963 b. Studies in Indian ethnobotany – II. Plants used in medicine by the tribals of Madhya Pradesh. *Bull. Reg. Res. Lab. Jammu.* 1: 126 128.

Jain, S.K. 1965 a. Medicinal plantlore of the tribals of Bastar. *Econ. Bot.* 19: 236 -250.

Jain, S.K. 1965 b. On the prospects of some new or less known medicinal plant resources. *Indian Med. J.* 59: 270 – 272.

Jain, S.K. & J.N. De. 1966. Observations on ethnobotany of Purulia district, West Bengal. *Bull. Bot. Suv. India.* 8: 237 – 251.

Jain, S.K. & C.R. Tarafder. 1970. Medicinal plant lore of the Santals. A revival of P O Bodding's work. *Econ. Bot.* 24: 241 – 278.

Jain, S.K., D.K. Banerjee & D.C. Pal. 1973. Medicinal plants among certain Adibasis in India. *Bull. Bot. Surv. India.* 15: 85 – 91.

Jain, S.K. & N. Dam. 1979. Some ethnobotanical notes from north – eastern India. *Econ. Bot.* 33: 52 – 56.

Jain, S.K. & S.K. Borthakur. 1980. Ethnobotany of the Mikirs of India. *Econ. Bot.* 34: 264 – 272.

Jain, S.K. 1981 (Ed.). Glimpses of Indian ethnobotany. Oxford and IBH Publishing Co., New Delhi.

Jain, S.K. 1984. Ethnobotany of Morni and Kalesar (Ambala – Haryana). *J. Econ. Taxon. Bot.* 5: 809 – 813.

Jain, S.K. 1991. Dictionary of Indian folk Medicine & Ethnobotany. Deep publication, New Delhi.

Jain, P. & Sahu, T.R. 1993. An ethnobotanical study of Noradehi Sanctuary Park of M. P., India: Native plant remedies for Scorpion sting & Snake bite. *J. Econ. Taxon. Bot.* 17: 315-328.

Jain, S.P. & Puri, H.S. 1994. A ethno-medico botanical survey of Parbati valley in H.P. (India), *J Econ. Tax. Bot.* 18: 321-327.

Jain, S. K. 1997. Contribution to Indian Ethnobotany. Scientific Publishers (India), Jodhpur.

Jain, S. P., S. C. Singh, J. Singh & Sushil Kumar. 2003. Ethno-medico-botanical survey of Raipur district, Chhattisgarh State. 266-271. In: Singh *et al.* (ed.). Ethnobotany and Medicinal Plants of India and Nepal. Vol-I. Scientific Publishers (India), Jodhpur.

Jain, S.K. 2004 (Ed.). A manual of ethnobotany. Scientific Publisher (India), Jodhpur.

Jamir, N.S. 1990. Some interesting medicinal plants used by Nagas. *J. Res. Edue Indian Med.* 9: 81-87.

Janardhanan, K.P. 1963. An enumeration of the medicinal plants of Khed Taluka, Maharashtra State. *Bull. Bot. Surv. India.* 5: 363 – 374.

Janmeda, B. S., Lokendra Singh & Preeti Vats. 2006. Folk claims on Monocotyledons plants in East- Sikkim. *J. NTFPs* 13(2):155-160.

Jha, P.K. Choudhary, R.S. & Choudhary, S.K. 1997. Studies of Medicinal plants of Palamau (Bihar)- (Part – II). *Bijournal.* 9: 21 – 38.

Joshi, M.C., M.B. Patel & P.J. Mehta. 1980. Some folk medicines of Dangs, Gujarat State. *Bull. Medico – ethnobot. Res.* 1: 8 – 24.

Joshi, P. 1982. An ethnobotanical study of Bhils– A preliminary survey. *J. Econ. Taxon. Bot.* 3: 257 – 266.

Jubilee, P. & Subhan, C. N. 2006. Biological activities of ethnomedicinal claims of some plant species of Assam. *IJTK.* 5(2):229-236.

Kadavul, K. & P. Jisha. 2006. Medicinal plants and their conservation in Mahe region, U. T. of Pondicherry, Malabar Coast, South India. *J. Econ. Taxon. Bot.* 30(Suppl.): 203-207.

Kala, C. P. & Nima Manjrekar. 2003. Ethnomedicobotany of Indian trans-Himalaya: A case study of Spiti. 177- 183. In: Maheshwari, J. K. (ed.). Ethnobotany and Medicinal Plants of Indian Subcontinent. Scientific Publishers (India), Jodhpur.

Kataria, R. L. & D. P. Gauchan. 2006. Ethnomedicinal plants used in Dysentery and diarrhoea in Hanumangarh district, Rajasthan. *J. Econ. Taxon. Bot.* 30(Suppl.): 128-132.

Kamble, S.Y. & S.G. Pradhan. 1980. Ethnobotany of Korkus in Maharashtra. *Bull. Bot. Surv. India.* 22: 201 – 202.

Kapoor, S.L. & Kapoor, L.D. 1980. Medicinal plant wealth of the Karimnagr district of A.P. Bull. Med. Ethnobot. Res. 1: 120-144.

Kapur, S. K. & S. Nanda. 1992. Traditionally important medicinal plants of Bhaderwah Hills- Jammu Province- I. *J. Econ. Taxon. Bot. Addl. Ser.* 10: 307-318.

Kapur, S.K. 1993. Ethno – Medico plants of Kangra Valley (Himachal Pradesh). *J. Econ. Taxon. Bot.* 17: 395 – 408.

Karnick, C.R., K.C. Tiwari, R. Majumdar & S. Bhattacharjee. 1981. Newer ethnobotanical and folklore studies of some medicinal plants of Gauhati and surrounding areas. *Nagarjun.*24: 240 – 245.

Katewa, S.S. & Arora, A. 1997. Some plants in folk medicines of Udaipur district. (Rajasthan). *Ethnobotany.* 9: 48 – 51.

Katewa, S.S. & Sharma, R. 1998. Ethnomedicinal observations from certain Watershed areas of Rajasthan. *Ethnobotany.* 10: 46 – 49.

Khan, A. A., S. Khan & M. P. Singh. 2003. Weeds of Soyabean [*Glycine max* (L.) Merr.] and their medicinal importance in Rewa division (M.P.). 245-248. In: Singh *et al.* (ed.). Ethnobotany and Medicinal Plants of India and Nepal. Vol-I. Scientific Publishers (India), Jodhpur.

Khan, A. A., A. K. Verma & M.P. Singh. 2003. Certain ethnobotanical informations on food and medicinal plants from Rewa division of Madhya Pradesh with special reference to rare and endangered species. 249-254. In: Singh *et al.* (ed.). Ethnobotany and Medicinal Plants of India and Nepal. Vol-I. Scientific Publishers (India), Jodhpur.

Kharkongor, P. & J. Joseph. 1981. Folklore medico – botany of rural Khasi and Jaintia tribes in Meghalaya. 124 – 136. In S.K. Jain (Ed.) *Glimpses of Indian Ethnobotany.*

Khory, J.K. 1981. Materia medica of India & their Therapeutics, Neeraj Publishing house, New Delhi.

Kothari, M. J. & K. M. Rao. 2003. Ethnobotanical studies of Thane district, Maharashtra. 265-272. In: Maheshwari, J.K. (ed.). Ethnobotany and Medicinal Plants of Indian Subcontinent. Scientific Publishers (India), Jodhpur.

Kothari, M. J. & A. N. Londhe. 2003. Ethnobotany in Human health care of Chikhaldara, Amaravati district in Maharashtra State. 273-281. In: Maheshwari, J.K. (ed.).

Ethnobotany and Medicinal Plants of Indian Subcontinent. Scientific Publishers (India), Jodhpur.

Kirtikar, K.R. & Basu, B.D. 2004. Indian medicinal plants, Vol. I, II, III &IV (Reprint). Bishen Singh Mahendra Pal Singh, Dehradun.

Kiruba, S., S. Jeeva, N. Venugopal, S. S. M. Das, G. S. Regini, R. C. Laloo & B. P. Mishra. 2006. Ethnomedicinal herbs of Koonthakulam water Sanctuary, Nellai, Tamilnadu, India. *J. NTFPs* 13(1):25-27.

Krishna, B. & S. Singh. 1987. Ethnobotanical observations in Sikkim. *J. Econ. Taxon. Bot.* 9: 1 – 7.

Kshirsagar, R. D. & N. P. Singh. 2003. Less-known herbal remedies from Soligas of Mysore, Southern India. 656- 661. In: Singh *et al.* (ed.). Ethnobotany and Medicinal Plants of India and Nepal. Vol-II. Scientific Publishers (India), Jodhpur.

Kumar, Y., K. Haridasan & R.R. Rao. 1980. Ethnobotanical notes on certain medicinal plants among some Garo people around Balphakram Sanctury in Meghalaya. *Bull. Bot. Surv. India.* 22: 161 – 165.

Kumar, Y., S. Fancy & R.R. Rao. 1987. Further contribution to the ethnobotany of Meghalaya: Plants used by War Jaintia of Jaintia Hill district. *J. Econ. Taxon. Bot.*11: 65 – 70.

Kumar, M. 1992. Ethnomedicinal studies of plants of chotanagpur plateau, Bihar, *Int. J. Mendel. 9: 137 – 139.*

Kumar, V. & Jain, S.K. 1998. A contribution to ethnobotany of Surguja district in M.P. *Ethnobotany.* 10: 89 – 96.

Kumar, S., F. Parveen & R. S. Mertia. 2003. Taxonomic analysis of medicinal plants of the Indian Thar: A Prioritisation strategy. 160-169. In: Singh *et al.* (ed.). Ethnobotany and Medicinal Plants of India and Nepal. Vol-I. Scientific Publishers (India), Jodhpur.

Kumar, Anand & Jagdish Lal. 2003. Medicinal plant resources of the Kanha tiger reserve, M. P. 255-265. In: Singh *et al.* (ed.). Ethnobotany and Medicinal Plants of India and Nepal. Vol-I. Scientific Publishers (India), Jodhpur.

Kumar, K. J. L., K. S. Kalesh & A. Mohandas. 2003. An account of the Economic potential and commercial exploitation of four lesser known *Garcinia* species from India. 692-694. In: Singh *et al.* (ed.). Ethnobotany and Medicinal Plants of India and Nepal. Vol-II. Scientific Publishers (India), Jodhpur.

Kumar, A., D. D. Tewari & Y. N. Pande. 2003. Ethno-phytotherapeutics among Tharus of Beerpur-Semra forest range of Balrampur district (U.P.). 839-844. In: Singh *et al.* (ed.). Ethnobotany and Medicinal Plants of India and Nepal. Vol-II. Scientific Publishers (India), Jodhpur.

Kumar, S. & Chauhan, A.K.K. 2005. Medicinal plants used by local inhabitants in Bharatpur district, Rajasthan. *Ethnobo.*17: 179 – 183.

Kumar, A., A. Singh, Y. Sharma & J. C. Rana. 2006. Ethno-medico-botany of some important plants in Mandhala watershed of Himachal Pradesh. *J. Econ. Taxon. Bot.* 30 (Suppl.): 145-150.

Kumar, A. & D. K. Yadav. 2006. Important Ethno-medicinal plants of family Poaceae in Gaya District, Bihar. *J. Econ. Taxon. Bot.* 30(Suppl.): 171-176.

Lakshamanan, K.K. & A.S. Sankaranarayanan. 1988. Some folklore medicines in the remote hemlets, Dhoomanoor & Champukarai of Anai Katty hills, Coimbatore, Tamil Nadu. *Indian J. Forestry.* 11: 217 – 219.

Lal, S.D. & B.K. Yadav. 1983. Folk medicines of Kurukshetra District (Haryana), India. *Econ. Bot.* 37: 299 – 305.

Lal, S.D. & K. Lata. 1980. Plants used by the Bhat Community for regulating fertility. *Econ. Bot.* 34: 273 – 275.

Lindley, John. 1981. Flora medica, Ajay book service, New Delhi.

Maheshwari, J. K., K. K. Singh & S. Saha. 1980. Ethnomedicinal uses of plants by Tharus in Kheri district, U. P. *Bull. Medico-ethnobot. Res.* 1:318-337.

Maheshwari, J.K. & K.K. Singh & S. Saha. 1981. The Ethonbotany of the Tharus of Kheri district. Uttar Pradesh. *Nation. Bot. Res. Inst.* Lucknow.

Maheshwari, J.K. & J.P. Singh. 1984. Contribution to the ethnobotany of Bhoxa tribe of Bijnor & Pauri Garhwal district, U.P. *J. Econ. Taxon. Bot.* 5: 251 – 259.

Maheshwari, J.K. B.S. Kalakoti & Brijlal. 1986. Ethnomedicine of Bhil Tribe of Jhabua district, Madhya Pradesh. *Anc. Sci. Life.* 5: 255 – 261.

Maheshwari, J.K. K.K. Singh & S. Saha. 1986. Ethnobotany of tribals of Mirzapur district. U.P. *Nation. Bot. Res. Inst.,* Lucknow.

Maheshwari, J.K. & J.P. Singh. 1987. Traditional phytotherapy amongst the Kol tribe of Banda district, Uttar Pradesh. *J. Econ. Taxon. Bot.* 9: 165 – 171.

Malhotra, S.K. & S. Moorthy. 1973. Some useful and medicinal plants of Chandrapur district (Maharasthra State). *Bull. Bot. Surv. India.* 15: 13 – 21.

Malhotra, C.L. & Balodi, B. 1984. Medicinal plants of Alpine region of Gori Valley, Kumaon, *J. Sci. Res. Plant Med* 5(1&2): 1-8.

Manandhav, N. P. 2003. Ethnobotanical notes on the family Leguminoseae in Nepal. 333-344. In: Singh *et al.* (ed.). Ethnobotany and Medicinal Plants of India and Nepal. Vol-I. Scientific Publishers (India), Jodhpur.

Megoneitso & R.R. Rao. 1983. Ethnobotanical studies in Nagaland – 4. Sixty two medicinal plants used by the Angami Nagas. *J. Econ. Taxon. Bot.*4: 167 – 172.

Meena, S.L., K.C. Sharma & R. Gopalan. 2003. Ethnomedicinal plants of Karauli district, Rajasthan. 177-180. In: Singh *et al.* (ed.). Ethnobotany and Medicinal Plants of India and Nepal. Vol-I. Scientific Publishers (India), Jodhpur.

Mishra, R. & R.D. Dxit. 1973. Vajradanti – An ethnobotanical study. I. *J. Res. Indian Med.* 8: 89 – 91.

Mishra, R. & K.V. Billore. 1983. Some ethnobotanical lores from Banswara district. Rajasthan. *Nagarjun.* 26: 229 – 231.

Mishra, D.P. & T.R. Sahu. 1984. Euphorbiaceous plants used in medicine by the tribals of Madhya Pradesh, India. *J. Econ. Taxon. Bot.* 5: 791 – 794.

Mishra, S.K. & Verma, R.M.P. 1995. Medicinal plants of Champaran (Bihar) used in various diseases. *Flora fauna.* 1: 75 – 76.

Mishra, B. & Vaisya, R. 2004. Bhavaprakasa, Vol. I & II. Chaukhambha Sanskrit Sansthan, Varanasi.

Mitaliya, K. D., D. C. Bhatt, J. N. Patel & S. K. Patel. 2003. Observations on plants used for joint disorders by rural and tribal people of Gujrat. 212-216. In: Singh *et al.* (ed.). Ethnobotany and Medicinal Plants of India and Nepal. Vol-I. Scientific Publishers (India), Jodhpur.

Mitaliya, K. D. & D. C. Bhatt 2003. Rare and endangered medicinal plants of Gujarat. 845-850. In: Singh *et al.* (ed.). Ethnobotany and Medicinal Plants of India and Nepal. Vol-II. Scientific Publishers (India), Jodhpur.

Mohanty, R.B. Padhy, S.N. & Dash, S.K. 1996. Traditional phytotherapy for diarrhoeal diseases in Ganjan and Phulbani district of South Orissa, India. *Ethnobotany.* 8: 60 – 65.

Mokat, D. N. & S. S. Deokule. 2006. Ethno-medico-botanical survey of Ratnagiri district of Maharashtra State. *J. Econ. Taxon. Bot.* 30(Suppl.): 140-144.

Molla, H.A. & B. Roy. 1985. Traditional uses of some medicinal plants by the Rabha tribals in Jalpaiguri district, West Bengal. *J. Econ. Taxon. Bot.* 7: 578 – 580.

Molla, H. A. & D. C. Pal. 1992. Observation on *Vetiveria zizanioides* (L.) Nash. (Khas-Khas). *J. Econ. Taxon. Bot. Addl. Ser.* 10: 101-103.

Mondal, P. & P. K. Mukherjee. 1992. Notes on Ethnobotany of Keonjhar district, Orissa. *J. Econ. Taxon. Bot. Addl. Ser.* 10: 7-18.

Mudgal, V. & D.C. Pal. 1980. Medicinal plants used by tribals of Mayurbhanj (Orissa). *Bull. Bot. Surv. India.* 22: 59 – 62.

Mudgal, V. Khanna, K.K. & Hajra, P.K. 1997. Flora of Madhya Pradesh. Vol. II. BSI. Calcutta.

Mukerji, B. 1953. The Indian pharmaceutical Codex, New Delhi.

Múkherjee, A.S. Mukherjee & M. Mukherjee. 1986. Less known medicinal plants of Rubiaceae in Darjeeling Hills, West Bengal (India). *Indian J. Appl. & Pure. Bot.* 1: 86 – 91.

Mukhopadhyay, C. R. 1992. Useful plants of Birbhum district, West Bengal. *J. Econ. Taxon. Bot. Addl. Ser.* 10: 83-95.

Murthy, K.S., P.C. Sharam & Prem Kishore. 1986. Tribal remedies for sanke bite from Orissa. *Anc. Sci. Life.* 6: 122 – 123.

Muthukumarasamy, S., V. R. Mohan, S. Kumaresan & V. Chelladurai. 2003. Herbal medicinal plants used by Palliyars to obtain relief from gastro-intestinal complaints. 711-714. In: Singh *et al.* (ed.). Ethnobotany and Medicinal Plants of India and Nepal. Vol-II. Scientific Publishers (India), Jodhpur.

Nadanakunjidam, S. 2003. Ethnomedicinal observation from Attapadi Hills of Western Ghats. 732-740. In: Singh *et al.* (ed.). Ethnobotany and Medicinal Plants of India and Nepal. Vol-II. Scientific Publishers (India), Jodhpur.

Nagar, M. 1985. The use of wild plant foods by aboriginal communities in Central India, 337 – 342. In Mishra, V.M. & Belwood, P. (Ed.) *Recent Adv. In Indo-Pacific Prehist.* Oxford & IBH, New Delhi.

Nagarjun, N. & Rao, K.N. 1989. Folk - medicine for diabetes from Rayalaseema of Andhra Pradesh, *Ancient. Sci. Life.* 9: 31 – 35.

Nagendra Prasad, P. & Z. Abraham. 1984. Ethnobotany of Nayadis of North Kerala. *J. Econ. Taxon. Bot.* 5: 41 – 48.

Namjoshi, A.N. 1960. Studies in Pharmacognosy of Ayurvedic Drugs. Board of Research on Ayurveda, Bombay.

Narain, S. & Singh, U. 2006a. Contribution to the Ethnobotanical plants of Mirzapur district (U. P.). *J. Econ. Taxon. Bot.* 30(Suppl.): 14 – 17.

Narain, S. & Singh, U. 2006b. Contribution to the Ethnobotanical plants of Sonbhadra district (U. P.). *J. Econ. Taxon. Bot.* 30(Suppl.): 18 – 20.

Nath, Ashis & G. G. Maiti. 2003. Ethnobotany of Barak valley (Southern Assam) with special reference to folk medicine. 964-971. In: Singh *et al.* (ed.). Ethnobotany and Medicinal Plants of India and Nepal. Vol-II. Scientific Publishers (India), Jodhpur.

Nath, P. C., Sarmah, R., Arunachalam, A. & Barbhuiya, A. 2006. NTFPs: Potential and their conservation in Dihing-patkai wildlife santuary of Assam. *Jou. Of NTFPs.* 13: 17-23.

Nautiyal, S. 1981. Some medicinal plants of Garhwal hills – A traditional use. *J. Sci. Res. Pl. Med.*2: 12 – 18.

Nautiyal, S., R. K. Maikhuri, K. S. Rao & K. G. Saxena. 2003. Ethnobotany of the tolchha bhotiya tribe of the buffer zone village in Nanda biosphere reserve, India. 119-142. In: Singh *et al.* (ed.). Ethnobotany and Medicinal Plants of India and Nepal. Vol-I. Scientific Publishers (India), Jodhpur.

Nayak, P. K., R. K. Nayak & B. P. Choudhury. 2003. A check list of medicinal plants of Kalahandi district in Orissa. 519-532. In: Singh *et al.* (ed.). Ethnobotany and Medicinal Plants of India and Nepal. Vol-II. Scientific Publishers (India), Jodhpur.

Nayak, R. K., P. K. Nayak & B. P. Choudhury. 2003. Some medicinal weeds of Mahanadi Delta. 533-538. In: Singh *et al.* (ed.). Ethnobotany and Medicinal Plants of India and Nepal. Vol-II. Scientific Publishers (India), Jodhpur.

Negi, K.S., J.K. Tiwari & R.D. Gaur. 1985. Economic importance of some common trees in Garhwal, Himalaya: An ethnobotanical study. *Indian J. Forestry.*8: 276 – 289.

Oommachan, M. 1977. The flora of Bhopal. J. K. Jain Brothers, Bhopal.

Pal, D.C. & J.N. Srivastava. 1976. Preliminary notes of ethnobotany of Singhbhum district, Bihar, *Bull. Bot. Surv. India.*18. 247 – 250.

Pal, D.C. 1980. Observations on folklore about plants used in veterinary medicine in Bengal, Orissa & Bihar. *Bull. Bot. Surv. India.*22: 96 – 99.

Pal, G.D. 1984. Observations on ethnobotany of tribals of Subansiri. Arunachal Pradesh. *Bull. Bot. Surv. India.*26: 26 - 37.

Pal, D.C. & S.K. Jain. 1989. Notes on Lodha medicine in Midnapur district. W.B. India. *Econ. Bot.*43: 464 – 470.

Pandey, G.S. 1969. Bhavaprakash Nighantu (With Commentary by Dr. K.C. Chunekar). Chowkhamba Sanskrit Sansthan, Varanasi.

Pandey, A. K. & S. D. Rout. 2006. Ethnobotanical uses of plants of Similipal Biosphere Reserve (Orissa). *Ethnobotany* 18: 102-106.

Pandit, B.R. Kotiwar, O.S., Oza, R. A. & Kumar, R.M. 1996. Ethno - medicinal plant lore from Gir forest, Gujarat. *Adv Plant Sci.* 9: 81 – 84.

Panigrahi, A.K. & Alka, S. 2000. Glossary of useful and economically important plants. New Central Book Agency. Calcutta.

Paranjpe, P. Indian medicinal plants: forgotten healers. 2005. Chaukhamba Sanskrit Pratisthan, Delhi.

Pawar, S. & Patil, D. A. 2006. Ethnobotanical aspects of naturalised exotic plants of Jalgaon district, Maharashtra. *Jour. of NTFPs.* 13:55-59.

Pearsall, J. & Trumble, B. 1996. The oxford english Reference Dictionary. Oxford University Press, Oxford.

Pereira, N. 2006. Ethnobotanical relevance in tribal life: A study on Warli tribe of Thane district, Maharashtra. *J. Econ. Taxon. Bot.* 30(Suppl.): 31-39.

Peter Paul Hembrom & Goel, A. K. 2005. Horopathy: Ethnomedicine of Mundas. *Ethnobotany*.17:89-95.

Prakash, A. & K. K. Singh. 2006. Useful medicinal plants for general tonic, sexual vigour, strength, vitality and venereal diseases among the tribals of Uttar Pradesh and Uttaranchal.. *J. Econ. Taxon. Bot.* 30(Suppl.): 326-331.

Prasad, V. K., T. Rajagopal & K. V. S. Badarinath. 2003. Notes on economic importance of wild plants of Rampa agency- East Godovari district, Andhra Pradesh. 603-612. In: Singh *et al.* (ed.). Ethnobotany and Medicinal Plants of India and Nepal. Vol-II. Scientific Publishers (India), Jodhpur.

Printya, J.V. 1963. The Sushruta Samhita. Vol. I&II, Motilal Banarsidas. Delhi.

Puri, H.S. 1983. Medicinal plants of Tejpur (Assam). *Bull. Medico-ethnobot. Res.*4: 1 – 13.

Purkayastha, J. & Subhan, C.N. 2005. Biological activitis of ethnomedicinal claims of some plant species of Assam. *IJTK.* 5(2), 229 – 236.

Purohit, V.P., R.A. Silas & R.D. Gaur. 1985. Ethnobotanical studies of some medicinal plants used in skin diseases from Raath (Pauri) Garhwal, Himalaya. *J. Sci. Res. Pl. Med.*6: 39 – 47.

Radhakrisnan, K., Pandurangan, A.G., Pusphangadan, P. & Sasidharan, A. 1996. Less known ethnomedicinal plants of Kerala state and their conservation. *Ethnobotany* 8: 82-84.

Rai, M.K. 1985. Plants used as medicine by tribals of Chhindwara District (M.P.). *J. Econ. Taxon. Bot.*7: 385 – 387.

Rai, Bharat, D. B. Khawas & Rabindra Chettri. 1992. Certain plants in the folklore and folklife of Darjeeling and Sikkim Hills. I: Used for the treatment of human ailments. *J. Econ. Taxon. Bot. Addl. Ser.* 10: 193-198.

Rajan, S. 1992. Medicinal Plants of Ootacamund, Nilgiris, Tamil Nadu. *J. Econ. Taxon. Bot. Addl. Ser.* 10: 429-460.

Rajan, S., D. Suresh Baburaj, M. Sethuraman & S. Parimala. 2003. Folk-Medicine among Nilgiri Irulas: An emerging trend in primary health care practice. 791-795. In: Singh *et al.* (ed.). Ethnobotany and Medicinal Plants of India and Nepal. Vol-II. Scientific Publishers (India), Jodhpur.

Rajendran, K., R. Balakrishnan & S. Chandrasekaran. 2003. Common medicinal plants and their utilization by villagers in east coast. 727-731. In: Singh *et al.* (ed.). Ethnobotany and Medicinal Plants of India and Nepal. Vol-II. Scientific Publishers (India), Jodhpur.

Rajendran, K. & S. K. Rengamani. 2006. Medicinal plants and their utilization by villagers in Southern districts of Tamilnadu. *J. Econ. Taxon. Bot.* 30(Suppl.): 208-216.

Rajwar, G.S. 1983. Low altitude medicinal plants of South Garhwal. *Bull. Medico-ethnobot. Res.* 4: 14 – 28.

Ramachandran, V.S. & N.C. Nair. 1981 a. Ethnobotanical studies in cannanore district, Kerala state (India). *J. Econ. Taxon. Bot.* 2: 65 - 72.

Ramachandran, V.S. & N.C. Nair. 1981 b. Ethnobotanical observations on 'lrulars' of Tamil Nadu (India). *J. Econ. Taxon. Bot.* 2: 183 – 190.

Rana, T.S., Datt & Rao, R.R. 1996. Strategies for sustainable utilization of plant resources by the tribals of the Tons – Valley, Western Himalayas. *Ethnobotany.*8: 96 – 104.

Rao, R.R. & B. Neogi, 1980. Observations on the ethnobotany of the Khasi & Garo tribes in Meghalaya. *J. Econ. Taxon. Bot.*1: 157 – 162.

Rao, R.R. 1981 a. Ethnobotanical stuidies on the flora of Meghalaya – Some interesting reports of herbal medicines. 137-148. In S.K. Jain (Ed.) *Glimpses of Indian Ethnobotany.*

Rao, R.R. 1981 b. Ethnobotany of Meghalaya – Medicinal plants used by Khasi and Garo tribes. *Econ. Bot.* 35: 4 – 9.

Rao, R.R. & N.S. Jamir. 1982a. Ethnobotanical studies in Nagaland – II: 54 Medicinal plants used by Nagas. *J. Econ. Taxon. Bot.* 3: 11 – 17.

Rao, R.R. & N.S. Jamir, 1982b. Ethnobotanical studies in Nagaland – I: Medicinal plants. *J. Econ. Bot.* 36: 176 – 181.

Rao, K.P. & Sreeramulu, S.H. 1985. Ethnobotany of selected medicinal plants of Srikakulam district, A.P. *Ancient Sci. life.* 4: 238-244.

Rao, R.R. & Haridasan, K. 1991. An ethnobotanical survey of medicinal and other useful plants form North-East India. *J. Eco. Tax. Bot.* 15: 423-436.

Rao, V L N., B. R. Busi, B. Dharma Rao, Ch. Seshagiri Rao, K Bharathi & M Venkaiah. 2006. Ethnomedicinal practices among Khonds of Visakhapatanam district, A. P. *IJTK* 5(2):217-219.

Rastogi & Mehrotra 1997. Compendium of Indian medicine Plant, Vol. I, II, III, IV & V. CDRI, Lucknow and PID Delhi.

Ravikumar, K. & R. Vijaya Sankar. 2003. Ethnobotany of Malayali tribes in Melpattu village, Javvadhu Hills of Eastern ghats, Tiruvannamalai district, Tamil Nadu. In:

Singh *et al.* (ed.). Ethnobotany and Medicinal Plants of India and Nepal. Vol-II. Scientific Publishers (India), Jodhpur.

Reddy, M.B., Reddy, K.R. & Reddy, M.N. 1991. Ethnobotany of Cuddapah district. A.P., India. *Int. J. Pharmacog.* 29; 273-280.

Rosakutty, P. J., A. Stella Roslin & S. Ignacimutha. 2003. Sone traditional folklore medicinal plants of Kanyakumari district, Tamil Nadu. 369-375. In: Maheshwari, J. K. (ed.). Ethnobotany and Medicinal Plants of Indian Subcontinent. Scientific Publishers (India), Jodhpur.

Roy, G.P. & K.K. Chuturvedi. 1986a. Plants used as tonic by the tribals of Abujh Marh Reserve area, Bastar district in Madhya Pradesh. *Vanyajati.* 34: 27 – 32.

Roy, G.P. & K.K. Chaturvedi. 1986b. Ethnomedicinal trees of Abujh-Marh area, Madhya Pradesh. *Folklore.* 27: 95 – 100.

Roy, G.P. & K.K. Chaturvedi. 1987. Less known medicinal uses of rare and endangered plants of Abujh Marh reserve area, Bastar (Madhya Pradesh). *J. Econ. Taxon. Bot.*9: 325 – 328.

Sadhale, A., Mujumdar, A.M. & Pendse, G.S. 1991. Ethnobotanical studies of sacred grove at Ajiwali, Pune district, *J. Econ. Taxon. Bot.* 15: 167-172.

Saikia, N. & S. C. Nath. 2003. Ethnomedicinal observations of some species of the genus *Curcuma* L. growing in Assam. 430-433. In: Singh *et al.* (ed.). Ethnobotany and Medicinal Plants of India and Nepal. Vol-I. Scientific Publishers (India), Jodhpur.

Saikh, N. & Subhan C. Nath. 2003. Indigenous practice of treating Dental disorders in Assam. 496-499. In: Singh *et al.* (ed.). Ethnobotany and Medicinal Plants of India and Nepal. Vol-I. Scientific Publishers (India), Jodhpur.

Sahoo, A. K. & D. D. Bahali. 2003. Plants used in less known ethnomedicines and medico-religious beliefs in Phulbani district of Orissa. 500-504. In: Singh *et al.* (ed.). Ethnobotany and Medicinal Plants of India and Nepal. Vol-I. Scientific Publishers (India), Jodhpur.

Samvatsar, S. & V. B. Diwanji. 2003. Plants used for Rheumatism by the tribals of Western M. P. 305-314. In: Maheshwari, J. K. (ed.). Ethnobotany and Medicinal Plants of Indian Subcontinent. Scientific Publishers (India), Jodhpur.

Saren, A. M., R. Sen & D. C. Pal. 2003. A contribution to the ethnobotany of Bankura district, West Bengal. 545-555. In: Maheshwari, J. K. (ed.). Ethnobotany and Medicinal Plants of Indian Subcontinent. Scientific Publishers (India), Jodhpur.

Sarkar, N., S. Rudra & S. K. Basu. 2003. Ethnobotany of Bangriposi, Mayurbhanj, Orissa. Traditional medicinal uses of plants of Himachal Hills. 509-514. In: Maheshwari, J. K. (ed.). Ethnobotany and Medicinal Plants of Indian Subcontinent. Scientific Publishers (India), Jodhpur.

Sarma, G. C. & R. S. Baishya. 1992. Studies on the medicinal uses of plants by the North-East tribes-IV. *J. Econ. Taxon. Bot. Addl. Ser.* 10: 177-184.

Sarma, S. K., B. Bevi & D. K. Bhattacharjya. 2006. Ethnomedicinal uses of plants by the Sarania tribe of Nalbari district of Assam. *J. Econ. Taxon. Bot.* 30(Suppl.): 133-139.

Sasidharan, N. & Augustine, Jomy. 2006. Ethnobotany of the tribes living in and around the Periyar Tiger Reserve, Southern Western Ghats, India. *J. Econ. Taxon. Bot.* 30(Suppl.): 45 - 58.

Satapathy, K. B. 1992. Medicinal uses of some Plants among the tribals of Sundargarh district, Orissa. *J. Econ. Taxon. Bot. Addl. Ser.* 10: 241-249.

Sattapathy, K. B. & M. Brahmam. 2003. Some interesting phytotherapeutic claims of tribals of Jajpur district, Orissa. 467-472. In: Maheshwari, J. K. (ed.). Ethnobotany and Medicinal Plants of Indian Subcontinent. Scientific Publishers (India), Jodhpur.

Saxena, H.O. & P.K. Dutta. 1975. Studies on the ethnobotany of Orissa. *Bull. Bot. Surv. India.*17: 124 – 131.

Saxena, A.P. & K.M. Vyas. 1981. Ethnobotanical records on infections diseases from tribals of Banda district. *J. Econ. Taxon. Bot.*2: 191 – 194.

Saxena, H.O., M. Brahman & P.K. Dutta. 1931. Ethnobotanical studies in Orissa, 232 – 244. In S.K. Jain (Ed.). *Glimpses of Indian Ethnobotany.*

Saxena, A.P. & K.M. Vyas. 1983. Ethnobotany of Dhasan Valley. *J. Econ. Taxon. Bot.* 4: 121 – 128.

Saxena, A.P. & K.M. Vyas. 1986. Antimicrobial activity of seeds of some ethnomedicinal plants. *J. Econ. Taxon. Bot.* 8: 291 – 299.

Saxena, H.O. 1986. Observations on the ethnobotany of Madhya Pradesh. *Bull. Bot. Surv. India.* 28: 149 – 156.

Samvatsar, Swati. 1996. The Flora of Western Tribal Madhya Pradesh, *Scientific Publisher,* Jodhpur.

Sebastian, M.K. & M.M. Bhandari. 1984. Medico-ethnobotany of Mount Abu, Rajasthan. India. *J. Ethnopharmacol.* 12: 223 – 230.

Sebastian, M.K. 1984. Plants used as veterinary medicines, galactagogues and fodder in the forest areas of Rajasthan. *J. Econ. Taxon. Bot.* 5: 785 – 788.

Sebastian, M.K. & Bhandari, M.M. 1984. Some plants used as veterinary medicines by bhils. *Int. J. Trop. Agric.* 2; 307-310.

Sen, R., D. C. Pal. & B. Roy. 1984. Botany and ethnobotany of Parashi. *J. Econ. Taxon. Bot.* 5: 857 – 858.

Sen, R.S. Bandopadhayay, E. Biswas & A. Guha. 1985. Ethnobotanical uses of Herbaria – IV. *J. Econ. Taxon. Bot.* 6: 331 – 335.

Sen, S.K. & Pradhan, N.B. 1999. Conservation of ethnomedicinal plants of Bargarh district in Orissa. *Adv. Plant Sci.*12: 207-213.

Shah, N.C. & M.C. Joshi. 1971. An ethnobotanical study of Kumaon region of India. *Econ. Bot.* 25: 414 – 422.

Shah, G.L., A.R. Menon & G.V. Gopal. 1981. An account of the ethnobotany of Saurashtra in Gujarat state (India). *J. Econ. Taxon. Bot.*2: 173 – 182.

Shah, N.C. 1982. Herbal folk medicines in northern India. *J. Ethnopharmacol.*6: 293 – 301.

Shah, G.L. & Gopal, G.V. 1982. An ethnobotanical profile of the Dangies. *J. Econ. Taxon. Bot.* 3: 355-364.

Shah, G.L., S.S. Yadav & N. Badri 1983. Medicinal plants from Dahanu Forest Division in Maharashtra State. *J. Econ. Taxon. Bot.* 4: 141 – 151.

Shah, G.L. 1984. Some economically important plants of Salsette Island near Bombay. *J. Econ. Taxon. Bot.* 5: 753 – 765.

Shah, G.L. & G.V. Gopal 1986. Folklore medicines of Vasavas, Gujarat, India. *Acta. Bot. Indica.*14: 48 – 53.

Shah, G.L. & G.V. Gopal 1992. An ethnobotanical profile of the Dangies. *J. Econ. Taxon. Bot.* 3: 355 – 364.

Shah, M. A. U. 2005. Ethnomedicinal plants of Bhakkar Tehsil in Punjab, Pakistan. *Ethnobotany.* 17: 171-175.

Sharma, R.K. & Bhagvan Dash. 1976. Charaka Samhita, Vol. I & II, Chaukhamba Sanskrit Series, Varansi, India.

Sharma, P.K., S.K. Dhyani & V. Shanker. 1979. Some useful and medicinal plants of the district Dehradun and Siwalik. *J. Sci. Res. Pl. Med.*1: 17 – 43.

Sharma, B.D. & S.K. Malhotra. 1984. A contribution to the ethnobotany of tribal areas in Maharashtra. *J. Econ. Taxon. Bot.*5: 533 – 537.

Sharma, K. K. & Shiva Sharma. 1992. Medicinal plants of Southern Aravalli Hills. *J. Econ. Taxon. Bot. Addl. Ser.* 10: 209-217.

Sharma, P.V. 2003. Dravyaguna - Vijnana. Chaukhamba bharti academy Varanasi.

Sharma, B. D. & J. C. Rana 2003. Traditional medicinal uses of plants of Himachal Hills. 173-176. In: Maheshwari, J. K. (ed.). Ethnobotany and Medicinal Plants of Indian Subcontinent. Scientific Publishers (India), Jodhpur.

Sharma, H. M., A. Radhapyari Devi & B. Manihar Sharma. 2003. Ethnomedicinal uses of Monocotyledonous plants by the Meiteis of Manipur. 473-480. In: Singh *et al.* (ed.). Ethnobotany and Medicinal Plants of India and Nepal. Vol-I. Scientific Publishers (India), Jodhpur.

Sharma, P. K., N. S. Chauhan & Brij lal. 2003. Comercially important medicinal and aromatic plants of Parvati valley, Himachal Pradesh. 937-942. In: Singh *et al.* (ed.). Ethnobotany and Medicinal Plants of India and Nepal. Vol-II. Scientific Publishers (India), Jodhpur.

Sharma, S. C., G. N. Sharma & R. K. Aggarwal. 2006. Traditional significant Medicinal plants of Nagaur district (Rajasthan). *J. Econ. Taxon. Bot.* 30(Suppl.): 320-325.

Shekhawat, G.S. & Sunil Anand. 1984. An ethnobotanical profile of Indian Desert. *J. Econ Taxon. Bot.* 5: 591 – 598.

Shubhangi Pawar & D.A. Patil. 2006. Ethnomedicinal aspects of naturalised exotic plants of Jalgaon district, Maharashtra, India. *J. NTFPs* 13(1):55-59.

Shukla, G., V. Mudgal & K. K. Khanna. 1992. Notes on medicinal uses of plants known amongst rural folk-lore of Pratapgarh and Sultanpur districts, U. P. *J. Econ. Taxon. Bot. Addl. Ser.* 10: 219-225.

Shukla, G., B. K. Verma & H. P. Pandey. 2003. Folk-lore herbotherapy of Jalaun district, U. P. India. 143-147. In: Singh *et al.* (ed.). Ethnobotany and Medicinal Plants of India and Nepal. Vol-I. Scientific Publishers (India), Jodhpur.

Siddiqui, M.B. & Husian, W. 1991. Traditional treatment of diarrhoea and dysentery through herbal drugs in rural India. *fitoterapia.*62: 325 – 329.

Siddque, M. A. A., Jhon, A. Q. & Paul, T. M. 1995. Status of some important medicinal and aromatic plants of Kashmir Himalaya. *Adv Plant Sci.* 8: 134-139.

Sikarwar, R.L.S. & Kaushik, J.P. 1993. Folk medicines of the Morena district, M.P., India. *Int J Pharmacog.* 31: 283-287.

Singh, Harbhajan. 1945. Home useful wild plants of the Delhi Province. *India. J. Agr. Sci.*15: 297 – 307.

Singh, K.K., S.K. Palvi & H.B. Singh. 1980. Survey of some medicinal plants of Dharchula block in Pithoragarh district of U.P. *Bull. Medico-ethnobot. Res.*1: 1– 7.

Singh, V. & R.P. Pandey. 1980. Medicinal plantlore of the tribals of eastern Rajasthan. *J. Econ. Taxon. Bot.*1: 137 – 147.

Singh, K.K. & J.K. Maheshwari. 1983. Traditional phytotherapy amongst the tribals of Varanasi district, Uttar Pradesh. *J. Econ. Taxon. Bot.*4: 829 – 838.

Singh, K.K. & Saha & J.K. Maheshwari. 1985. Ethnobotany of *Helicteres isora* L., in Kheri district, Uttar Pradesh. *J. Econ. Taxon. Bot.* 7: 487 – 492.

Singh, A.K., R.N. Singh & S.K. Singh. 1987. Some ethnobotanical plants of Terai region of Gorakhpur, district- I. *J. Econ. Taxon. Bot.* 9: 407 – 410.

Singh, H. 1988. Ethnobiological treatment of Piles by Bhoxas of Uttar Pradesh. *Anc. Sci. Life.* 8: 167 – 170.

Singh, L. B., A. K. Verma & S. S. N. Sinha. 1992. Preliminary observations on the Ethnomedicinal plants of Godda district (Bihar). *J. Econ. Taxon. Bot. Addl. Ser.* 10: 205-208.

Singh, H. & Maheshwari, J.K. 1992. Traditional remedies for snake bite & Scorpion – sting among the Bhoxas of Nainital district. U.P. *Aryavaidyah.*6: 120 123.

Singh, L.B. & Singh, C.L. 1992. An Ethno-Medico-botanical study of Deoghar district (Bihar). *Biojournal.* 4: 83 – 86.

Singh, P.B. & Aswal, B.S. 1992. Medicinal plants of Himachal Pradesh used in Pharmaceutical Industry. *Bull. Med. Ethno. Res.* 13: 172 – 208.

Singh, J. P., Suchita Kumar, Th. Puinyabati Devi & Sudhir Kumar. 1992. Medicinal Plants of Manipur – I. *J. Econ. Taxon. Bot. Addl. Ser.* 10: 233-239.

Singh, P.B. 1993. Medicinal plants of Ayurvedic importance from Mandi district of Himachal Pradesh. *Bull. Med. Ethnobot. Res.* 14: 126 – 136.

Singh, K.K. and Prakash, A. 1994. Indigenous phytotherapy among the Gond tribes of Uttar Pradesh, India. *Ethnobotany.* 6: 37 – 41.

Singh, K.K. 1997. Studies on native medicine of Jaunsari tribe of Dehradun district, U.P. India. *Int. J Pharmacog.*35: 105 – 110.

Singh, V.K., Ali, Z.A., & Siddique, M.K. 1997. Folk medicinal plaats of the Garwal and Kumaon forest of U.P. India. *Hamdard Med* 40(4): 35-47.

Singh, H.B.K. 1997. Studies on Medico-botany of Meitel community in Manipur State, India (II). *Adv. Plant. Sci.* 10: 13 – 18.

Singh, V.K., Ali, Z.A. & Siddiqui, M.K. 1997. Medicinal plants used by the forest ethnics of Gorakhpur district (U.P.). *Int. J. Pharmacog.*35: 194 – 206.

Singh, S.K., Das. P.K. & Das, M.N. 1998. Ethnobotanical studies on some medicinal plants of Rajgir, Bihar. *Int. J. Mendeol.*15: 145 – 148.

Singh, V. & R. P. Pandey. 1998. Ethnobotany of Rajasthan. Scientific publisher, Jodhpur.

Singh, G. S. 2003. Ethnobotanical study of useful plants of Kullu district in North Western Himalaya. 185-198. In: Maheshwari, J. K. (ed.). *Ethnobotany and Medicinal Plants of Indian Subcontinent.* Scientific Publishers (India), Jodhpur.

Singh, A. K. 2003. A contribution to the ethnobotany of Sub-Himalayan region of Eastern U. P. 237-246. In: Maheshwari, J. K. (ed.). Ethnobotany and Medicinal Plants of Indian Subcontinent. Scientific Publishers (India), Jodhpur.

Singh, G. S. 2003. Ethnobotanical inventory of Sariska national park in the Aravalli Hills of Eastern Rajasthan. 181-195. In: Singh *et al.* (ed.). Ethnobotany and Medicinal Plants of India and Nepal. Vol-I. Scientific Publishers (India), Jodhpur.

Singh, P. K. & K. Ibotombi Singh. 2003. Mother and Child birth: I- An ethnobotanical study of the Meitei community of Manipur State. 457-465. In: Singh *et al.* (ed.). Ethnobotany and Medicinal Plants of India and Nepal. Vol-I. Scientific Publishers (India), Jodhpur.

Singh, P. K. & K. Ibotombi Singh. 2003. First-aid remedies: An ethno-medico-botanical study of the Meitei community of Manipur State. 466-472. In: Singh *et al.* (ed.). Ethnobotany and Medicinal Plants of India and Nepal. Vol-I. Scientific Publishers (India), Jodhpur.

Singh, V. P. & R. C. Srivastava. 2003. Economic importance of Sedges of Uttar Pradesh. 978-981. In: Singh *et al.* (ed.). Ethnobotany and Medicinal Plants of India and Nepal. Vol-II. Scientific Publishers (India), Jodhpur.

Sinha, B. K., B. K. Shukla & P. Sharma. 2006. Ethnomedicinal plants of Chhatisgarh with sporadic distribution. *J. Econ. Taxon. Bot.* 30(Suppl.):70-109.

Sivakumar, A., M. S. Subramanian, M. Karunakaran & A. Burkanudeen. 2003. Ethnobotany of Poliyars of Anaimalai Hills, Tamil Nadu. 679-685. In: Singh *et al.* (ed.). Ethnobotany and Medicinal Plants of India and Nepal. Vol-II. Scientific Publishers (India), Jodhpur.

Sood, S. K. & S. Thakur. 2004. *Ethnobotany of Rewalsar Himalaya.* Deep publications. New Delhi.

Srivastava, D.K. & S.K. Varma. 1981. An ethnobotanical study of Santhal Pargana, Bihar, *Inidan. Forester.* 107: 30 – 41.

Srivastava, P. K., K. K. Khanna & V. Mudgal. 1992. New Traditional herbal remedies from the rural folklore of Hamirpur district, U.P. *J. Econ. Taxon. Bot. Addl. Ser.* 10: 399-404.

Srivastava, S.C. and Rout, N. 1994. Some plants of ethnopaediatric importance in district Koraput, Orissa. *Bull. Bot. Surv. India.* 36: 166 – 168.

Srivastava, R. C., V. P. Singh & M. K. Singh. 2003. Medicinal plants of Jaunpur district U. P. India. 148-159. In: Singh *et al.* (ed.). Ethnobotany and Medicinal Plants of India and Nepal. Vol-I. Scientific Publishers (India), Jodhpur.

Srivastava, A. K. & Monika Singh. 2003. Medicinal potential of grasses in Rajasthan. 170-176. In: Singh *et al.* (ed.). Ethnobotany and Medicinal Plants of India and Nepal. Vol-I. Scientific Publishers (India), Jodhpur.

Srivastava, S. C., S. Mitra & S. Bandyopadhyay. 2003. Some plants of ethnomedicinal importance from Darjeeling district, West Bengal. 972-977. In: Singh *et al.* (ed.). Ethnobotany and Medicinal Plants of India and Nepal. Vol-II. Scientific Publishers (India), Jodhpur.

Subramani, S. P. & G. S. Goraya. 2003. Some folklore medicinal plants of kolli Hills record of a Natti Vaidyas Sammelan. 665-678. In: Singh *et al.* (ed.). Ethnobotany and Medicinal Plants of India and Nepal. Vol-II. Scientific Publishers (India), Jodhpur.

Subramanian, A., V. R. Mohan, S. Kumaresan & A. Chelladurai. 2003. Medicinal plants used by the valaiyans of Madurai district, Tamil Nadu. 785-787. In: Singh *et al.* (ed.). Ethnobotany and Medicinal Plants of India and Nepal. Vol-II. Scientific Publishers (India), Jodhpur.

Sudhakar, S. & R.S. Rolla. 1985. Medicinal plants of Upper East Godavari District, Andhra Pradesh, and need for establishment of Medicinal Farm. *J. Econ. Taxon. Bot.* 7: 399 – 406.

Sudhakar, A. & Chetty, K.M. 1998. Medicinal importance of some angiospermic weeds used by the rural people of Chittoor district of Andhra Pradesh, India. *Fitoterapia.* 69: 390-400.

Sur, P. R., R. Sen & A. C. Halder. 1992. Ethnobotanical study of Purulia district, West Bengal. *J. Econ. Taxon. Bot. Addl. Ser.* 10: 259-264.

Tarafder, C. R. 1978. Some interesting new uses of the well known plant Vitex negundo L. (NISINDA). Bull. Bot. Surv. India 20: 176-177.

Tarafder, C.R. & H.N. Rai Chaudhuri. 1981. Less known medicinal uses of plants among the tribals of Hazaribagh district of Bihar. 208 – 217. In S.K. Jain (Ed.). *Glimpses of Indian Ethnobotany.*

Tarafder, C.R. 1985. *Acacia catechu* (L.f.) Willd. (Fabaceae) - Inddigenous and less known uses of the plant. *Folklore.* 26: 158 – 159.

Tarafder, C.R. 1983. Traditional medicinal plants used by the tribals of Ranchi & Hazaribagh district, Bihar- Plants used in stomach troubles. *J. Econ. Taxon. Bot.* 4: 891 – 896.

Tarafder, C.R. 1983a. Ethnogynaecology in relation to plants – II. Plants used in abortion. *J. Econ. Taxon. Bot.* 4: 507 – 516.

Tarafder, C.R. 1983b. Ethnogynaecology in relation to plants – I. Plants used in antifertility and conception. *J. Econ. Taxon. Bot.* 4: 483 – 490.

Tarafder, C.R. 1986. Ethnobotany of Chhotanagpur (Bihar). *Folklore.* 27: 95 – 100.

Tarafder, C.R. 1987. Some traditional knowledge about tribal health. *Folklore.* 28: 37–42.

Tarafder, C.R. 1984a. Ethnogynaecology in relation to plants. Part- III. Plants used to accelerate delivery & in pre & post-natal complaints. *J. Econ. Taxon. Bot.* 5: 572 – 576.

Tarafder, C.R. 1984b. Less known nine medicinal plants used by the tribals for curing gonorrhoea in Ranchi and Hazaribagh district, Bihar. *Folklore.* 25: 47- 49.

Tarafder, C.R. 1984c. Less known twenty three medicinal plants used by the tribals for curing boils in Ranchi and Hazaribagh district. Bihar. *Vanyajati.* 32: 14 – 19.

Tewari, L.C., Agrawal, R.G. Pandey, M.J. Uniyal, M.R. & Pandey, G. 1990. Some traditional folk medicine from the Himalayas (U.P. region), *Aryavaidyan* 4: 49-57.

Thomas, Jery & Jhon De Britto. 2003. Weeds of medicinal importance in Tirunelveli district in Tamil Nadu. 363-367. In: Maheshwari, J.K. (ed.). *Ethnobotany and Medicinal Plants of Indian Subcontinent.* Scientific Publishers (India), Jodhpur.

Thomas, J. & A. John De Britto. 2003. Ethnobotanical study in Wynad district in Kerala. 815-824. In: Singh *et al.* (ed.). *Ethnobotany and Medicinal Plants of India and Nepal.* Vol-II. Scientific Publishers (India), Jodhpur.

Tigga, M., G. S. Lakra & P. S. N. Rao. 2003. Medicinal value of latex yielding plants from Andman & Nicobar Islands. 765-772. 60. In: Singh *et al.* (ed.). *Ethnobotany and Medicinal Plants of India and Nepal.* Vol-II. Scientific Publishers (India), Jodhpur.

Tiwari, K.C., R. Majumdar & S. Bhattacharjee. 1979. Folklore medicine from Assam and Arunachal Pradesh (district Tirap). *Quart. J. Crude Drug Res.* 17: 61 – 67.

Tiwari, K.C. & Majumdar, R. 1996. Medicinal plant form upper Assam borders having specific folk uses. *Sachitra Ayurved* 49: 207-214.

Tribedi, G.N., R.N. Kayal & H.N. Rai Chaudhuri. 1982. Some medicinal plants of Mayurbhanj (Orissa). *Bull. Bot. Surv. India.* 24: 117 – 120.

Tribedi, G.N., H.A. Mulla & D.C. Pal. 1985. Some uses of plants from the tribal areas of Chotanagpur, Bihar. *Nagarjun.* 29: 15 – 18.

Tripathi *et al.* 1996. Medicinal plants of Rajasthan in Indian system of medicine. *Ancient Sci. Life.* 15: 190 – 212.

Udayan, P. S., S. George, K. V. Tushar, S. Sudhakar Raja & I. Balachandran. 2006 a. A note on the Ethnomedicinal plants used by the Kaadar Tribes, Kariyan Shola, Top Slip, Tamil Nadu. *J. Econ. Taxon. Bot.* 30(Suppl.): 5 – 12.

Udayan, P. S., S. George, K. V. Tushar, S. Sudhakar Raja & I. Balachandran. 2006 b. Ethnobotanical information from the Muduga tribe of Mukkali, near Silent Valley National Park, Palakkad district, Kerala. *J. Econ. Taxon. Bot.* 30(Suppl.):27 –30.

Uniyal, M.R. 1968. Medicinal plants of Bhagirathi valley lying in Uttarkashi forest division. *Indian Forester.* 94: 407 – 420.

Uniyal, M.R. & M.S. Chauhan. 1973. Traditionally important medicinal plants of Kangra Valley in Dharamsala forest circle, Himachal Pradesh. *J. Res. Indian. Med.*8: 76 – 85.

Upadhye, A., Kumbhojkar, M.S. & Vartak, V.D. 1986. Observations on wild plants used in folk medicine in the rural areas of the Kolhapur district. *Ancient Sci Life* 6: 119-121.

Upadhyay, R. & Jaswant singh. 2005. Ethnomedicinal uses of plants from Tikri forest of Gonda district. *Ethnobotany*. 17: 167– 170.

Upadhye, A. M.S. Kumbhojkar & V.D. Vartak. 1986. Observations on wild plants used in folk medicine in the rural areas of the Kolhapur district. *Anc. Sci. Life*. 6: 119 – 121.

Upadhay, O.P., Kumar, K. & Tiwari, R.K. 1998. Ethnobotanical study of skin treatment uses of medicinal plants of Bihar, *Pharmaceut Biol.* 36: 161 – 172.

Upadhyay, R. & S. V. S. Chauhan. 2003. Ethnobotanical uses of plant gums by the tribals. 601-602. In: Singh *et al.* (ed.). *Ethnobotany and Medicinal Plants of India and Nepal.* Vol-II. Scientific Publishers (India), Jodhpur.

Venugopal, K. & K. Raghunathan. 1982 (Ed.). Medicobotanical-cum-ethnomedicinal survey of district Jhabua (M.P.). *Centr. Counc. Res. Ayurv. Siddha Newsletter.* 4 - 5.

Ved Prakash & S.K. Jain. 1984. Poaceae: Tribe - Isachneae. *Fasc. Fl. India.*14: 41 – 42. Bot. Surv. India, Calcutta.

Ved Prakash & B.N. Mehrotra. 1987. Ethnobotanical studies on the flora of Khandala, Maharashtra State. *J. Econ. Taxon. Bot.* 9: 205 – 208.

Ved Prakash & B.N. Mehrotra. 1988. Unrecorded traditional medicines-I. *Anc. Sci. Life.* 3: 110-112.

Verma, D. M., Balakrishan, N. P. & Dixit, R. P. 1993. Flora of Madhya Pradesh. BSI, Calcatta.

Vijaya Kumar, R. & Pullaiah, T. 1998. Medicinal Plants used by the tribals of Prakasham District, A.P. *Ethnobotany*. 10: 97-102.

Vir Jee, G.H. Dar, P. Kachroo & G.M. Bhat. 1984. Taxo – ethnobotanical studies of the rural areas in district Rajouri (Jammu). *J. Econ. Taxon. Bot.* 5: 831 – 838.

Viswanathan, K. 1995. Survey on medicinal spices of the Nilgiris. *Ancient Sci. life.* 14: 258-267.

Warrier, P. K., V. P. K. Nambiar & C. Ramankutty. 1994. Indian medicinal plants. Vol. I-V. oriental longum, Chennai.

Yesodharan, K. & K. A. Sujana. 2006. Ethnomedicinal plants used by the trbals of Parambikulam Wildlife Sanctuary, Kerala to cure cuts and wounds. *J. Econ. Taxon. Bot.* 30(Suppl.): 365-369.

INDEX OF ENGLISH, HINDI & SANSKRIT NAMES OF PLANTS

Aristolachia bracteolata	Worm killer	Kirmar	Kitamari	27
Artemisia nilagirica	Indian wormwood	Nagdona, Dauna	Damanah	28
Artocarpus heterophyllus	Jackfruit tree	Kathal	Panasah	29
Asclepias curassavica	Wild epicacunha	Kauathori	Bharadvaji	31
Asparagus adscendens	Asparagus	Safed musallee	Musali	32
Averrhoa carambola	Carambola apple	Kamarakh	Karmarangah	33
Baliospermum montanum	-	Danti	Danti	34
Bambusa arundinacea	Thorny bamboo	Bans	Vamsah	35
Barringtonia acutangula	Small Indian oak	Samudraphal	Samudraphala	36
Basella alba L. var. *rubra*	Indian spinach	Poi	Upodika	38
Bauhinia racemosa	Downy mountain ebony	Jhinjhora	Ashmantak	39
Benincasa hispida.	White gourd melon	Petha	Kusmandah	40
Berberis aristata	Tree termeric	Daaruhallada	Daruharidra	41
Beta vulgaris	Garden beet	Cukkandar	Palakya	42
Betula utilis	Himalayan silver birch	Bhojpatra	Bhurjah	43
Bixa orellana	Arnotta plant	Sinduriya	Sinduri	44
Blumea lacera	Blumea	Kukaraunda	Kukundarah	45
Borassus flabellifer	Palmyra palm	Tar	Talah	46
Boswellia serrata	Indian olibanum tree	Salai	Sallaki	47
Brassica juncea	Indian mustard	Rayi	Sarsapah	48
Buchanania lanzan	-	Ciraumci	Priyalah	49
Caesalpinia sappan	Sappan wood	Patang	Patrangah	51
Callicarpa macrophylla	Calicarpa	Priyangu	Priyangu	52
Calophyllum inophyllum	Alexandrian laureal	Sultan campa	Punnagah	53
Calycopteris floribunda	Kokkarai	Marsadabaguli	Susavi	54
Camellia sinensis	Tea plant	Cay	Syamaparni	55
Capparis decidua	Caper plant	Karil	Karirah	55
Capsicum annuum	Chillis	Lalmircah	Katuvirah	57
Cardiospermum halicacabum	Ballom vine	Kanphuti	Sakralata	58
Careya arborea	Wild guava	Kumbi	Kumbhi	59
Carica papaya	Papaya	Pappita	Erandakakati	60

Ferula asafoetida	Asafoetida	Hing	Hingu	94
Ficus hispida	-	Katguleriya	Malayu	95
Ficus microcarpa	-	Kamarup	Plaksah	96
Flacourtia indica	Madagascar plum	Kancu	Aghori	96
Foeniculum vulgare	Fennel	Saunph	Madhurika	98
Fritillaria roylei	Fritillary	Kakoli	Kakoli	99
Garcinia gummi-gutta	-	Billati-amli	Vrksamlah	99
Garcinia morella	Indian gamboge tree	Tamal	Hiravi	100
Gardenia gummifera	Cumbi-gum tree	Dikamali	Nadihingu	101
Glycomis arborea	Ash sheora	Potali	Asvasakhotah	102
Gossypium arboreum	Tree cotton	Kapas	Raksatika	103
Gossypium herbaceum	Indian cotton	Kapas	Karpasah	104
Helianthus annus	Sunflower	Surajmukhi	Adityabhakta	105
Hiptage benghalensis	Clustered hiptage	Madhumalati	Madhavi	106
Hordeum vulgare	Barley	Jau	Yavah	108
Hydnocarpus laurifolia	Chaulmurga	Calmogara	Tuvarakah	109
Hyoscyamus niger	Henbane	Khurasani ajavayan	Parasikayavani	110
Ichnocarpus frutescens	-	Kalidudhi	Palindi	111
Indigofera tinctoria	Indian indigo	Nil	Nilini	112
Inula racemosa	-	Puskarmul	Pauskaram	113
Ipomoea batatas	Sweet potato	Sakkarkand	Pindaluh	114
Ipomoea mauritiana	Giant potato	Bhilaykand	Ksiravidari	115
Ipomoea nil	Morning glory	Kaladana	Krsnabija	116
Jasminum grandiflorum	Common jasmin	Cameli	Malati	117
Jasminm sambac	Arabian jasmin	Mogra	Mallika	118
Juglans regia	Common walnut	Akhrot	Aksotah	119
Justicia gendarussa	-	Nilinirgundi	Vataghni	120
Kaempferia rotunda	Indian crocus	Bhuyicampa	Bhumicampaka	121
Kyllinga nemoralis	-	Nirbisi	Svetanirvisa	122
Lablab purpureus	Lablab bean	Sem	Nispavah	123
Lagenaria siceraria	Bitter bottle gourd	Kadvi lauki	Katutumbi	124
Lens culinaris	Lentil	Masur	Masurah	125
Lepidium sativum	Water cress	Halim	Asalika	126
Linum usitatissimum	Flax plant	Alsi	Atasi	127
Lodoicea maldivica	Sea coconut palm	Darya ka Nariyal	Arkaragah	128

Pistacia chinensis	Kakra	Karkatakasrngi	Karkatasrngi	160
Pisum sativum	Garden pea	Mathar	Kalayah	161
Plantago ovata	Spongel seeds	Isabgol	Snigdhajirakah	162
Pluchea lanceolata	Rasna	Rasana	Rasna	163
Plumeria rubra	Pogodo tree	Cameli	Svetacampaka	164
Premna corymbosa	-	Ageta	Agnimanthah	165
Prunus amygdalus	Almond tree	Badam	Vatamah	166
Prunus cerasoides	Himalayan wild cherry	Patmakh	Padmakah	167
Prunus domestica	Common plum	Alubukhara	Arukam	168
Prunus persica	Peach tree	Aru	Aruka	169
Pterocarpus santalinus	Red sanders	Raktcandan	Raktacandanah	170
Pueraria tuberosa	Indian kudzu	Vidarikand	Vidari	171
Punica granatum	Pomegranate	Anar	Dadimah	172
Pyrus malus	Apple	Seb	Badara	173
Quisqualis indica	Rangoon creeper	Rangunachi veli	-	174
Randia dumetorum	Emetic nut	Mainphal	Madana	175
Raphanus sativus	Radish	Muli	Mulika	176
Rhinacanthus nasuta	-	Juyipani	Yuthikaparni	177
Rosa damascena	Persian rose	Gulaaba	Satapatri	178
Sansevieria roxburghiana	Indian bow-string hemp	Murva	Maruva	178
Saccharum officinarum	Sugarcane	Ganna	Asipatra	179
Shorea robusta	Sal tree	Sal	Agnivallabha	180
Smilax china	China root	Chopchini	Madhusnuhi	182
Solanum melongena	Brinjal	Baingan	Vartaki	183
Soymida febrifuga	Indian redwood tree	Rohan	Manasrohini	184
Spinacea oleracea	Spinach	Palak	Chhurika	185
Strychnos nux-vomica	Nux vomica	Kuchala	Karaskara	186
Swertia chirayita	Chiretta	Chiraayata	Kirata	187
Tabernaemontana divaricata	East India Rosebay	Chandni	Tagar	188
Tagetus erecta	Marigold	Zenddu	Jhandu	190
Teramnus labialis	Wild udad	Masparni	Ardramasha	191
Terminalia crenulata	Black murdah	Asaina	Chagakarnah	192
Thespesia populnea	Portia tree	Paraspipal	Haripucchah	193